CURRIC QA 445 .A27 Text

Developmental Editor
Nirmala Nutakki

Managing Editor
Enid Haley

Senior Consulting Mathematics Editor
Lesley Haynes

Coordinating Editor
Mei Lin Cheung

Production Coordinator
Stephanie Cox

Editorial Contributors
Nancy Andraos   Kelly Davis
Gina Jackson   Gary Merritt

Product Manager
Susan Cox

Publisher
Claire Burnett

Design/Production
Pronk&Associates

Art Direction
Pronk&Associates

Electronic Assembly/Technical Art
Pronk&Associates

2 3 4 5 GG 06 05 04 03 02

Geometry and Discrete Mathematics 12

**Addison-Wesley
Secondary
Mathematics
Authors**

Elizabeth Ainslie
Paul Atkinson
Maurice Barry
Cam Bennet
Barbara J. Canton
Ron Coleborn
Fred Crouse
Garry Davis
Mary Doucette
Bonnie Edwards
Jane Forbes
George Gadanidis
Liliane Gauthier
Florence Glanfield
Katie Pallos-Haden
Carol Besteck Hope
Terry Kaminski
Brendan Kelly
Stephen Khan
Ron Lancaster
Duncan LeBlanc
Kevin Maguire
Rob McLeish
Jim Nakamoto
Nick Nielsen
Paul Pogue
Brent Richards
David Sufrin
Paul Williams
Elizabeth Wood
Rick Wunderlich
Paul Zolis
Leanne Zorn

Robert Alexander

Peter J. Harrison

Antonietta Lenjosek

Peter Taylor

Addison Wesley

Toronto

Program Consultants and Reviewers

Ron Bender
Faculty of Engineering
University of Ottawa

Gord Doctorow
ASE 1
Toronto District School Board

John Kitney
Head of Mathematics
Bayridge Secondary School
Kingston

Kevin Maguire
Mathematics Consultant
Toronto District School Board

John McGrath
Former Head of Mathematics
Adam Scott Secondary School
Peterborough

Ray Nowak
Head of Mathematics
Bramalea Secondary School
Bramalea

Jamie Pyper
ESSO Centre for Mathematics Education
University of Western Ontario

Wendy Solheim
Head of Mathematics
Thornhill Secondary School
Thornhill

Deidre Wilson
Head of Mathematics
Orangeville District Secondary School
Orangeville

Assessment Consultant

Lynda E.C. Colgan
Department of Education
Queen's University
Kingston

Contents

Unit I Geometry

Unit II Proof and Problem Solving

4 Examples of Proof

Performance Problems for Proof

5 Deductive Reasoning

Performance Problems for Deductive Reasoning

Contents

The **Solutions** to Examples model clear, concise mathematical communication. Reading and understanding an Example solution will help develop your communication skills.

Something to Think About prompts you to reflect on solutions or the implications of new concepts, and to share your thinking.

Selected **Exercises** ask you to explain your reasoning, or describe your findings. Each numbered section also contains an exercise highlighted with a "Communication" emphasis.

Unit II, with its focus on the methods of proof, provides new strategies for developing communication skills.

Independent Learning

Performance Problems provide opportunities for you to explore new areas of content in self-directed study, with other students and on your own.

This text includes appendices that can help you develop independent learning skills:

- **Answers** are provided for all content-based exercises; proofs are available in the Solutions section of the Teacher's Resource Book. Conscientious students can use both answers and solutions to support their learning.
- A **Student Reference** provides a comprehensive review of prerequisite results, terms, concepts, and skills. There are cross-references to this appendix when prerequisite material is required during core development.

Assessment

Several features of this book relate to a balanced assessment approach.

- **Achievement Chart Categories** highlighted in each exercise set
- **Communication** opportunities in Examples and exercises
- **Self-Tests** at the end of each chapter
- **Performance Problems** with rich, extended problems that address all four categories of the Achievement Chart

GEOMETRY

Welcome to *Addison-Wesley Geometry and Discrete Mathematics 12...*

This book is about methods of proof, and your independent investigation of extended problems, as well as the development of new mathematical content.

The Ontario curriculum for *Geometry and Discrete Mathematics* has three strands: Geometry, Proof and Problem Solving, and Discrete Mathematics. The structure of ***Addison-Wesley Geometry and Discrete Mathematics 12*** mirrors the structure of the course, with a unit that relates to each strand in the curriculum.

Unit I   Geometry

Unit II   Proof and Problem Solving

Unit III   Discrete Mathematics

The methods of proof, and opportunities for problem solving, appear throughout **Units I** and **III**. **Unit II** presents insights into the reason for proof, specific methods of proof, and many thought-provoking examples and exercises in which you devise your own approach to solve a problem.

The curriculum includes several expectations that invite content extensions, and larger, more comprehensive problems for you to solve. The course emphasizes the solving of a problem over an extended period of time, with opportunities to reflect, and then return to find new perspectives, and to generate alternative solutions. You will use a variety of tools to explore many aspects of a problem. For example, you will solve a linear system by hand, by using a graphing calculator, and by using a spreadsheet.

Many exercises in ***Addison-Wesley Geometry and Discrete Mathematics 12*** will challenge your thinking. Opportunities for extensions of content, and for solving classic problems, are provided in **Performance Problems**, which appear five times in the book, after chapters 3, 4, 5, and 7, and with **Cumulative Performance Problems** at the end. **Performance Problems** include sections that focus on:

> Vector proofs using linear combinations
> Circle properties to investigate and prove
> Probability

Chapter Elements
Numbered Sections

These develop the new content of the course.

Take Note boxes highlight important results or definitions, and should be part of your study notes.

Something to Think About appears regularly. It prompts you to reflect on the thinking behind an example or problem solution, to think about alternative methods of approach, or to consider connections with other topics.

Exercises are organized into A, B, and C categories according to their level of difficulty.

Each exercise set identifies exercises for specific categories of the provincial **Achievement Chart**. These exercises show you what to expect when you are assessed on any of the four categories. We have highlighted exercises as examples only. A labelled exercise may not be limited to one category, but the focus helps to simplify assessment.

Ongoing Review

The **Mathematics Toolkit** in each Chapter Review summarizes important chapter results. Use the toolkit and the **Review Exercises** to study for a chapter test.

The **Self-Test** at the end of each chapter helps you prepare for a class test.

Performance Problems provide extended problems of the type that are emphasized in this course. These problems may relate to content from any or all units in the book.

Communication

Communication is a key part of all learning. Clear communication is essential in the process of proving results. A valid proof requires clear, logical communication that presents a compelling case. This book, with its stress on proof and problem solving, emphasizes communication. It also provides many ways for you to improve your mathematical communication.

Curriculum Expectations

By the end of this chapter, you will:

- Represent vectors as directed line segments.
- Perform the operations of addition, subtraction, and scalar multiplication on geometric vectors.
- Determine the components of a geometric vector and the projection of a geometric vector.

- Model and solve problems involving velocity and force.
- Determine and interpret the dot product … of geometric vectors.
- Represent Cartesian vectors in two-space … as ordered pairs ….
- Perform the operations of addition, subtraction, scalar multiplication, dot product, … on Cartesian vectors.

Your previous work in mathematics has been based on quantities called *scalars* that can be described by a single real number that specifies their magnitude, or size. Distance, area, and the value of a trigonometric function are all examples of scalar quantities. In this unit, we will look at other quantities called *vectors* that are described by specifying both a magnitude and a direction. The acceleration due to gravity is an example of a vector. It is described by specifying a magnitude (usually about 9.8 m/s^2) and a direction (always vertically downward).

Some scalar quantities have corresponding vector quantities.

Scalar quantity	Vector quantity
Distance is a scalar quantity.	Displacement is distance travelled in a given direction. It is a vector quantity.
Maya lives 100 km from Kitchener. Maya lives somewhere on the circle.	Maya lives 100 km northeast of Kitchener.
Speed is a scalar quantity.	Velocity is speed in a given direction. It is a vector quantity.
The airplane is travelling at a speed of 900 km/h. 	The velocity of the airplane is 900 km/h west.

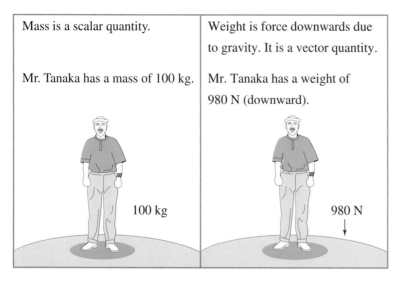

Mass is a scalar quantity.	Weight is force downwards due to gravity. It is a vector quantity.
Mr. Tanaka has a mass of 100 kg.	Mr. Tanaka has a weight of 980 N (downward).
100 kg	980 N

N is the symbol for newtons, the metric unit of force.

A *geometric vector* is represented by an arrow called a *directed line segment*. The length of the line segment represents the magnitude of the vector and the arrowhead points in the direction of the vector.

A vector from point A to point B is written $\overrightarrow{AB}$, where A is the tail or initial point of the vector and B is the head or terminal point. A vector can also be labelled by a lowercase letter with an arrow above, such as $\overrightarrow{v}$. The magnitude of the vector is written as $|\overrightarrow{AB}|$ or $|\overrightarrow{v}|$. The absolute value bars remind us that the magnitude must be non-negative because it represents a length.

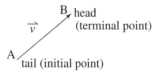

The direction of a vector can be described using the main compass directions of north, south, east, or west. Bearings can also be used. North is taken as 000°. Then, moving clockwise, all other directions are assigned a number up to 359°. For example, northeast is 045°, due south is 180°, and southwest is 225°.

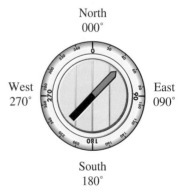

Vectors are usually drawn to scale so that the length and direction of a line segment accurately reflects the magnitude and direction of the vector. Unless otherwise stated, we will assume that north is at the top of the page.

Example 1

Draw vectors to represent:

a) a displacement of 30 km northeast

b) a weight of 50 N acting vertically downward

c) a velocity of 230 km/h on a bearing of 310°

Solution

a) Choose a convenient scale such as 1 cm : 10 km. Select a convenient initial point. Use a protractor to mark a direction 45° east of north. Construct a line segment 30 ÷ 10, or 3 cm long. Add an arrowhead at the terminal point. Label the vector.

b) Use the scale 1 cm : 20 N. Construct a line segment 50 ÷ 20, or 2.5 cm long. Draw the arrowhead pointing to the bottom of the page.

c) Use the scale 1 cm : 50 km/h. To find a bearing of 310°, measure 310° clockwise from north, or measure 360° − 310° = 50° counterclockwise from north. Mark the bearing and construct a line segment 230 ÷ 50, or 4.6 cm long.

N

45° 30 km

50 N

N

230 km/h

310°

In mathematics, we often use vectors to represent a translation or a slide. In the diagram at the right, △ABC is mapped under a slide onto △XYZ. The mapping is represented geometrically by drawing vectors $\overrightarrow{AX}$, $\overrightarrow{BY}$, and $\overrightarrow{CZ}$ from points A, B, and C to their respective images X, Y, and Z. The length of the vectors indicates the distance moved under the translation and their direction indicates the direction of the translation.

B

Y

A

X

C

Z

When a figure is translated, each point on the figure moves the same distance in the same direction. Hence, the vectors $\overrightarrow{AX}$, $\overrightarrow{BY}$, and $\overrightarrow{CZ}$ have the same magnitude and direction. They are equivalent or equal vectors.

Observe that equal vectors need not have the same location in space; they need not have the same initial point and the same terminal point. Therefore, a single vector can have many representations. This is a key property of geometric vectors.

Take Note

Equal Vectors

Equal vectors have the same magnitude and direction.

The vectors $\vec{a}$ and $\vec{b}$ below are equal since $|\vec{a}| = |\vec{b}|$ and the direction of $\vec{a}$ is the same as the direction of $\vec{b}$. We write $\vec{a} = \vec{b}$.

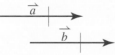

On page 6, we used the vectors $\overrightarrow{AX}$, $\overrightarrow{BY}$, and $\overrightarrow{CZ}$ to represent the translation that maps △ABC onto △XYZ. We can represent the inverse translation that maps △XYZ onto △ABC by reversing the directions of $\overrightarrow{AX}$, $\overrightarrow{BY}$, and $\overrightarrow{CZ}$ to get their respective opposites, $\overrightarrow{XA}$, $\overrightarrow{YB}$ and $\overrightarrow{ZC}$. We indicate that $\overrightarrow{AX}$ and $\overrightarrow{XA}$ are opposites by writing $\overrightarrow{XA} = -\overrightarrow{AX}$.

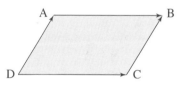

Take Note

Opposite Vectors

Opposite vectors have the same magnitude, but act in opposite directions. The vectors $\overrightarrow{a}$ and $\overrightarrow{b}$ below are opposites since $|\overrightarrow{a}| = |\overrightarrow{b}|$ and the direction of $\overrightarrow{a}$ is opposite to the direction of $\overrightarrow{b}$. We write $\overrightarrow{a} = -\overrightarrow{b}$.

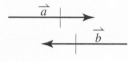

Example 2

In the diagram, ABCD is a parallelogram.

List 2 pairs of equal vectors.

List 2 pairs of opposite vectors.

Solution

Since opposite sides of a parallelogram are equal, $|\overrightarrow{AB}| = |\overrightarrow{DC}|$.

Furthermore, $\overrightarrow{AB}$ and $\overrightarrow{DC}$ have the same direction.

Hence, $\overrightarrow{AB}$ and $\overrightarrow{DC}$ are equal vectors.

Similarly, $\overrightarrow{DA}$ and $\overrightarrow{CB}$ are equal vectors.

One pair of opposite vectors is $\overrightarrow{AB}$ and $\overrightarrow{CD}$.

Another pair of opposite vectors is $\overrightarrow{DA}$ and $\overrightarrow{BC}$.

A

1. State whether each quantity is a vector or a scalar.

   a) age   **b)** volume   **c)** displacement   **d)** mass

   e) force   **f)** area   **g)** temperature   **h)** weight

   i) speed   **j)** density

2. Which of the following can be described by a vector?

   a) a wind of 35 km/h from the northeast

   b) a barbell of mass 40 kg

   c) a time of 14 min

   d) a distance of 14.7 km

   e) a weight on Mars of 300 N

   f) an advance of 15 km due east

   g) a speed of 85 km/h

   h) a force of 15 N directed downward

3. Find the magnitude and direction of each vector. Use a ruler and the given scale to determine the magnitude. Use north, south, east, west, northwest, northeast, southwest, or southeast to describe the directions.

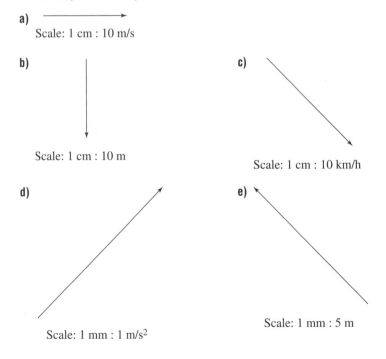

   a)
   Scale: 1 cm : 10 m/s

   b)
   Scale: 1 cm : 10 m

   c)
   Scale: 1 cm : 10 km/h

   d)
   Scale: 1 mm : 1 m/s²

   e)
   Scale: 1 mm : 5 m

4. Identify pairs of vectors that appear to be equal.

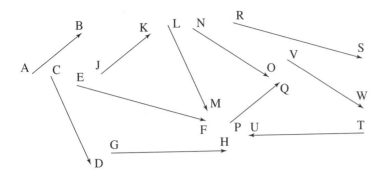

B

5. Knowledge/Understanding Use the geometric properties of each figure to list all pairs of equal vectors.

a)

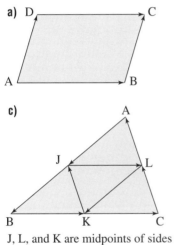

b)

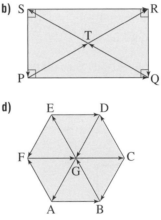

c)

J, L, and K are midpoints of sides AB, AC, and BC, respectively.

d)

ABCDEF is a regular hexagon with centre G.

6. List two pairs of equal vectors and two pairs of opposite vectors.

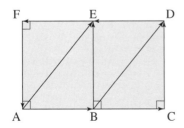

E and B are midpoints of sides DF and AC respectively.

7. Communication If X is the midpoint of YZ, explain why $\overrightarrow{XY} = -\overrightarrow{XZ}$.

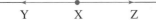

8. Construct a scale drawing of each vector. The direction of each vector is given in the square brackets.

a) 50 km/h [north]

b) 12m/s [095°]

c) 500 N [southeast]

d) 2.5 m/s² [335°]

e) 7 m [270°]

9. For each vector in exercise 8, describe and draw the opposite vector.

10. ABCD is a square of side length 3 cm.

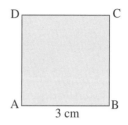

a) State whether each statement is true or false. Explain.

i) $\overrightarrow{AB} = \overrightarrow{BC}$

ii) $|\overrightarrow{AB}| = |\overrightarrow{BC}|$

iii) $|\overrightarrow{BA}| = -|\overrightarrow{CB}|$

b) Calculate the magnitude of $\overrightarrow{AC}$.

11. Thinking/Inquiry/Problem Solving Explain your answer to each question. Use a diagram.

a) If $\overrightarrow{u} = \overrightarrow{v}$, is it always true that $|\overrightarrow{u}| = |\overrightarrow{v}|$?

b) If $|\overrightarrow{u}| = |\overrightarrow{v}|$, is it always true that $\overrightarrow{u} = \overrightarrow{v}$?

12. Application The fractions $\frac{2}{3}, \frac{4}{6}, \frac{6}{9}, \ldots$ are all equivalent to the fraction $\frac{2}{3}$. Explain how the concept of equivalent fractions is analogous to the concept of equivalent vectors.

Cathleen S. Morawetz (1923–)
Born: Toronto, Canada

Born into a mathematical family of Irish descent, Morawetz attended the University of Toronto to study mathematics. She received a PhD from New York University and was a professor there for many years. Morawetz became director of the university's Courant Institute of Mathematical Sciences in 1984—the first woman to hold such a position. In 1998, Morawetz was awarded the National Medal of Science, the highest scientific honour bestowed by the USA. Her current research includes work in fluid dynamics and wave propagation.

1.2 Adding Vectors

In Section 1.1, we used vectors to represent displacements such as translations.

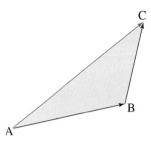

In the diagram at the right, point A has been translated to point B then to point C under the displacements $\overrightarrow{AB}$ and $\overrightarrow{BC}$ respectively. Observe that the single displacement $\overrightarrow{AC}$ is equivalent to successive displacements $\overrightarrow{AB}$ and $\overrightarrow{BC}$. We call $\overrightarrow{AC}$ the *resultant* or sum of $\overrightarrow{AB}$ and $\overrightarrow{BC}$, and write $\overrightarrow{AC} = \overrightarrow{AB} + \overrightarrow{BC}$. Since the three vectors form a triangle, we call this method of adding vectors the *Triangle Law*.

Observe that the vectors being added are arranged sequentially from head-to-tail.

Take Note

Triangle Law of Vector Addition

Let $\overrightarrow{a}$ and $\overrightarrow{b}$ be any two vectors arranged head-to-tail, as shown. The sum, $\overrightarrow{a} + \overrightarrow{b}$, is the vector from the tail of $\overrightarrow{a}$ to the head of $\overrightarrow{b}$.

Example 1

Given the vectors $\overrightarrow{a}$ and $\overrightarrow{b}$:

a) Draw the vector $\overrightarrow{a} + \overrightarrow{b}$.

b) Draw the vector $\overrightarrow{b} + \overrightarrow{a}$.

c) Prove that $\overrightarrow{a} + \overrightarrow{b} = \overrightarrow{b} + \overrightarrow{a}$.

Solution

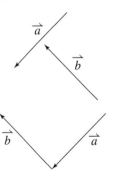

a) Arrange the vectors sequentially by translating the tail of $\overrightarrow{b}$ to the head of $\overrightarrow{a}$ (see diagram at the right).

Draw a vector from the tail of $\overrightarrow{a}$ to the head of $\overrightarrow{b}$.

This is the vector $\overrightarrow{a} + \overrightarrow{b}$.

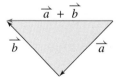

b) Translate the tail of $\overrightarrow{a}$ to the head of $\overrightarrow{b}$. Draw a vector from the tail of $\overrightarrow{b}$ to the head of $\overrightarrow{a}$.

This is the vector $\overrightarrow{b} + \overrightarrow{a}$.

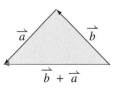

c) Use parts a and b. The vectors $\overrightarrow{a} + \overrightarrow{b}$ and $\overrightarrow{b} + \overrightarrow{a}$ have the same magnitude and direction. So, they are equal vectors.

That is, $\overrightarrow{a} + \overrightarrow{b} = \overrightarrow{b} + \overrightarrow{a}$.

Vector addition has properties that are similar to the properties of addition in arithmetic. For example, two numbers can be added in either order: $x + y = y + x$. This property is called the *commutative law of addition*. *Example 1* shows that vector addition also satisfies the commutative law. That is, if $\vec{a}$ and $\vec{b}$ are any two vectors, then:

$$\vec{a} + \vec{b} = \vec{b} + \vec{a}$$

In the exercises, you will prove two other properties of vector addition (exercises 8 and 10).

To add three or more vectors, we place them head-to-tail so that the tail of the second vector is at the head of the first vector, the tail of the third vector is at the head of the second vector, and so on.

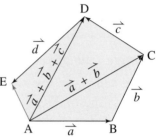

$$\vec{a} + \vec{b} + \vec{c} + \vec{d} = \overrightarrow{AB} + \overrightarrow{BC} + \overrightarrow{CD} + \overrightarrow{DE}$$
$$= \overrightarrow{AC} + \overrightarrow{CD} + \overrightarrow{DE}$$
$$= \overrightarrow{AD} + \overrightarrow{DE}$$
$$= \overrightarrow{AE}$$

The sum is the vector with tail at A (tail of the first vector) and head at E (head of the last vector).

Something to Think About

- Does order matter when adding three or more vectors?

Example 2

The diagram at the right shows a rectangular box. Determine a vector equal to each sum.

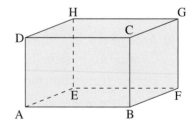

a) $\overrightarrow{AD} + \overrightarrow{DH}$

b) $\overrightarrow{AB} + \overrightarrow{BF} + \overrightarrow{FG}$

c) $\overrightarrow{AE} + \overrightarrow{HC}$

d) $\overrightarrow{AD} + \overrightarrow{AE} + \overrightarrow{AB}$

Solution

Place the vectors sequentially and add them head-to-tail. Where necessary, replace a vector with an equivalent vector to perform the addition.

a) $\overrightarrow{AD} + \overrightarrow{DH} = \overrightarrow{AH}$

b) $\overrightarrow{AB} + \overrightarrow{BF} + \overrightarrow{FG} = \overrightarrow{AF} + \overrightarrow{FG}$
$$= \overrightarrow{AG}$$

c) $\overrightarrow{AE} + \overrightarrow{HC} = \overrightarrow{AE} + \overrightarrow{EB}$

$\qquad\qquad\quad = \overrightarrow{AB}$

d) $\overrightarrow{AD} + \overrightarrow{AE} + \overrightarrow{AB} = \overrightarrow{AD} + \overrightarrow{DH} + \overrightarrow{HG}$

$\qquad\qquad\qquad\qquad\quad = \overrightarrow{AH} + \overrightarrow{HG}$

$\qquad\qquad\qquad\qquad\quad = \overrightarrow{AG}$

Something to Think About

- When adding vectors that are arranged sequentially head-to-tail, what is the pattern of letters in the vectors being added and their sum?

In *Example 2*, some answers can be expressed in different ways. For example, in part c we can write:

$\qquad \overrightarrow{AE} + \overrightarrow{HC} = \overrightarrow{DH} + \overrightarrow{HC}$

$\qquad\qquad\qquad\quad = \overrightarrow{DC}$

This is equivalent to the vector $\overrightarrow{AB}$ because $\overrightarrow{DC}$ and $\overrightarrow{AB}$ have the same magnitude and the same direction.

When we add vectors sequentially by arranging them head-to-tail, it is possible to return to the initial point. In the diagram on page 12, this situation occurs with $\overrightarrow{AB} + \overrightarrow{BE} + \overrightarrow{EA}$ and $\overrightarrow{AB} + \overrightarrow{BA}$. According to the definition of addition, each sum is the vector with head and tail at the same point. We call this the *zero vector*, and represent it by $\overrightarrow{0}$. Hence, $\overrightarrow{AB} + \overrightarrow{BE} + \overrightarrow{EA} = \overrightarrow{0}$ and $\overrightarrow{AB} + \overrightarrow{BA} = \overrightarrow{0}$.

We define the zero vector to have zero length and no specified direction. The sum of any vector and its opposite is the zero vector.

$\qquad \overrightarrow{a} + (-\overrightarrow{a}) = \overrightarrow{0}$

Something to Think About

- The zero vector, $\overrightarrow{0}$, is defined to be a vector so that the sum of any two vectors is always a vector. Hence, $\overrightarrow{0}$ is different from the number 0.

In many applications, two vectors act simultaneously on the same point and are arranged tail-to-tail. In such cases, we add the vectors using an alternative to the Triangle Law called the *Parallelogram Law*.

In the diagram at the right, vectors $\overrightarrow{OA} = \overrightarrow{a}$ and $\overrightarrow{OB} = \overrightarrow{b}$ have a common tail, O. To find their sum, we construct parallelogram OACB in which OA and OB are adjacent sides. Hence, $\overrightarrow{BC} = \overrightarrow{OA} = \overrightarrow{a}$ and $\overrightarrow{AC} = \overrightarrow{OB} = \overrightarrow{b}$.

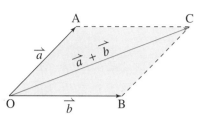

The sum $\overrightarrow{a} + \overrightarrow{b}$ can be obtained by applying the Triangle Law to △OAC. Alternatively, $\overrightarrow{a} + \overrightarrow{b}$ can be obtained as the diagonal $\overrightarrow{OC}$ of parallelogram OACB.

Parallelogram Law of Vector Addition

Let $\overrightarrow{a}$ and $\overrightarrow{b}$ be any two vectors arranged tail-to-tail. Complete the parallelogram determined by $\overrightarrow{a}$ and $\overrightarrow{b}$. The sum, $\overrightarrow{a} + \overrightarrow{b}$, is the vector with the same tail as $\overrightarrow{a}$ and $\overrightarrow{b}$, and with its head at the opposite vertex of the parallelogram.

A common application of vector addition involves finding the combined effect of two vectors. For example, when a boat is travelling in a current, the actual velocity of the boat (its velocity relative to the shore) is the resultant of the boat's velocity in still water and the velocity of the current.

Example 3

A boat with a forward velocity in still water of 14 m/s is travelling across a river, directly towards the opposite shore. At the same time, a current of 5 m/s carries the boat down the river. Determine the resultant velocity of the boat.

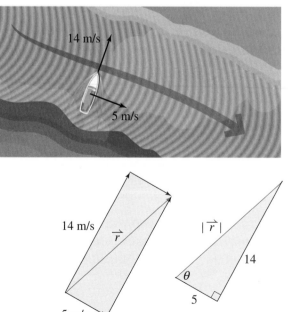

Solution

The diagram, above right, shows the vectors acting on the boat.

Draw vector-sum diagram. Draw the resultant as the side of a triangle or as the diagonal of a parallelogram. Extract a triangle from the vector sketch, and indicate which lengths and angles are to be calculated.

The boat's heading is at right angles to the current, so the velocity parallelogram is a rectangle, and the triangles are right triangles.

Use the Pythagorean Theorem to calculate the magnitude of the resultant $\vec{r}$.

$$|\vec{r}|^2 = 14^2 + 5^2$$
$$|\vec{r}| = \sqrt{221}$$
$$|\vec{r}| \doteq 15$$

Use the tangent ratio to calculate the direction of $\vec{r}$.

$$\tan \theta = \frac{14}{5}$$
$$\theta \doteq 70°$$

The boat is travelling at 15 m/s at an angle of 70° relative to the shore.

1.2 Exercises

A

1. Express each sum as a single vector (below left).

   a) $\overrightarrow{AB} + \overrightarrow{BC}$

   b) $\overrightarrow{AC} + \overrightarrow{CD}$

   c) $(\overrightarrow{BC} + \overrightarrow{CD}) + \overrightarrow{DA}$

   d) $\overrightarrow{BC} + (\overrightarrow{CD} + \overrightarrow{DA})$

   e) $\overrightarrow{CA} + \overrightarrow{AD} + \overrightarrow{DB}$

   f) $\overrightarrow{BD} + \overrightarrow{DB}$

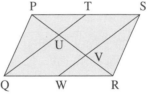

2. Express each sum as a single vector (above right).

   a) $\overrightarrow{PT} + \overrightarrow{TQ}$

   b) $\overrightarrow{QR} + \overrightarrow{RU}$

   c) $\overrightarrow{RV} + \overrightarrow{VS}$

   d) $\overrightarrow{PV} + \overrightarrow{VS}$

   e) $\overrightarrow{UQ} + \overrightarrow{QW} + \overrightarrow{WV}$

   f) $\overrightarrow{SW} + \overrightarrow{WQ} + \overrightarrow{QR}$

3. In the diagram (top left of the following page), ABCD and CEFG are parallelograms. Express each sum as a single vector.

   a) $\overrightarrow{HG} + \overrightarrow{HD}$

   b) $\overrightarrow{HG} + \overrightarrow{HA}$

   c) $\overrightarrow{FG} + \overrightarrow{FE}$

   d) $\overrightarrow{CD} + \overrightarrow{HG}$

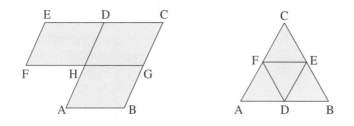

B

4. In the diagram (above right), △ABC is equilateral and D, E, F are the midpoints of its sides. Express each sum as a single vector.

a) $\overrightarrow{AF} + \overrightarrow{DB}$

b) $\overrightarrow{DE} + \overrightarrow{DB}$

c) $\overrightarrow{FA} + \overrightarrow{EB}$

d) $\overrightarrow{DA} + \overrightarrow{EC}$

e) $\overrightarrow{AF} + \overrightarrow{DE}$

f) $\overrightarrow{EC} + \overrightarrow{FD}$

5. Copy each pair of vectors and draw $\vec{u} + \vec{v}$.

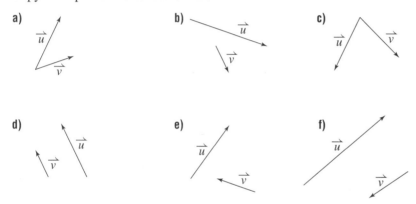

6. Knowledge/Understanding The diagram (below left) shows a square-based right pyramid. Determine each sum.

a) $\overrightarrow{KN} + \overrightarrow{NR}$

b) $\overrightarrow{RS} + \overrightarrow{KR}$

c) $\overrightarrow{MN} + \overrightarrow{MS}$

d) $\overrightarrow{KM} + \overrightarrow{NK}$

e) $\overrightarrow{KN} + \overrightarrow{RS}$

f) $\overrightarrow{KR} + \overrightarrow{NM} + \overrightarrow{SK}$

7. Use the diagram at the bottom right of the previous page. Express each vector as the sum of two other vectors. It may be possible to do this in more than one way.

a) $\overrightarrow{DA}$ **b)** $\overrightarrow{CD}$

c) $\overrightarrow{CB}$ **d)** $\overrightarrow{AB}$

e) $\overrightarrow{DB}$ **f)** $\overrightarrow{BC}$

8. Below is a property of addition in arithmetic and algebra.
   Adding 0: $x + 0 = x$

   a) Write the corresponding property of addition of vectors.

   b) Use the definition of addition to prove the property in part a.

9. Copy each pair of vectors and draw $\overrightarrow{u} + \overrightarrow{v} + \overrightarrow{w}$.

a)

b)

10. **Communication** When we add more than two numbers in arithmetic, it does not matter which ones we add first: $(x + y) + z = x + (y + z)$. This property is called the *associative law of addition*. Explain how the diagram at the right can be used to show that vector addition is associative; that is, $(\overrightarrow{a} + \overrightarrow{b}) + \overrightarrow{c} = \overrightarrow{a} + (\overrightarrow{b} + \overrightarrow{c})$.

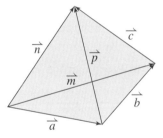

11. Use a diagram to explain how each vector sum can be expressed as a single vector.

a) $\overrightarrow{WX} + \overrightarrow{XY} + \overrightarrow{YZ}$ **b)** $\overrightarrow{PQ} + \overrightarrow{RP}$

c) $\overrightarrow{AB} + \overrightarrow{CA}$ **d)** $\overrightarrow{ST} + \overrightarrow{US} + \overrightarrow{VU}$

12. In any $\triangle ABC$, determine the sum $\overrightarrow{AB} + \overrightarrow{BC} + \overrightarrow{CA}$.

13. **Thinking/Inquiry/Problem Solving** ABCDE is a regular pentagon.

   a) Determine the sum $\overrightarrow{AC} + \overrightarrow{CE} + \overrightarrow{EB} + \overrightarrow{BD} + \overrightarrow{DA}$.

   b) Suppose the vectors in part a were all drawn tail-to-tail. What pattern would they form? Explain.

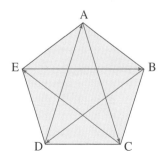

14. **Application** In his rowboat, Pierre heads directly across a river at a speed of 10 km/h. The river is flowing at 6 km/h.

 a) What is the resultant speed of the boat?

 b) What angle will the resultant path of the boat make with the shoreline?

 c) If the river is 120 m wide, how far downstream will Pierre land on the opposite shore?

15. Refer to exercise 14. Suppose Pierre wants to row directly across the river.

 a) At what angle relative to the shore should he head?

 b) How long will this trip take?

16. Refer to the diagram in exercise 6. Express each sum as a single vector.

 a) $\overrightarrow{KR} + \overrightarrow{NM} + \overrightarrow{MK}$ b) $\overrightarrow{KS} + \overrightarrow{RN} + \overrightarrow{RK}$

C

17. Two forces with magnitudes 8 N and 11 N act on a large object. The angle between the forces is 30°.

 a) Draw a diagram to represent the combined effect of the forces.

 b) Calculate the magnitude of the resultant force.

18. a) For any vectors $\overrightarrow{a}$ and $\overrightarrow{b}$, can $\left|\overrightarrow{a} + \overrightarrow{b}\right| = \left|\overrightarrow{a}\right| + \left|\overrightarrow{b}\right|$? Use a diagram to explain.

 b) Prove that for any vectors $\overrightarrow{a}$ and $\overrightarrow{b}$, $\left|\overrightarrow{a} + \overrightarrow{b}\right| \leq \left|\overrightarrow{a}\right| + \left|\overrightarrow{b}\right|$.

 c) Is it possible to have $\left|\overrightarrow{a} + \overrightarrow{b}\right| > \left|\overrightarrow{a}\right| + \left|\overrightarrow{b}\right|$? Use a diagram to explain.

1.3　Subtracting Vectors

In arithmetic, subtraction is defined as the inverse operation of addition. For example, $5 - 3$ equals 2 because 2 is the number that must be added to 3 to obtain 5.

We define subtraction of vectors in the same way. Let $\vec{a} = \overrightarrow{OA}$ and $\vec{b} = \overrightarrow{OB}$ be two vectors drawn tail-to-tail. We define $\vec{a} - \vec{b}$ to be the vector that must be added to $\vec{b}$ to obtain $\vec{a}$. This is the vector $\overrightarrow{BA}$ that goes from the head of $\vec{b}$ to the head of $\vec{a}$.

$$\vec{a} - \vec{b} = \overrightarrow{BA} \qquad ①$$

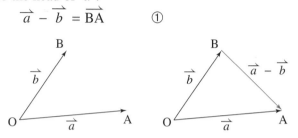

The Triangle Law shows that this is reasonable. If we start at O and go to B and then go to A, the result is $\vec{b} + \vec{a} - \vec{b} = \vec{a}$.

We can use the Triangle Law in a different way to find another expression for $\overrightarrow{BA}$.

$$\overrightarrow{BA} = \overrightarrow{BO} + \overrightarrow{OA}$$
$$\overrightarrow{BA} = -\vec{b} + \vec{a}$$
$$\overrightarrow{BA} = \vec{a} + (-\vec{b}) \qquad ②$$

Compare equations ① and ②:

$$\vec{a} - \vec{b} = \vec{a} + (-\vec{b})$$

This equation tells us that we can subtract a vector by adding its opposite. The diagram below shows two ways to do this.

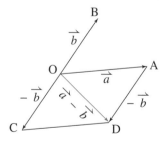

Using the Parallelogram Law:

$$\vec{a} - \vec{b} = \vec{a} + (-\vec{b})$$
$$= \overrightarrow{OA} + \overrightarrow{OC}$$
$$= \overrightarrow{OD}$$

Using the Triangle Law:

$$\vec{a} - \vec{b} = \vec{a} + (-\vec{b})$$
$$= \overrightarrow{OA} + \overrightarrow{AD}$$
$$= \overrightarrow{OD}$$

Observe that the result is equivalent to the one shown in equation ① because the vectors $\overrightarrow{OD}$ and $\overrightarrow{BA}$ are equal.

Vector Subtraction

Let $\overrightarrow{a}$ and $\overrightarrow{b}$ be any two vectors. Either of the two methods shown below can be used to determine $\overrightarrow{a} - \overrightarrow{b}$.

Identify head and tail
Arrange $\overrightarrow{a}$ and $\overrightarrow{b}$ tail-to-tail.
Then $\overrightarrow{a} - \overrightarrow{b}$ is the vector from the head of $\overrightarrow{b}$ to the head of $\overrightarrow{a}$.

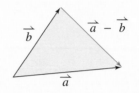

Add the opposite
$\overrightarrow{a} - \overrightarrow{b}$ is the sum of $\overrightarrow{a}$ and the opposite of $\overrightarrow{b}$.
$$\overrightarrow{a} - \overrightarrow{b} = \overrightarrow{a} + (-\overrightarrow{b})$$

A special case of subtraction occurs when the two vectors are equal. According to the definition of subtraction, $\overrightarrow{a} - \overrightarrow{a}$ is the vector from the head of $\overrightarrow{a}$ to the head of $\overrightarrow{a}$. This is the *zero vector*, and we write $\overrightarrow{a} - \overrightarrow{a} = \overrightarrow{0}$.

Example 1

Given the vectors $\overrightarrow{u}$ and $\overrightarrow{v}$, draw the vector $\overrightarrow{u} - \overrightarrow{v}$.

a)

b)

Solution

a) $\overrightarrow{u} - \overrightarrow{v}$ is the vector from the head of $\overrightarrow{v}$ to the head of $\overrightarrow{u}$.

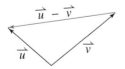

b) *Method 1*

Arrange the vectors tail-to-tail by translating $\overrightarrow{v}$ so that it has the same tail as $\overrightarrow{u}$. Then $\overrightarrow{u} - \overrightarrow{v}$ is the vector from the head of $\overrightarrow{v}$ to the head of $\overrightarrow{u}$.

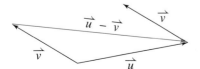

Method 2

Add the opposite of $\vec{v}$ to $\vec{u}$. Use the Triangle Law.

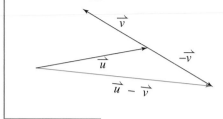

Something to Think About

- What other way is there to apply each method in part b?

Example 2

ABCD is a square. Express each difference as a single vector.

a) $\overrightarrow{BC} - \overrightarrow{BA}$ b) $\overrightarrow{AC} - \overrightarrow{BC}$

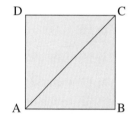

Solution

a) $\overrightarrow{BC}$ and $\overrightarrow{BA}$ have the same tail, B.

$\overrightarrow{BC} - \overrightarrow{BA}$ is the vector from the head of $\overrightarrow{BA}$ to the head of $\overrightarrow{BC}$; that is, from A to C.

$\overrightarrow{BC} - \overrightarrow{BA} = \overrightarrow{AC}$

b) $\overrightarrow{AC}$ and $\overrightarrow{BC}$ do not have the same tail.

Since $\overrightarrow{BC} = \overrightarrow{AD}$, we may replace $\overrightarrow{BC}$ with $\overrightarrow{AD}$.

$\overrightarrow{AC} - \overrightarrow{BC} = \overrightarrow{AC} - \overrightarrow{AD}$

$\overrightarrow{AC} - \overrightarrow{BC} = \overrightarrow{DC}$

The difference in *Example 2b* can be determined in a different way. Instead of subtracting $\overrightarrow{BC}$, we can add its opposite, $\overrightarrow{CB}$.

$\overrightarrow{AC} - \overrightarrow{BC} = \overrightarrow{AC} + \overrightarrow{CB}$

$\overrightarrow{AC} - \overrightarrow{BC} = \overrightarrow{AB}$

Since $\overrightarrow{AB} = \overrightarrow{DC}$, the two results are equivalent.

A

1. The diagram (below left) shows three congruent equilateral triangles. Express each difference as a single vector.

a) $\overrightarrow{BA} - \overrightarrow{BC}$

b) $\overrightarrow{BA} - \overrightarrow{BD}$

c) $\overrightarrow{CE} - \overrightarrow{AE}$

d) $\overrightarrow{AE} - \overrightarrow{ED}$

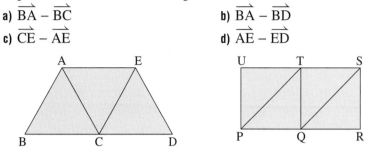

2. The diagram (above right) contains two squares. Express each difference as a single vector.

a) $\overrightarrow{SQ} - \overrightarrow{ST}$

b) $\overrightarrow{QT} - \overrightarrow{QP}$

c) $\overrightarrow{PR} - \overrightarrow{QS}$

d) $\overrightarrow{PT} - \overrightarrow{TS}$

3. a) Explain why $\vec{a} - \vec{b}$ is the vector from the head of $\vec{b}$ to the head of $\vec{a}$.

   b) How could you use subtraction to represent the vector from the head of $\vec{a}$ to the head of $\vec{b}$?

B

4. **Knowledge/Understanding** Copy each pair of vectors and draw $\vec{u} - \vec{v}$.

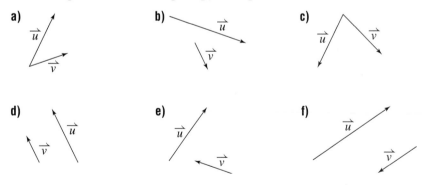

5. In parallelogram ABCD (top left of the following page), $\overrightarrow{AB} = \vec{u}$ and $\overrightarrow{BC} = \vec{v}$.

   a) State a single vector equal to each of the following.

   i) $\vec{u} + \vec{v}$

   ii) $\vec{u} - \vec{v}$

   iii) $-\vec{u} - \vec{v}$

   iv) $\vec{v} - \vec{u}$

   b) Express $\overrightarrow{AC}$ in terms of $\vec{u}$ and $\vec{v}$ in two ways. What property of vector addition is illustrated?

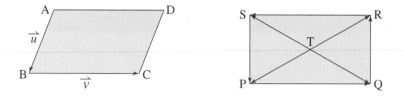

6. PQRS is a rectangle, above right. Express each vector as the difference of two other vectors. It may be possible to do this in more than one way.

a) $\overrightarrow{TQ}$

b) $\overrightarrow{RT}$

c) $\overrightarrow{PS}$

d) $\overrightarrow{PR}$

7. Thinking/Inquiry/Problem Solving ABCDEF is a regular hexagon.
Determine $\overrightarrow{AB} - \overrightarrow{BC} + \overrightarrow{CD} - \overrightarrow{DE} + \overrightarrow{EF} - \overrightarrow{FA}$

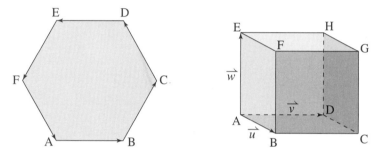

8. Application The diagram (above right) shows a cube, where $\overrightarrow{AB} = \overrightarrow{u}$, $\overrightarrow{AD} = \overrightarrow{v}$, and $\overrightarrow{AE} = \overrightarrow{w}$. Determine a single vector equivalent to each of the following.

a) $\overrightarrow{u} + \overrightarrow{v} + \overrightarrow{w}$

b) $\overrightarrow{u} + \overrightarrow{v} - \overrightarrow{w}$

c) $\overrightarrow{u} - \overrightarrow{v} + \overrightarrow{w}$

d) $\overrightarrow{u} - \overrightarrow{v} - \overrightarrow{w}$

9. Decide whether each statement is true or false. Draw diagrams to support your answers.

a) $\overrightarrow{a} + \overrightarrow{b}$ and $\overrightarrow{a} - \overrightarrow{b}$ always have the same length.

b) $\overrightarrow{a} + \overrightarrow{b}$ is always longer than $\overrightarrow{a} - \overrightarrow{b}$.

10. Communication Suppose you have a diagram of any two vectors $\overrightarrow{u}$ and $\overrightarrow{v}$ drawn tail-to-tail. Explain how you can tell, just by looking at the diagram, whether $\left|\overrightarrow{u} + \overrightarrow{v}\right|$ is greater than, equal to, or less than $\left|\overrightarrow{u} - \overrightarrow{v}\right|$.

C

11. a) Prove that for any vectors $\overrightarrow{a}$ and $\overrightarrow{b}$, $\left|\overrightarrow{a} - \overrightarrow{b}\right| \le \left|\overrightarrow{a}\right| + \left|\overrightarrow{b}\right|$.

b) Is it possible to have any or all of the following? Use diagrams to explain.

i) $\left|\overrightarrow{a} - \overrightarrow{b}\right| \le \left|\overrightarrow{a}\right| - \left|\overrightarrow{b}\right|$

ii) $\left|\overrightarrow{a} - \overrightarrow{b}\right| \ge \left|\overrightarrow{a}\right| - \left|\overrightarrow{b}\right|$

iii) $\left|\overrightarrow{a} - \overrightarrow{b}\right| \le \left|\overrightarrow{b}\right| - \left|\overrightarrow{a}\right|$

iv) $\left|\overrightarrow{a} - \overrightarrow{b}\right| \ge \left|\overrightarrow{b}\right| - \left|\overrightarrow{a}\right|$

1.4 Multiplying a Vector by a Scalar

In arithmetic, multiplication is defined as repeated addition. For example, $2 + 2 + 2 = 3 \times 2$. In this *Investigation*, you will explore a similar concept with vectors. Remember that the magnitude of a vector is always a non-negative scalar.

Investigation

Scalar Multiples of Vectors

1. Draw any vector $\vec{a}$, with $\left| \vec{a} \right| = 3$ cm.

2. a) Draw the vector $\vec{u} = \vec{a} + \vec{a}$; this is represented as $\vec{u} = 2\vec{a}$.

   b) How do the magnitude and direction of $\vec{u}$ compare with the magnitude and direction of $\vec{a}$?

3. a) Draw the vector $\vec{v} = \vec{a} + \vec{a} + \vec{a} + \vec{a} + \vec{a}$; this is represented as $\vec{v} = 5\vec{a}$.

   b) How do the magnitude and direction of $\vec{v}$ compare with the magnitude and direction of $\vec{a}$?

4. a) Draw the vector $\vec{w} = -\vec{a}$.

   b) What is the magnitude of $\vec{w}$? What is the direction of $\vec{w}$?

5. a) Draw the vector $\vec{z} = -\vec{a} - \vec{a} - \vec{a}$; this is represented as $\vec{z} = -3\vec{a}$.

   b) What is the magnitude of $\vec{z}$? What is the direction of $\vec{z}$?

6. How are the vectors $\vec{a}$, $\vec{u}$, $\vec{v}$, $\vec{w}$, and $\vec{z}$ related geometrically?

The operation of multiplying a vector by a scalar is called *scalar multiplication*.

Take Note

Scalar Multiplication

Let $\vec{v}$ be any vector and let k be a scalar. Then $k\vec{v}$ is a vector that is $|k|$ times as long as $\vec{v}$.

- If $k > 0$, $k\vec{v}$ has the same direction as $\vec{v}$.
- If $k < 0$, $k\vec{v}$ is opposite in direction to $\vec{v}$.
- If $k = 0$, $k\vec{v}$ is the zero vector.

Scalar multiplication has some properties that are similar to properties in arithmetic and algebra. For example, if $\vec{a}$ and $\vec{b}$ are vectors and m is a scalar, then:

$$m(\vec{a} + \vec{b}) = m\vec{a} + m\vec{b}$$

We say that scalar multiplication is *distributive* over vector addition.

Proof that $m(\vec{a} + \vec{b}) = m\vec{a} + m\vec{b}$

Consider the diagram below in which $\triangle DOC$ is similar to $\triangle BOA$ and has sides m times as long ($m > 0$).
Suppose $\overrightarrow{OA} = \vec{a}$ and $\overrightarrow{AB} = \vec{b}$.

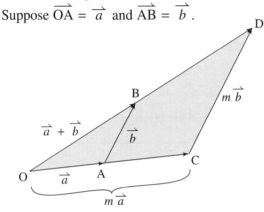

Since OD is m times as long as OB:	Using the Triangle Law:
$\overrightarrow{OD} = m\overrightarrow{OB}$	$\overrightarrow{OD} = \overrightarrow{OC} + \overrightarrow{CD}$
$= m(\vec{a} + \vec{b})$	$= m\vec{a} + m\vec{b}$

Therefore, $m(\vec{a} + \vec{b}) = m\vec{a} + m\vec{b}$, when $m > 0$. To complete the proof, this property must also be proved for the case $m \leq 0$. You will do this in exercise 20. See exercises 18 and 19 for other properties of scalar multiplication.

When one vector is a scalar multiple of another vector, we say that these vectors are *collinear*. For example, on the diagram above, $\overrightarrow{OA}$ and $\overrightarrow{OC}$ are collinear. Vectors $\overrightarrow{AB}$ and $\overrightarrow{CD}$ are also collinear. Observe that if these vectors are drawn tail-to-tail, their heads and tails lie on a line, just as do the heads and tails of vectors $\overrightarrow{OA}$ and $\overrightarrow{OC}$.

Example 1

In rectangle ABCD, X and Y are the midpoints of AB and AD respectively. If $\overrightarrow{AX} = \vec{a}$ and $\overrightarrow{AY} = \vec{b}$, express each vector in terms of $\vec{a}$ and/or $\vec{b}$.

a) $\overrightarrow{AB}$ b) $\overrightarrow{DA}$ c) $\overrightarrow{XY}$

d) $\overrightarrow{YC}$ e) $\overrightarrow{XC}$ f) $\overrightarrow{BD}$

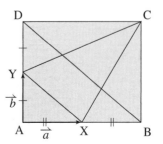

Solution

a) $\overrightarrow{AB} = 2\overrightarrow{AX}$
$$= 2\overrightarrow{a}$$

b) $\overrightarrow{DA} = -2\overrightarrow{AY}$
$$= -2\overrightarrow{b}$$

c) $\overrightarrow{XY} = \overrightarrow{XA} + \overrightarrow{AY}$
$$= -\overrightarrow{a} + \overrightarrow{b}$$

d) $\overrightarrow{YC} = \overrightarrow{YD} + \overrightarrow{DC}$
$$= \overrightarrow{b} + 2\overrightarrow{a}$$

e) $\overrightarrow{XC} = \overrightarrow{XY} + \overrightarrow{YC}$
$$= -\overrightarrow{a} + \overrightarrow{b} + \overrightarrow{b} + 2\overrightarrow{a}$$
$$= \overrightarrow{a} + 2\overrightarrow{b}$$

f) $\overrightarrow{BD} = \overrightarrow{BA} + \overrightarrow{AD}$
$$= -2\overrightarrow{a} + 2\overrightarrow{b}$$

Something to Think About

- In this solution, where are we using the fact that scalar multiplication is distributive over vector addition?

Scalar multiplication of vectors is often combined with addition and subtraction. For example, the diagram shows vectors $\overrightarrow{a} = \overrightarrow{OA}$ and $\overrightarrow{b} = \overrightarrow{OB}$ drawn tail-to-tail. Points M and N are located such that $3\overrightarrow{a} = \overrightarrow{OM}$ and $2\overrightarrow{b} = \overrightarrow{ON}$. Vectors $\overrightarrow{OM}$ and $\overrightarrow{ON}$ form two adjacent sides of a parallelogram. The remaining vertex of the parallelogram is C. According to the Parallelogram Law,

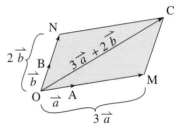

$$3\overrightarrow{a} + 2\overrightarrow{b} = \overrightarrow{OM} + \overrightarrow{ON}$$
$$3\overrightarrow{a} + 2\overrightarrow{b} = \overrightarrow{OC}$$

To get from O to C, we go in the direction of $\overrightarrow{OA}$ and 3 times its length to M. Then we go in the direction of $\overrightarrow{OB}$ and 2 times its length to C. If we replace the numbers 3 and 2 in $3\overrightarrow{a} + 2\overrightarrow{b}$ with other numbers, we proceed in a similar way (if either number is negative, we go in the opposite direction). Doing this is similar to plotting points on a grid.

In the diagram on the following page, vectors $\overrightarrow{a}$ and $\overrightarrow{b}$ define a grid of parallelograms. We can use the grid to express any vector in terms of $\overrightarrow{a}$ and $\overrightarrow{b}$. For example:

$$\overrightarrow{OC} = 3\overrightarrow{a} + 2\overrightarrow{b}$$
$$\overrightarrow{OD} = -\overrightarrow{a} + 4\overrightarrow{b}$$
$$\overrightarrow{OE} = -1.5\overrightarrow{a} - 2\overrightarrow{b}$$
$$\overrightarrow{OF} = 5\overrightarrow{a} - 3\overrightarrow{b}$$

These expressions are called *linear combinations* of $\vec{a}$ and $\vec{b}$. A linear combination of $\vec{a}$ and $\vec{b}$ has the form $s\vec{a} + t\vec{b}$, where s and t are scalars. Since we can use any real numbers for s and t, these linear combinations include all vectors in the plane of the diagram. This is true as long as $\vec{a}$ and $\vec{b}$ are not collinear.

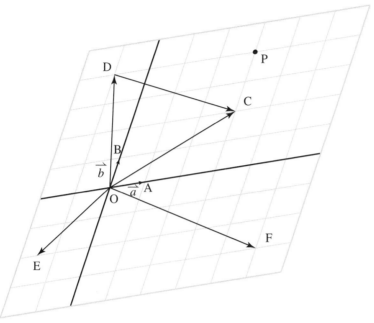

We can express any vector in the plane of the diagram as a linear combination of $\vec{a}$ and $\vec{b}$. For example:

$$\overrightarrow{DC} = \overrightarrow{OC} - \overrightarrow{OD}$$
$$= (3\vec{a} + 2\vec{b}) - (-\vec{a} + 4\vec{b})$$
$$= 4\vec{a} - 2\vec{b}$$

To verify this result, we start at D and go in the direction of $\vec{a}$ and 4 times its length to P. Then we go in the opposite direction of $\vec{b}$ and 2 times its length to C.

Any vector $\vec{c}$ in the plane can be expressed in only one way as a linear combination of two non-collinear vectors $\vec{a}$ and $\vec{b}$ in the plane. That is, $\vec{c} = s\vec{a} + t\vec{b}$ for unique scalars s and t. This is a fundamental property of vectors.

Proof that $\vec{c} = s\vec{a} + t\vec{b}$

Draw $\overrightarrow{OA} = \vec{a}$, $\overrightarrow{OB} = \vec{b}$, and $\overrightarrow{OC} = \vec{c}$.

Construct the parallelogram OA′CB′ with OC as its diagonal, where OA′ contains OA and OB′ contains OB. Then, from the definition of a scalar multiple, $\overrightarrow{OA'} = s\overrightarrow{OA}$ and $\overrightarrow{OB'} = t\overrightarrow{OB}$ for unique numbers s and t. So, $\vec{c} = s\vec{a} + t\vec{b}$ for unique numbers s and t.

Linear Combinations of Vectors

If $\vec{a}$ and $\vec{b}$ are non-zero, non-collinear vectors, then any vector $\overrightarrow{OP}$ in the plane containing $\vec{a}$ and $\vec{b}$ can be expressed as a linear combination of $\vec{a}$ and $\vec{b}$.

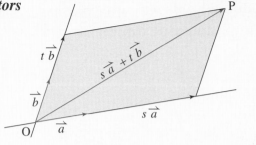

Example 2

Draw any two non-collinear vectors $\vec{u}$ and $\vec{v}$. Then draw each vector on the same diagram.

a) $\vec{w} = 2\vec{u} + 4\vec{v}$ **b)** $\vec{z} = -3\vec{u} - \vec{v}$

Solution

a) Draw $\vec{u}$ and $\vec{v}$ with a common tail, O.
Draw the line l containing $\vec{u}$.
Locate point P on l such that $\overrightarrow{OP} = 2\vec{u}$. Through P, draw a line parallel to $\vec{v}$. Locate point Q on this line such that $\overrightarrow{PQ} = 4\vec{v}$. Then $\vec{w} = \overrightarrow{OQ}$.

b) Locate point R on l such that $\overrightarrow{OR} = -3\vec{u}$. Through R, draw a line parallel to $\vec{v}$. Locate point S on this line such that $\overrightarrow{RS} = -\vec{v}$. Then $\vec{z} = \overrightarrow{OS}$.

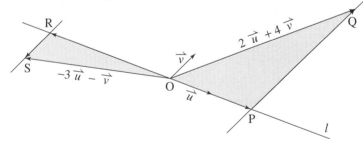

Something to Think About

• Suppose $\vec{u}$ and $\vec{v}$ were collinear. Could the linear combinations still be formed? How would the diagram be affected?

Example 3

The triangles DOC, OCA, and CAB in the diagram are equilateral; $\overrightarrow{OA} = \vec{u}$, and $\overrightarrow{OD} = \vec{v}$. Express each vector as a linear combination of $\vec{u}$ and $\vec{v}$.

a) $\overrightarrow{OC}$

b) $\overrightarrow{AB}$

c) $\overrightarrow{OB}$

d) $\overrightarrow{AD}$

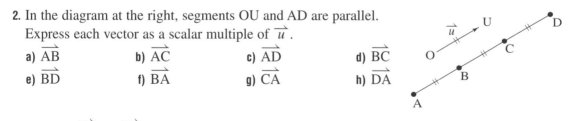

Solution

a) $\overrightarrow{OC} = \overrightarrow{OA} + \overrightarrow{OD}$
$= \vec{u} + \vec{v}$

b) $\overrightarrow{AB} = \overrightarrow{OC}$
$= \vec{u} + \vec{v}$

c) $\overrightarrow{OB} = \overrightarrow{OA} + \overrightarrow{AB}$
$= \vec{u} + \vec{u} + \vec{v}$
$= 2\vec{u} + \vec{v}$

d) $\overrightarrow{AD} = \overrightarrow{AO} + \overrightarrow{OD}$
$= -\vec{u} + \vec{v}$

Observe that parts of *Example 3* can be done in different ways. For example, in part c we could write:

$\overrightarrow{OB} = \overrightarrow{OD} + \overrightarrow{DB}$
$= \vec{v} + 2\vec{u}$
$= 2\vec{u} + \vec{v}$

1.4) Exercises

A

1. A car is travelling northeast at 85 km/h. Draw a scale diagram of its velocity. The car increases its speed by a factor of 1.5. Draw the new velocity vector.

2. In the diagram at the right, segments OU and AD are parallel. Express each vector as a scalar multiple of $\vec{u}$.

a) $\overrightarrow{AB}$

b) $\overrightarrow{AC}$

c) $\overrightarrow{AD}$

d) $\overrightarrow{BC}$

e) $\overrightarrow{BD}$

f) $\overrightarrow{BA}$

g) $\overrightarrow{CA}$

h) $\overrightarrow{DA}$

3. Suppose $\overrightarrow{XZ} = 3\overrightarrow{XY}$. Draw diagrams to support your answers to each question.

a) What conclusions can you draw about line segments XZ and XY?

b) What conclusions can you draw about points X, Y, and Z?

4. Refer to the answers in *Example 1c* and *1f*. What conclusions can you draw about line segments XY and BD?

B

5. In rectangle ABCD (below left), E is the midpoint of AB, $\overrightarrow{AE} = \overrightarrow{u}$, and $\overrightarrow{AD} = \overrightarrow{v}$. Express each vector in terms of $\overrightarrow{u}$ and/or $\overrightarrow{v}$.

   a) $\overrightarrow{AB}$ b) $\overrightarrow{AC}$ c) $\overrightarrow{CE}$

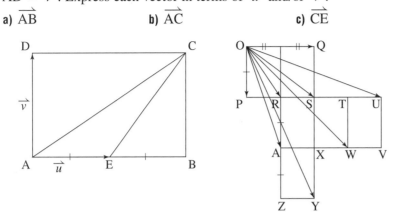

6. Use the diagram above right. Express each vector in terms of $\overrightarrow{OP}$ and $\overrightarrow{OQ}$.

   a) $\overrightarrow{OR}$ b) $\overrightarrow{OU}$ c) $\overrightarrow{OW}$

   d) $\overrightarrow{OS}$ e) $\overrightarrow{OA}$ f) $\overrightarrow{OY}$

7. Use the diagram on page 27.

   a) Determine whether or not $\overrightarrow{DC}$ and $\overrightarrow{OF}$ are parallel.

   b) Express each vector as a linear combination of $\overrightarrow{a}$ and $\overrightarrow{b}$.

     i) $\overrightarrow{DE}$ ii) $\overrightarrow{EF}$ iii) $\overrightarrow{DF}$

8. **Knowledge/Understanding** Use the diagram below.

   a) Express each vector as a linear combination of $\overrightarrow{a}$ and $\overrightarrow{b}$.

     i) $\overrightarrow{OC}$ ii) $\overrightarrow{OD}$ iii) $\overrightarrow{OE}$ iv) $\overrightarrow{OF}$

   b) Use the results of part a to express each vector as a linear combination of $\overrightarrow{a}$ and $\overrightarrow{b}$. Use the diagram to verify your results.

     i) $\overrightarrow{CD}$ ii) $\overrightarrow{DE}$ iii) $\overrightarrow{EF}$ iv) $\overrightarrow{FC}$

     v) $\overrightarrow{DF}$ vi) $\overrightarrow{EC}$

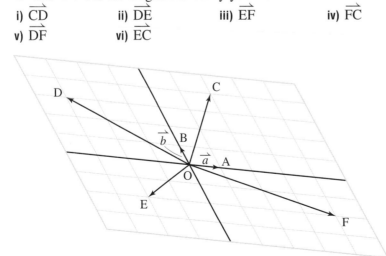

9. Draw a diagram like the one at the right. Then draw each of the following on your diagram.

   a) $3\vec{u}$
   b) $-\frac{1}{4}\vec{v}$
   c) $2\vec{u} - 3\vec{v}$
   d) $-2\vec{u} + 3\vec{v}$
   e) $1.5\vec{u} + 0.5\vec{v}$
   f) $-\vec{u} + 2\vec{v}$

10. Draw any two non-collinear vectors $\vec{u}$ and $\vec{v}$ tail-to-tail. Then draw each of the following on the same diagram.

    a) $3\vec{u} + 4\vec{v}$
    b) $-5\vec{u} + 2\vec{v}$
    c) $2\vec{u} - 3\vec{v}$

11. **Communication** Draw any two non-collinear vectors $\vec{a}$ and $\vec{b}$ tail-to-tail.

    a) Draw each linear combination on the same diagram.
       i) $-2\vec{a} + 3\vec{b}$
       ii) $-\vec{a} + 2\vec{b}$
       iii) $0\vec{a} + \vec{b}$
       iv) $\vec{a} + 0\vec{b}$
       v) $2\vec{a} - \vec{b}$
       vi) $3\vec{a} - 2\vec{b}$

    b) Describe the pattern formed by vectors $\vec{a}$, $\vec{b}$, and all the vectors in part a.

12. **Application** ABCD is a square. The midpoints of BC and CD are M and N respectively.

    a) Express $\overrightarrow{AM}$ and $\overrightarrow{AN}$ as linear combinations of $\overrightarrow{AB}$ and $\overrightarrow{AD}$.

    b) Express $\overrightarrow{AB}$ and $\overrightarrow{AD}$ as linear combinations of $\overrightarrow{AM}$ and $\overrightarrow{AN}$.

13. In the diagram (below left), A and D are the midpoints of opposite sides of parallelogram OBCE, $\overrightarrow{OA} = \vec{u}$, and $\overrightarrow{OE} = \vec{v}$. Express each vector as a linear combination of $\vec{u}$ and $\vec{v}$.

    a) $\overrightarrow{OD}$
    b) $\overrightarrow{OC}$
    c) $\overrightarrow{AC}$
    d) $\overrightarrow{EB}$

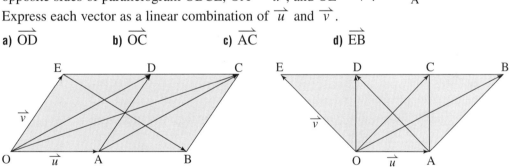

14. The diagram (above right) shows a square and two isosceles right triangles. Also, $\overrightarrow{OA} = \vec{u}$ and $\overrightarrow{OE} = \vec{v}$. Express each vector as a linear combination of $\vec{u}$ and $\vec{v}$.

    a) $\overrightarrow{OD}$
    b) $\overrightarrow{OC}$
    c) $\overrightarrow{OB}$
    d) $\overrightarrow{AD}$

15. OABCDE is a regular hexagon with centre F. Also, $\overrightarrow{OA} = \overrightarrow{u}$ and $\overrightarrow{OE} = \overrightarrow{v}$. Express the vectors in each list as linear combinations of $\overrightarrow{u}$ and/or $\overrightarrow{v}$.

a) $\overrightarrow{OA}, \overrightarrow{AB}, \overrightarrow{BC}, \overrightarrow{CD}, \overrightarrow{DE}, \overrightarrow{EO}$

b) $\overrightarrow{OB}, \overrightarrow{AC}, \overrightarrow{BD}, \overrightarrow{CE}, \overrightarrow{DO}, \overrightarrow{EA}$

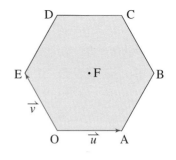

16. Complete parts a and b for each list in exercise 15.

a) Draw a diagram of the vectors drawn tail-to-tail.

b) Describe the pattern formed by the heads of the vectors. Explain the pattern.

17. Thinking/Inquiry/Problem Solving In the diagram below, the points marked on each line are equally spaced.

a) Express each coloured vector as a linear combination of $\overrightarrow{u}$ and $\overrightarrow{v}$.

b) Draw a diagram showing these vectors with a common tail. Describe the pattern formed by the heads of the vectors.

c) Explain the pattern.

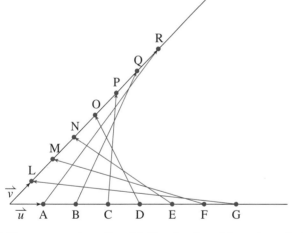

18. Two properties of multiplication in arithmetic and algebra are:

Multiplying by 0: $0x = 0$

Multiplying by 1: $1x = x$

a) Write the corresponding properties of scalar multiplication of vectors.

b) Use the definition of scalar multiplication to prove the properties in part a.

19. Use the definition of scalar multiplication to show that each property is true for positive scalars m and n.

a) $(m + n)\overrightarrow{a} = m\overrightarrow{a} + n\overrightarrow{a}$

b) $m(n\overrightarrow{a}) = (mn)\overrightarrow{a}$

20. On page 25, we used the definition of scalar multiplication to prove that
$m(\vec{a} + \vec{b}) = m\vec{a} + m\vec{b}$ when $m > 0$. Prove this property when $m \leq 0$.

21. Refer to exercise 9. Suppose that $\left|\vec{u}\right| = 1$, $\left|\vec{v}\right| = 1$, and that the angle between $\vec{u}$ and $\vec{v}$ is 120°. Determine the magnitude of each resultant vector in exercise 9.

22. Let $\vec{u} = s\vec{a} + t\vec{b}$ and $\vec{v} = m\vec{a} + n\vec{b}$, where $\vec{a}$ and $\vec{b}$ are any two non-collinear vectors. If $\vec{u}$ and $\vec{v}$ are collinear, show that $s : m = t : n$.

**Hypatia
(c. 370–415)
Born:
Alexandria,
Egypt**

Hypatia of Alexandria was the daughter of a scholar and mathematician. She studied astronomy, astrology, and mathematics, and lectured on mathematics and philosophy at the Platonist school in Alexandria around 400 A.D.

With her father, Hypatia wrote commentaries on the major mathematical works of the time, including those of Ptolemy, Euclid, Diophantus, and Apollonius. She is considered an excellent preserver of early mathematical work.

Despite her early demise, philosophers considered Hypatia a woman of great knowledge and a profound orator.

1.5 Cartesian Vectors

In previous sections, we represented vectors geometrically as directed line segments. If we draw vectors on a coordinate grid, we can represent them as ordered pairs.

Five vectors are shown on the diagram at the right. They are all equal because they have the same magnitude and the same direction. Starting at the tail, the head of each vector is reached by moving 3 right and 2 up. We represent all of these vectors by the same ordered pair, [3, 2]. The square brackets distinguish ordered pairs that represent vectors from ordered pairs that represent points.

We say that [3, 2] is a *Cartesian vector* because it can be plotted on a grid. The numbers 3 and 2 are called *components* of the vector [3, 2]. Observe that the five vectors shown are equal because their corresponding components are equal.

> We often omit the word "Cartesian" because the ordered pair and the square brackets indicate that this vector is on a grid.

Each vector [3, 2] whose tail is not at the origin can be translated to the vector $\overrightarrow{OP}$ whose tail is at the origin. We call $\overrightarrow{OP}$ the *position vector* for [3, 2]. The head of the position vector $\overrightarrow{OP} = [3, 2]$ is the point P(3, 2). In general, the components of a position vector are the coordinates of its head.

Operations on Cartesian Vectors

We often graph Cartesian vectors with tails at the origin. The diagram at the right shows vectors $\overrightarrow{u} = [4, 1]$ and $\overrightarrow{v} = [2, 3]$. To add and subtract these vectors, or to calculate a scalar multiple, we apply the methods developed in earlier sections.

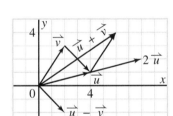

Addition

If we add $\overrightarrow{u}$ and $\overrightarrow{v}$ using the Triangle or Parallelogram Laws, we obtain $\overrightarrow{u} + \overrightarrow{v} = [6, 4]$. We can obtain the same result by adding the corresponding components of $\overrightarrow{u}$ and $\overrightarrow{v}$.

$$\overrightarrow{u} + \overrightarrow{v} = [4, 1] + [2, 3]$$
$$= [4 + 2, 1 + 3]$$
$$= [6, 4]$$

Subtraction

By the definition of subtraction, $\overrightarrow{u} - \overrightarrow{v}$ is the vector from the head of $\overrightarrow{v}$ to the head of $\overrightarrow{u}$ when they are drawn tail-to-tail. The result is the vector [2, –2].

Hence, $\vec{u} - \vec{v} = [2, -2]$. We can obtain the same result by subtracting the corresponding components of $\vec{u}$ and $\vec{v}$.

$$\begin{aligned} \vec{u} - \vec{v} &= [4, 1] - [2, 3] \\ &= [4 - 2, 1 - 3] \\ &= [2, -2] \end{aligned}$$

Scalar Multiplication

By the definition of scalar multiplication, $2\vec{u}$ has the same direction as $\vec{u}$ and is twice as long. Hence, $2\vec{u} = [8, 2]$. We can obtain this result by multiplying the components of $\vec{u}$ by 2.

$$\begin{aligned} 2\vec{u} &= 2[4, 1] \\ &= [2 \times 4, 2 \times 1] \\ &= [8, 2] \end{aligned}$$

By applying the same methods to the general vectors $\vec{u} = [x_1, y_1]$ and $\vec{v} = [x_2, y_2]$, we obtain the following results.

Take Note

Operations on Cartesian Vectors

If $\vec{u} = [x_1, y_1]$ and $\vec{v} = [x_2, y_2]$, then:

$$\vec{u} + \vec{v} = [x_1 + x_2, y_1 + y_2]$$
$$\vec{u} - \vec{v} = [x_1 - x_2, y_1 - y_2]$$
$$k\vec{u} = [kx_1, ky_1]$$

Example 1

Given $\vec{u} = [3, -1]$ and $\vec{v} = [1, 2]$, determine:

a) $\vec{u} + \vec{v}$ b) $\vec{u} - \vec{v}$ c) $3\vec{u} + 2\vec{v}$

Solution

a) $\begin{aligned}[t] \vec{u} + \vec{v} &= [3, -1] + [1, 2] \\ &= [3 + 1, -1 + 2] \\ &= [4, 1] \end{aligned}$

b) $\begin{aligned}[t] \vec{u} - \vec{v} &= [3, -1] - [1, 2] \\ &= [3 - 1, -1 - 2] \\ &= [2, -3] \end{aligned}$

c) $\begin{aligned}[t] 3\vec{u} + 2\vec{v} &= 3[3, -1] + 2[1, 2] \\ &= [9, -3] + [2, 4] \\ &= [11, 1] \end{aligned}$

Components may be used to prove the distributive properties of scalar multiplication you saw in the previous section.

For example: $(m + n)\vec{a} = m\vec{a} + n\vec{a}$

Proof that $(m + n)\vec{a} = m\vec{a} + n\vec{a}$

Suppose $\vec{a} = [a_1, a_2]$.

For any scalars m and n,

$$(m + n)\vec{a} = (m + n)[a_1, a_2]$$
$$= [(m + n)a_1, (m + n)a_2]$$
$$= [ma_1 + na_1, ma_2 + na_2]$$
$$= [ma_1, ma_2] + [na_1, na_2]$$
$$= m\vec{a} + n\vec{a}$$

Example 2

Segment PQ has endpoints P(−2, 3) and Q(4, 1).

a) Find the components of the vector $\vec{PQ}$.

b) Graph both $\vec{PQ}$ and its corresponding position vector.

c) Determine $|\vec{PQ}|$.

Solution

a) Plot the points P and Q.
   Q is 6 units to the right of P and 2 down.
   Thus, $\vec{PQ} = [6, -2]$.

b) Name the corresponding position vector $\vec{u}$.
   Draw $\vec{u}$ with its tail at the origin and its head at $(6, -2)$.
   $\vec{u} = [6, -2]$ is the corresponding position vector.

c) Use the Pythagorean Theorem.
   $$|\vec{PQ}| = \sqrt{6^2 + (-2)^2}$$
   $$|\vec{PQ}| = \sqrt{40}$$
   $$= 2\sqrt{10}$$

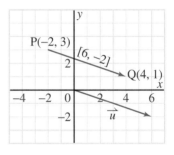

Student Reference

Radical

In Example 2, we can determine $\vec{PQ}$ by subtracting the coordinates of P from the corresponding coordinates of Q.
$$\vec{PQ} = [4 - (-2), 1 - 3]$$
$$= [6, -2]$$

This result can be generalized.

If $A(x_1, y_1)$ and $B(x_2, y_2)$ are any two points, $\vec{AB} = [x_2 - x_1, y_2 - y_1]$.

Proof that $\overrightarrow{AB} = [x_2 - x_1, y_2 - y_1]$

$\overrightarrow{AB} = \overrightarrow{OB} - \overrightarrow{OA}$

$\quad = [x_2, y_2] - [x_1, y_1]$

$\quad = [x_2 - x_1, y_2 - y_1]$

The Vector with Given Head and Tail

If $A(x_1, y_1)$ and $B(x_2, y_2)$ are any two points, the components of the vector $\overrightarrow{AB}$ are found by subtracting the coordinates of its tail, A, from those of its head, B.

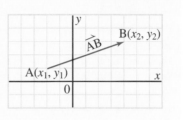

$\overrightarrow{AB} = [x_2 - x_1, y_2 - y_1]$

To determine the magnitude of this vector, use the Pythagorean Theorem.

$\left|\overrightarrow{AB}\right| = \sqrt{(x_2 - x_1)^2 + (y_2 - y_1)^2}$

The results of *Example 1* are illustrated in the diagram below left. The heads of $\overrightarrow{u}$ and $\overrightarrow{v}$ are the points $(3, -1)$ and $(1, 2)$ respectively. Observe that:

- The head of $\overrightarrow{u} + \overrightarrow{v}$ is the point $(4, 1)$.
- The head of $\overrightarrow{u} - \overrightarrow{v}$ is the point $(2, -3)$.
- The head of $3\overrightarrow{u} + 2\overrightarrow{v}$ is the point $(11, 1)$.

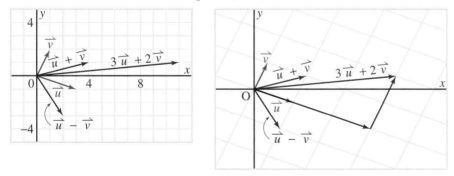

In *Example 1c*, the given expression $3\overrightarrow{u} + 2\overrightarrow{v}$ is a linear combination of $\overrightarrow{u}$ and $\overrightarrow{v}$. Hence, the answer $[11, 1]$ is a linear combination of $[3, -1]$ and $[1, 2]$:

$\quad [11, 1] = 3[3, -1] + 2[1, 2]$

Recall from Section 1.4 that any vector can be expressed as a linear combination of two non-collinear vectors. Therefore, if we are given two such vectors we should be able to express any other vector as a linear combination of them. This is illustrated above right, and in the next example.

Example 3

Given the vectors $\vec{u} = [3, -1]$ and $\vec{v} = [1, 2]$:

a) Express the vector $\vec{w} = [-3, 8]$ as a linear combination of $\vec{u}$ and $\vec{v}$.

b) Illustrate the result in part a on a diagram.

Solution

a) Let $\vec{w} = s\vec{u} + t\vec{v}$ for some real numbers s and t.

$[-3, 8] = s[3, -1] + t[1, 2]$
$[-3, 8] = [3s, -s] + [t, 2t]$
$[-3, 8] = [3s + t, -s + 2t]$

Since these vectors are equal, their components are equal.

$3s + t = -3$ ①
$-s + 2t = 8$ ②

Solve the linear system formed by ① and ②.

Copy ①: $3s + t = -3$
② × 3: $\underline{-3s + 6t = 24}$
Add: $7t = 21$
                         $t = 3$

Substitute $t = 3$ in ①:

$3s + 3 = -3$
$3s = -6$
$s = -2$

Therefore, $\vec{w} = -2\vec{u} + 3\vec{v}$.

b) Vectors $\vec{u}$ and $\vec{v}$ define a grid of parallelograms. On this grid, $\vec{w} = -2\vec{u} + 3\vec{v}$, or $[-3, 8] = -2[3, -1] + 3[1, 2]$

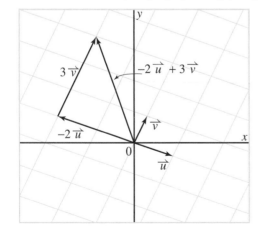

Alternate Representation of Cartesian Vectors

Another way to represent Cartesian vectors is based on linear combinations. In the diagram, $\vec{i}$ and $\vec{j}$ are vectors with length 1 with tails at the origin and heads at (1, 0) and (0, 1) respectively.

A vector with length 1 is called a *unit vector*.

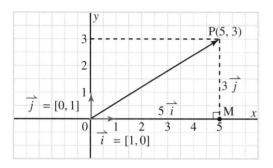

Any Cartesian vector can be represented as a linear combination of these unit vectors, $\vec{i}$ and $\vec{j}$, along the coordinate axes.

We can write the vector $\overrightarrow{OP} = [5, 3]$ as a linear combination of $\vec{i}$ and $\vec{j}$.

$$\overrightarrow{OP} = \overrightarrow{OM} + \overrightarrow{MP}$$
$$\overrightarrow{OP} = 5\,\vec{i} + 3\,\vec{j}$$

Writing $\overrightarrow{OP} = 5\,\vec{i} + 3\,\vec{j}$ and $\overrightarrow{OP} = [5, 3]$ are equivalent ways to express $\overrightarrow{OP}$ in terms of its components.

All operations in *Examples 1* and *3* can be done using vectors written as linear combinations of $\vec{i}$ and $\vec{j}$ instead of as ordered pairs. For example, if $\vec{u} = 3\,\vec{i} - \vec{j}$ and $\vec{v} = \vec{i} + 2\,\vec{j}$, then:

$$3\vec{u} + 2\vec{v} = 3(3\,\vec{i} - \vec{j}) + 2(\vec{i} + 2\,\vec{j})$$
$$= 9\,\vec{i} - 3\,\vec{j} + 2\,\vec{i} + 4\,\vec{j}$$
$$= 11\,\vec{i} + \vec{j}$$

Compare this result with *Example 1c*.

Something to Think About

- Given any Cartesian vector, how can you generate a unit vector with the same direction?

A

1. Represent each vector as an ordered pair.

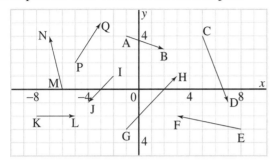

2. The coordinates of the head and tail of vector $\overrightarrow{PQ}$ are given. Represent $\overrightarrow{PQ}$ as an ordered pair, and graph both $\overrightarrow{PQ}$ and its corresponding position vector.

   a) P(3, 4), Q(4, 7)   b) P(4, −1), Q(7, 2)

   c) P(11, 1), Q(6, −3)   d) P(−3, 4), Q(1, −1)

3. The vector $\overrightarrow{v}$ = [−6, −2] has tail A and head B. Graph each point A, and determine the coordinates of B.

   a) A(8, 5)   b) A(−2, −1)   c) A(−4, 3)

4. Point A(5, −3) is the head of vector $\overrightarrow{v}$. Graph each vector $\overrightarrow{v}$ and determine the coordinates of its tail.

   a) $\overrightarrow{v}$ = [8, −5]   b) $\overrightarrow{v}$ = [−2, −4]   c) $\overrightarrow{v}$ = [11, 7]

B

5. Let $\overrightarrow{u}$ = [3, 2].

   a) Determine each vector.
      i) $2\overrightarrow{u}$ ii) $3\overrightarrow{u}$ iii) $5\overrightarrow{u}$ iv) $-4\overrightarrow{u}$

   b) Graph $\overrightarrow{u}$ and the vectors in part a.

   c) Determine the length of each vector in part a.

6. Find a vector that has the same direction as $\overrightarrow{v}$ = [4, 3] and:

   a) is 3 times as long as $\overrightarrow{v}$.   b) is half as long as $\overrightarrow{v}$.

   c) has length 10.   d) has length 1.

7. A quadrilateral has vertices A(4, 1), B(10, 3), C(6, 5), and D(0, 3).

   a) Determine $\overrightarrow{AB}$, $\overrightarrow{BC}$, $\overrightarrow{CD}$, and $\overrightarrow{DA}$.

   b) Determine the magnitudes of the vectors in part a.

   c) What kind of quadrilateral is it? Explain.

8. Repeat exercise 7 for the quadrilateral with vertices A(−2, −1), B(−1, 7), C(6, 3), and D(5, −5).

9. Application

a) Describe how you could use vectors to determine if three given points are collinear.

b) Test your method using each set of points.
  i) P(−3, 1), Q(2, 4), R(5, 6)   ii) D(5, 1), E(1, −5), F(−3, −11)

10. Knowledge/Understanding If $\vec{u} = [−2, 4]$ and $\vec{v} = [3, −1]$, determine:

a) $-\dfrac{1}{2}\vec{u}$ b) $4\vec{v}$ c) $\vec{u} + \vec{v}$

d) $\vec{u} - \vec{v}$ e) $-\vec{u} + 2\vec{v}$ f) $2\vec{u} - 3\vec{v}$

11. Draw a diagram to illustrate the results of exercise 10.

12. If $\vec{a} = [5, 3]$ and $\vec{b} = [2, −4]$, determine:

a) $\vec{a} + 3\vec{b}$ b) $2\vec{a} - 4\vec{b}$ c) $-3\vec{a} + 5\vec{b}$

13. Draw a diagram to illustrate the results of exercise 12.

14. If $\vec{u} = 3\vec{i} - 2\vec{j}$ and $\vec{v} = 2\vec{i} + \vec{j}$, determine:

a) $2\vec{u}$ b) $-3\vec{v}$ c) $\vec{u} + \vec{v}$

d) $\vec{u} - \vec{v}$ e) $4\vec{u} - 2\vec{v}$ f) $-2\vec{u} + 3\vec{v}$

15. Communication Let $\vec{a} = [4, 1]$ and $\vec{b} = [2, 3]$.

a) Determine $\vec{a} + \vec{b}$ and $\vec{a} - \vec{b}$.

b) Graph the vectors $\vec{a}$, $\vec{b}$, $\vec{a} + \vec{b}$, and $\vec{a} - \vec{b}$.

c) Determine $|\vec{a} + \vec{b}|$ and $|\vec{a} - \vec{b}|$.

d) Use your graph to explain why $|\vec{a} + \vec{b}|$ is greater than $|\vec{a} - \vec{b}|$.

e) Suppose $\vec{b}$ were changed to some other vector. Would it always be true that $|\vec{a} + \vec{b}|$ is greater than $|\vec{a} - \vec{b}|$? Illustrate your answer with some examples.

16. Given the vectors $\vec{u} = [3, 0]$ and $\vec{v} = [−1, 2]$:

a) Express the vector $\vec{w} = [2, 8]$ as a linear combination of $\vec{u}$ and $\vec{v}$.

b) Illustrate the results of part a on a diagram.

17. Use the results of exercise 16.

a) Express $\vec{u}$ as a linear combination of $\vec{v}$ and $\vec{w}$.

b) Express $\vec{v}$ as a linear combination of $\vec{u}$ and $\vec{w}$.

18. Given the vectors $\vec{u} = [2, 1]$ and $\vec{v} = [−1, 3]$:

a) Express the vector $\vec{w} = [12, −1]$ as a linear combination of $\vec{u}$ and $\vec{v}$.

b) Illustrate the results of part a on a diagram.

19. Use the results of exercise 18.

    a) Express $\vec{u}$ as a linear combination of $\vec{v}$ and $\vec{w}$.

    b) Express $\vec{v}$ as a linear combination of $\vec{u}$ and $\vec{w}$.

20. Thinking/Inquiry/Problem Solving Let $\vec{m} = [2, -1]$ and $\vec{b} = [0, 5]$.

    a) Determine the components of each vector in this list:

$$\vec{b} + 3\vec{m},\ \vec{b} + 2\vec{m},\ \vec{b} + \vec{m},\ \vec{b} + 0\vec{m},\ \vec{b} - \vec{m},\ \vec{b} - 2\vec{m},\ \vec{b} - 3\vec{m}$$

    b) Graph all seven vectors in part a with tail at $(0, 0)$.

    c) Explain the pattern in the results.

    d) How would the above results be affected if vector $\vec{b}$ were replaced with each vector?

        i) $\vec{b} = [2, 4]$ **ii)** $\vec{b} = [-1, 2]$

21. Let $\vec{u} = [3, -1]$ and $\vec{v} = [1, 2]$.

    a) Determine the components of each vector in this list:

$$-2\vec{u} + 3\vec{v},\ -\vec{u} + 2\vec{v},\ \vec{v},\ \vec{u},\ 2\vec{u} - \vec{v},\ 3\vec{u} - 2\vec{v}$$

    b) Graph all six vectors in part a with tail at $(0, 0)$.

    c) Explain the pattern in the results.

    d) Would you get similar results if you had started with any other non-zero vectors $\vec{u}$ and $\vec{v}$? Explain.

22. Let $\vec{a} = [a_1, a_2]$, $\vec{b} = [b_1, b_2]$, and $\vec{c} = [c_1, c_2]$. Let s and t be any scalars. Prove each property.

    a) $\vec{a} + \vec{b} = \vec{b} + \vec{a}$

    b) $(\vec{a} + \vec{b}) + \vec{c} = \vec{a} + (\vec{b} + \vec{c})$

    c) $s(\vec{a} + \vec{b}) = s\vec{a} + s\vec{b}$

    d) $(s + t)\vec{a} = s\vec{a} + t\vec{a}$

    e) If $\vec{a} + \vec{v} = \vec{0}$, then $\vec{v} = -\vec{a}$.

23. Find a vector whose magnitude is 4 and whose x-component is twice its y-component.

24. If $\vec{u} = [2, -1]$ and $\vec{v} = [x, 3]$, determine all numbers x such that $|\vec{u} + \vec{v}| = 5$.

C

25. Let $\vec{a}$ and $\vec{b}$ be any two non-collinear vectors. Let $\vec{c}$ be a non-zero vector such that $\vec{c} = s\vec{a} + t\vec{b}$, where s and t are constants. Is it always possible to express $\vec{a}$ as a linear combination of $\vec{b}$ and $\vec{c}$? Use a diagram to illustrate your answer.

We have represented vectors geometrically as directed line segments and algebraically as ordered pairs. This means that we have a choice of methods for solving problems involving vectors. In applied situations, a vector is usually described in terms of its magnitude and direction rather than its components. To solve the problem algebraically, we need to determine the components. The procedure for doing this is called *resolving* a vector into its components.

Consider the position vector $\overrightarrow{r} = [a, b]$ shown at the right. The components a and b can be expressed in terms of the magnitude of $\overrightarrow{r}$ and the smallest non-negative angle θ that $\overrightarrow{r}$ makes with the positive x-axis. This angle is called the *direction angle* of $\overrightarrow{r}$.

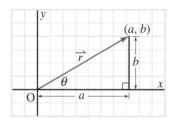

We can use the definitions of cosine and sine to determine the horizontal and vertical components of $\overrightarrow{r}$.

$$\cos \theta = \frac{a}{|\overrightarrow{r}|} \qquad\qquad \sin \theta = \frac{b}{|\overrightarrow{r}|}$$
$$a = |\overrightarrow{r}| \cos \theta \qquad\qquad b = |\overrightarrow{r}| \sin \theta$$

Hence, $\overrightarrow{r} = [a, b]$ or $\left[|\overrightarrow{r}| \cos \theta, |\overrightarrow{r}| \sin \theta \right]$.

Take Note

Writing a Vector Using Magnitude and Direction Angle

Let $\overrightarrow{r}$ be a non-zero vector that makes an angle θ with the positive x-axis. Then:

$$\overrightarrow{r} = \left[|\overrightarrow{r}| \cos \theta, |\overrightarrow{r}| \sin \theta \right]$$

Example 1

An airplane is flying on a bearing of 320° at 500 km/h. Express the velocity in component form.

Solution

Let $\overrightarrow{v}$ represent the velocity of the airplane.
Sketch $\overrightarrow{v}$ on a coordinate grid. A bearing of 320° corresponds to a direction angle of 130°. The plane's speed is 500 km/h, so $|\overrightarrow{v}| = 500$.

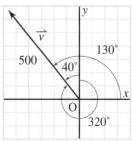

$$\begin{aligned} \overrightarrow{v} &= \left[|\overrightarrow{v}| \cos \theta, |\overrightarrow{v}| \sin \theta \right] \\ &= [500 \cos 130°, 500 \sin 130°] \\ &\doteq [-321, 383] \end{aligned}$$

In component form, the velocity of the airplane is approximately $[-321, 383]$.

Velocities are an important application of vectors. When a boat or airplane is steered toward a particular direction, that direction is called the *heading*. A wind, or a current, can add another velocity component to the craft, so that the actual bearing relative to the ground is not the same as the heading.

The wind or current also affects the velocity of the craft. Recall from *Example 3* in Section 1.2 that the actual velocity of a boat relative to the shore is the resultant of its velocity in still water and the velocity of the current. Similarly, the velocity of an airplane relative to the ground is the resultant of the airplane's velocity in still air and the velocity of the wind.

Example 2

A small aircraft is flying on a heading of 330° at a constant speed of 150 km/h. The wind is blowing on a bearing of 085° with a speed of 40 km/h. Determine the actual speed and direction of the aircraft relative to the ground.

Solution

Method 1: Using geometric vectors

Draw a diagram. $\overrightarrow{OW}$ represents the wind velocity. $\overrightarrow{OH}$ represents the heading.

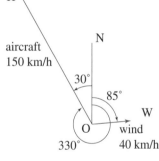

Complete parallelogram OWRH. Then $\overrightarrow{OR}$ represents the velocity of the aircraft relative to the ground.

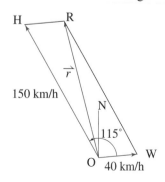

From the given bearings:

$\angle WOH = 30° + 85°$

$\qquad = 115°$

Since OWRH is a parallelogram,

$\angle OHR = 180° - 115°$

$\qquad = 65°$

Use the Cosine Law in $\triangle OHR$ to calculate $|\vec{r}|$.

$|\vec{r}|^2 = 40^2 + 150^2 - 2(40)(150)\cos 65°$

$|\vec{r}| \doteq 138$

Student Reference

Cosine Law
Sine Law

Let $\theta = \angle ROH$. Use the Sine Law to determine θ.

$\dfrac{\sin\theta}{40} = \dfrac{\sin 65°}{138}$

$\sin\theta = \left(\dfrac{40}{138}\right)\sin 65°$

$\theta \doteq 15°$

The bearing of $\overrightarrow{OH}$ is 330°, so the bearing of $\vec{r}$ is 330° + 15°, or 345°.

The aircraft's speed relative to the ground is 138 km/h on a bearing of 345°.

Method 2: Using Cartesian vectors

Draw a diagram on a coordinate system where north is along the positive y-axis. Bearings of 330° and 085° correspond to direction angles of 120° and 5° respectively.

Let $\vec{a}$ represent the velocity of the aircraft in still air.
Let $\vec{w}$ represent the velocity of the wind.
Let $\vec{r}$ represent the velocity of the aircraft relative to the ground.

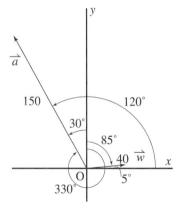

Express $\vec{a}$, $\vec{w}$, and $\vec{r}$ algebraically.

$\vec{a} = [150\cos 120°,\ 150\sin 120°]$

$\vec{w} = [40\cos 5°,\ 40\sin 5°]$

$\vec{r} = \vec{a} + \vec{w}$

$\quad = [150\cos 120°,\ 150\sin 120°] + [40\cos 5°,\ 40\sin 5°]$

$\quad = [150\cos 120° + 40\cos 5°,\ 150\sin 120° + 40\sin 5°]$

$\quad \doteq [-35.2,\ 133.4]$

The magnitude of the resultant is:

$|\vec{r}| = \sqrt{(-35.2)^2 + (133.4)^2}$

$\quad \doteq 138$

The bearing of the aircraft is $270° + \theta$

$\tan\theta = \dfrac{133.4}{35.2}$

$\theta \doteq 75°$

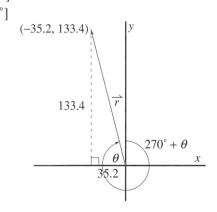

Hence, the bearing is $270° + 75°$, or $345°$.

The aircraft's speed relative to the ground is 138 km/h on a bearing of $345°$.

Another important application of vectors is that of forces acting on an object. When two or more forces act on an object, the forces can be added together. The resultant force produces the same net effect as the individual forces combined.

Example 3

Two tractors are being used to pull a tree stump out of the ground. The larger tractor pulls with a force of 3000 N east. The smaller tractor pulls with a force of 2300 N northeast. Find the magnitude of the resultant force and the angle it makes with the 3000 N force.

Solution

Method 1: Using geometric vectors

Draw a diagram. $\overrightarrow{OA}$ and $\overrightarrow{OB}$ represent the forces exerted by the two tractors.

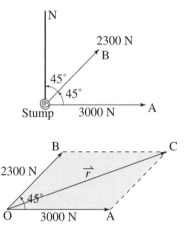

Complete parallelogram OACB. Then $\overrightarrow{OC}$ represents the resultant force.

$\angle BOA = 45°$

OACB is a parallelogram, so:

$\angle OAC = 180° - 45°$
$\qquad = 135°$

Use the Cosine Law to calculate $\left| \overrightarrow{r} \right|$.

$$\left| \overrightarrow{r} \right|^2 = 3000^2 + 2300^2 - 2(3000)(2300)\cos 135°$$
$$\left| \overrightarrow{r} \right| \doteq 4904$$

Let $\theta = \angle COA$. Use the Sine Law to determine θ.

$$\frac{\sin \theta}{2300} = \frac{\sin 135°}{4904}$$

$$\sin \theta = \left(\frac{2300}{4904} \right) \sin 135°$$

$$\theta \doteq 19°$$

The resultant force has a magnitude of 4904 N and acts at an angle of $19°$ to the 3000 N force.

Method 2: Using Cartesian vectors

Draw a diagram on a coordinate system where north is along the positive y-axis.

Let $\overrightarrow{l}$ and $\overrightarrow{s}$ represent the forces exerted by the large and small tractors respectively.

Let $\overrightarrow{r}$ be the resultant force.

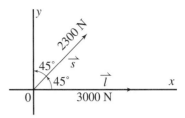

Represent $\overrightarrow{r}$, $\overrightarrow{l}$, and $\overrightarrow{s}$ algebraically.

$$\overrightarrow{l} = [3000, 0]$$
$$\overrightarrow{s} = [2300 \cos 45°, 2300 \sin 45°]$$

$$\begin{aligned}
\overrightarrow{r} &= \overrightarrow{l} + \overrightarrow{s} \\
&= [3000, 0] + [2300 \cos 45°, 2300 \sin 45°] \\
&= [3000 + 2300 \cos 45°, 2300 \sin 45°] \\
&\doteq [4626.3, 1626.3]
\end{aligned}$$

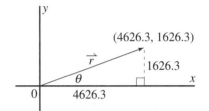

The magnitude of the resultant is:

$$|\overrightarrow{r}| = \sqrt{(4626.3)^2 + (1626.3)^2}$$
$$\doteq 4904$$

The direction of the resultant is:

$$\tan \theta = \frac{1626.3}{4626.3}$$
$$\theta \doteq 19°$$

The resultant force has a magnitude of 4904 N and acts at an angle of 19° to the 3000 N force.

Sometimes an object is acted upon by forces, but does not move. The object is said to be in *equilibrium*, and the sum of the forces acting on the object is the zero vector.

For example, in the diagram at the right, the object at point A is in equilibrium under the forces $\overrightarrow{F_1}$, $\overrightarrow{F_2}$, and $\overrightarrow{F_3}$. Observe that $\overrightarrow{F_3}$ is equal in magnitude but opposite in direction to the resultant of $\overrightarrow{F_1}$ and $\overrightarrow{F_2}$. We can write $\overrightarrow{F_3} = -(\overrightarrow{F_1} + \overrightarrow{F_2})$ or $\overrightarrow{F_1} + \overrightarrow{F_2} + \overrightarrow{F_3} = \overrightarrow{0}$.

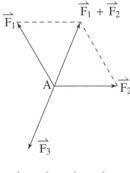

$\overrightarrow{F_3}$ is called the *equilibrant* of $\overrightarrow{F_1}$ and $\overrightarrow{F_2}$ since it counterbalances their resultant. In general, the equilibrant force is equal in magnitude but opposite in direction to the resultant force.

A 100-N weight is suspended from the ceiling by two ropes that make angles of 30° and 45° with the ceiling. Determine the tension in each rope.

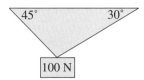

Solution

Draw a diagram. The forces are in equilibrium. The force exerted by the weight is directed downward. The forces in the ropes are along the ropes directed away from the weight.

Let $\overrightarrow{T_1}$ and $\overrightarrow{T_2}$ represent the forces in the two ropes respectively. The tension in each rope is the magnitude of the corresponding force.

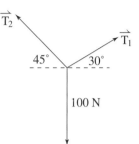

Method 1: Using geometric vectors

Draw a vector diagram and the corresponding triangle diagram. Since the forces are in equilibrium, the resultant of the forces in the two ropes is equal and opposite to the force exerted by the 100 N weight.

Use the Sine Law to find $\left|\overrightarrow{T_1}\right|$ and $\left|\overrightarrow{T_2}\right|$.

$$\frac{\left|\overrightarrow{T_1}\right|}{\sin 45°} = \frac{\left|\overrightarrow{T_2}\right|}{\sin 60°} = \frac{100}{\sin(30° + 45°)}$$

$$\left|\overrightarrow{T_1}\right| = \frac{100\sin 45°}{\sin 75°} \qquad \left|\overrightarrow{T_2}\right| = \frac{100\sin 60°}{\sin 75°}$$

$$\doteq 73 \qquad\qquad\qquad \doteq 90$$

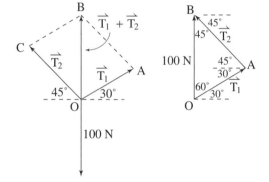

The tensions in the two ropes are 73 N and 90 N respectively.

Method 2: Using Cartesian vectors

Place the diagram on a coordinate system and represent each vector algebraically. Let $\overrightarrow{W}$ represent the force exerted by the 100 N weight.
Let $t_1 = \left|\overrightarrow{T_1}\right|$ and $t_2 = \left|\overrightarrow{T_2}\right|$.

$$\overrightarrow{T_1} = [t_1 \cos 30°, t_1 \sin 30°]$$

$$\overrightarrow{T_2} = [t_2 \cos 135°, t_2 \sin 135°]$$

$$\overrightarrow{W} = [0, -100]$$

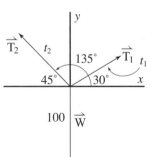

$\overrightarrow{W}$ is equal and opposite to the resultant of $\overrightarrow{T_1}$ and $\overrightarrow{T_2}$.

$$\overrightarrow{T_1} + \overrightarrow{T_2} = -\overrightarrow{W}$$

$$[t_1 \cos 30°, \, t_1 \sin 30°] + [t_2 \cos 135°, \, t_2 \sin 135°] = [0, \, 100]$$

Equate the x- and y-components.

$$t_1 \cos 30° + t_2 \cos 135° = 0 \qquad\qquad ①$$

$$t_1 \sin 30° + t_2 \sin 135° = 100 \qquad\qquad ②$$

Equations ① and ② form a system of linear equations. Solve the system.
Solve equation ① for t_1.

$$t_1 \cos 30° + t_2 \cos 135° = 0$$

$$t_1 = \frac{-t_2 \cos 135°}{\cos 30°} \qquad\qquad ③$$

Substitute equation ③ in equation ② then solve for t_2.

$$\left(\frac{-t_2 \cos 135°}{\cos 30°}\right) \sin 30° + t_2 \sin 135° = 100 \qquad\qquad\qquad \textbf{Recall that } \frac{\sin \theta}{\cos \theta} = \tan \theta.$$

$$-t_2 \cos 135° \tan 30° + t_2 \sin 135° = 100$$

Simplify by removing a common factor of t_2.

$$t_2(-\cos 135° \tan 30° + \sin 135°) = 100$$

$$t_2 = \frac{100}{-\cos 135° \tan 30° + \sin 135°}$$

$$\doteq 90$$

Solve for t_1 by substituting $t_2 = 90$ into equation ③.

$$t_1 \doteq \frac{-90 \cos 135°}{\cos 30°}$$

$$\doteq 73$$

The tensions in the two ropes are 73 N and 90 N respectively.

Something to Think About

- Refer to the solutions for *Examples 2, 3,* and *4.* When is a geometric approach easier to use? When is an algebraic approach easier to use?

Unless stated otherwise, use the method of your choice to complete the following exercises.

A

1. Express each velocity in component form.

   a) a velocity of 150 km/h north

   b) a velocity of 80 km/h southwest

   c) a velocity of 350 km/h on a heading of 035°

   d) a velocity of 140 km/h on a heading of 150°

   e) a velocity of 30 km/h on a heading of 290°

B

2. Buffy and Chie push a crate across a smooth horizontal floor. If Buffy pushes with a force of 50 N west and Chie pushes with a force of 35 N south, determine the resultant force exerted on the crate.

3. **Knowledge/Understanding** Two forces of 220 N and 400 N act on an object. The angle between the forces is 55°.

   a) Determine the magnitude of the resultant force.

   b) Determine the direction of the resultant relative to the 220 N force.

4. Two forces of 20 N and 30 N act on an object at an angle of 120° to each other. Determine the magnitude of the equilibrant force and the angle it makes with the 30 N force.

5. **Application** Two forces act on an object at an angle of 75°. One force is 195 N. The resultant force is 225 N. Determine the second force and the angle that it makes with the resultant.

6. Each of three brothers has tied a rope to a buoy floating on a lake. Paco pulls towards the east with a force of 40 N. Louis pulls towards the southwest with a force of 30 N. What force should Pepe exert to hold his brothers' efforts in equilibrium?

7. **Communication** Two cables hold a 225-N crate as shown in the diagram at the right. Explain how to find the tension in each cable.

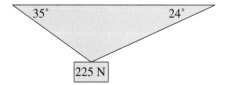

8. A child with weight 100 N is sitting on a swing. Her mother pulls the swing back until the chain makes an angle of 30° with the vertical. Determine the tension in the chain and the magnitude of the pulling force exerted by the mother.

9. A picture of weight 10 N hangs from two wires as shown in the diagram at the right. Determine the tension in each wire assuming that the picture is hung symmetrically on the wires.

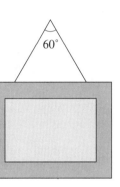

10. A plane is flying southeast at a constant speed of 900 km/h. The wind is blowing towards the north at 100 km/h. Determine the resultant velocity of the plane relative to the ground.

11. A plane flies on a heading of 030° at a constant speed of 600 km/h. If the velocity of the wind is 80 km/h on a bearing of 113°, what is the velocity of the plane relative to the ground?

12. A pilot wishes to fly from Toronto to Montreal, a distance of 508 km on a bearing of 075°. The cruising speed of the plane is 550 km/h. An 80 km/h wind is blowing on a bearing of 125°.

a) What heading should the pilot take to reach his destination?

b) What will be the speed of the plane relative to the ground?

c) How long will the trip take?

13. Thinking/Inquiry/Problem Solving A pilot wishes to fly to a city 80 km due east of her current location. She finds that she must steer the airplane on a bearing 080° to stay on course because there is a wind from the north. If the flight takes 20 min, find the speed of the wind.

1.7) The Dot Product

In earlier sections, you learned how to add and subtract vectors, and how to multiply a vector by a scalar. It is natural to ask whether a useful product of two vectors can be defined and whether the result is a scalar or a vector. There are two products of vectors that have great significance in mathematics and science. We will introduce one of these products in this section, and the other product, the cross product, in Chapter 2.

In your study of science, you may have encountered the concept of the work done by a force when it displaces an object. Both force and displacement have magnitude and direction, and so are vector quantities. The concept of work, a scalar quantity, involves a product of two vectors that is called the *dot product* (see exercises 20 and 21). We define this product as follows.

Take Note

Definition of the Dot Product

Suppose $\vec{a}$ and $\vec{b}$ are two non-zero vectors arranged tail-to-tail forming an angle θ, where $0° \leq \theta \leq 180°$. The dot product, $\vec{a} \cdot \vec{b}$, is defined as follows:

$$\vec{a} \cdot \vec{b} = |\vec{a}||\vec{b}| \cos \theta$$

The dot product is the product of the magnitudes of the two vectors and the cosine of the angle between them. Therefore, the dot product of two vectors is a scalar *not* a vector. It is a real number.

We define the angle between two vectors to be the smaller (non-negative) angle formed when the vectors are arranged tail-to-tail. To calculate the dot product of two vectors, we multiply their magnitudes and the cosine of the angle between them. For example:

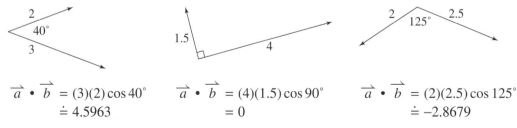

$$\vec{a} \cdot \vec{b} = (3)(2) \cos 40°$$
$$\doteq 4.5963$$

$$\vec{a} \cdot \vec{b} = (4)(1.5) \cos 90°$$
$$= 0$$

$$\vec{a} \cdot \vec{b} = (2)(2.5) \cos 125°$$
$$\doteq -2.8679$$

The three examples above show why the cosine of the angle between the vectors is included in the definition. It introduces a simple relationship between the values of the dot product and the angle between the vectors.

- Since $\cos 90° = 0$, the dot product of perpendicular vectors is 0.
- Since the cosine of an acute angle is positive, vectors forming an acute angle have a positive dot product.
- Since the cosine of an obtuse angle is negative, vectors forming an obtuse angle have a negative dot product.

The definition of the dot product is well suited for calculating dot products of vectors in geometric form. If the vectors are in Cartesian form, we would need to calculate their magnitudes and the angle between them to determine the dot product. Instead of doing that, we can develop a general formula.

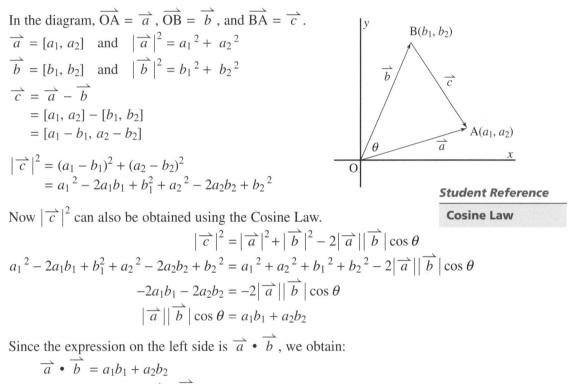

In the diagram, $\overrightarrow{OA} = \vec{a}$, $\overrightarrow{OB} = \vec{b}$, and $\overrightarrow{BA} = \vec{c}$.

$\vec{a} = [a_1, a_2]$ and $|\vec{a}|^2 = a_1{}^2 + a_2{}^2$

$\vec{b} = [b_1, b_2]$ and $|\vec{b}|^2 = b_1{}^2 + b_2{}^2$

$\vec{c} = \vec{a} - \vec{b}$

$\phantom{\vec{c}} = [a_1, a_2] - [b_1, b_2]$

$\phantom{\vec{c}} = [a_1 - b_1, a_2 - b_2]$

$|\vec{c}|^2 = (a_1 - b_1)^2 + (a_2 - b_2)^2$

$\phantom{|\vec{c}|^2} = a_1{}^2 - 2a_1b_1 + b_1^2 + a_2{}^2 - 2a_2b_2 + b_2{}^2$

Student Reference

Cosine Law

Now $|\vec{c}|^2$ can also be obtained using the Cosine Law.

$$|\vec{c}|^2 = |\vec{a}|^2 + |\vec{b}|^2 - 2|\vec{a}||\vec{b}|\cos\theta$$

$$a_1{}^2 - 2a_1b_1 + b_1^2 + a_2{}^2 - 2a_2b_2 + b_2{}^2 = a_1{}^2 + a_2{}^2 + b_1{}^2 + b_2{}^2 - 2|\vec{a}||\vec{b}|\cos\theta$$

$$-2a_1b_1 - 2a_2b_2 = -2|\vec{a}||\vec{b}|\cos\theta$$

$$|\vec{a}||\vec{b}|\cos\theta = a_1b_1 + a_2b_2$$

Since the expression on the left side is $\vec{a} \cdot \vec{b}$, we obtain:

$$\vec{a} \cdot \vec{b} = a_1b_1 + a_2b_2$$

This equation expresses $\vec{a} \cdot \vec{b}$ in terms of its components in Cartesian form.

Take Note

Dot Product of Cartesian Vectors

If $\vec{a} = [a_1, a_2]$ and $\vec{b} = [b_1, b_2]$, then

$\vec{a} \cdot \vec{b} = a_1b_1 + a_2b_2$

The dot product of two Cartesian vectors is the sum of the products of their corresponding components. For example:

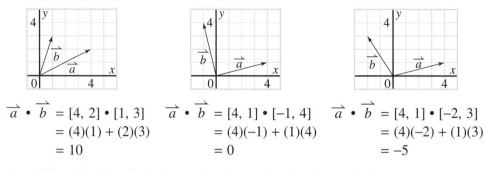

$$\vec{a} \cdot \vec{b} = [4, 2] \cdot [1, 3]$$
$$= (4)(1) + (2)(3)$$
$$= 10$$

$$\vec{a} \cdot \vec{b} = [4, 1] \cdot [-1, 4]$$
$$= (4)(-1) + (1)(4)$$
$$= 0$$

$$\vec{a} \cdot \vec{b} = [4, 1] \cdot [-2, 3]$$
$$= (4)(-2) + (1)(3)$$
$$= -5$$

A useful application of the dot product is to calculate the angle between two vectors. We use the formula below, which we obtain by solving $\vec{a} \cdot \vec{b} = |\vec{a}||\vec{b}| \cos \theta$ for $\cos \theta$.

Take Note

The Angle between Two Vectors

Let $\vec{a}$ and $\vec{b}$ be any two non-zero vectors forming an angle θ.

$$\cos \theta = \frac{\vec{a} \cdot \vec{b}}{|\vec{a}||\vec{b}|}$$

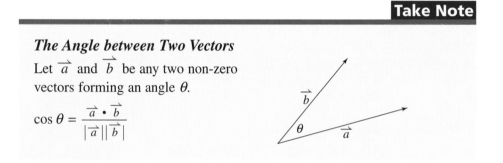

Example

Triangle DEF has vertices D(−2, 6), E(1, 2), and F(5, 4). Calculate ∠DEF.

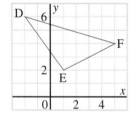

Solution

$$\vec{EF} = [5 - 1, 4 - 2] \quad \text{and} \quad \vec{ED} = [-2 - 1, 6 - 2]$$
$$= [4, 2] \qquad\qquad\qquad = [-3, 4]$$

$$\cos \angle E = \frac{\overrightarrow{EF} \cdot \overrightarrow{ED}}{|\overrightarrow{EF}||\overrightarrow{ED}|}$$

$$= \frac{[4, 2] \cdot [-3, 4]}{\sqrt{4^2 + 2^2}\sqrt{(-3)^2 + 4^2}}$$

$$= \frac{(4)(-3) + (2)(4)}{\sqrt{20}\sqrt{25}}$$

$$= \frac{-2}{5\sqrt{5}}$$

$$\doteq -0.179$$

$$\angle E \doteq 100°$$

Therefore, $\angle DEF \doteq 100°$.

In the *Example*, we could use the same method to calculate the other two angles of the triangle.

1.7 Exercises

A

1. State the angle between the two vectors.

a)

b) 45°

c) 120°

45°

2. Calculate the dot product of each pair of vectors.

a)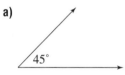

3

5 70°

b) 2   3

150°

c)

2.4

3

3. Calculate the dot product of each pair of vectors.

   a) $\overrightarrow{a} = [6, 2]$, $\overrightarrow{b} = [3, 4]$ **b)** $\overrightarrow{a} = [-2, 5]$, $\overrightarrow{b} = [3, 1]$

   c) $\overrightarrow{a} = [3, 1]$, $\overrightarrow{b} = [-2, 6]$ **d)** $\overrightarrow{a} = [-1, -7]$, $\overrightarrow{b} = [2, -3]$

4. The vectors $\overrightarrow{i} = [1, 0]$ and $\overrightarrow{j} = [0, 1]$ define a unit square. Determine each dot product in two different ways.

   a) $\overrightarrow{i} \cdot \overrightarrow{i}$ **b)** $\overrightarrow{j} \cdot \overrightarrow{j}$ **c)** $\overrightarrow{i} \cdot \overrightarrow{j}$

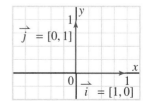

5. Communication The dot product of two vectors $\vec{a}$ and $\vec{b}$ is defined to be $|\vec{a}||\vec{b}|\cos\theta$, where θ is the angle between them. Explain why this is a better definition than $|\vec{a}||\vec{b}|$ or $|\vec{a}||\vec{b}|\sin\theta$.

B

6. Calculate the angle between the given vectors.

a) $\vec{u} = [0, 4]$, $\vec{v} = [5, 1]$ b) $\vec{u} = [3, -2]$, $\vec{v} = [-1, 2]$

c) $\vec{u} = [4, -1]$, $\vec{v} = [-2, -5]$ d) $\vec{u} = [6, 3]$, $\vec{v} = [2, -4]$

7. Suppose the only thing you know about vectors $\vec{u}$ and $\vec{v}$ is that $\vec{u} \cdot \vec{v} = 0.5$. What, if anything, does this tell you about these vectors?

8. Knowledge/Understanding Calculate the angles in each triangle.

a) $\triangle ABC$ with vertices A(−1, 0), B(−2, 1), and C(1, 4)

b) $\triangle PQR$ with vertices P(2, 6), Q(8, 3), and R(−4, 0)

9. a) Graph the quadrilaterals with these vertices:
    Quadrilateral ABCD: A(−4, 2), B(5, 5), C(6, 2), D(−3, −1)
    Quadrilateral PQRS: P(−3, 5), Q(9, 1), R(7, −6), S(−5, −2)

b) Use vectors to show that only one of these quadrilaterals is a rectangle.

10. Use the graph of $\triangle PQR$ (below left).

a) Determine each dot product.
    i) $\overrightarrow{PQ} \cdot \overrightarrow{PR}$ ii) $\overrightarrow{QP} \cdot \overrightarrow{QR}$ iii) $\overrightarrow{RQ} \cdot \overrightarrow{RP}$

b) Explain why two of the dot products in part a are equal.

c) If the triangle was equilateral, how would the three dot products be related?

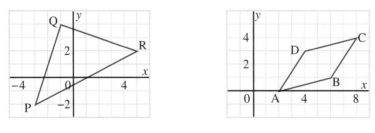

11. Use the graph of parallelogram ABCD (above right).

a) Determine each dot product.
    i) $\overrightarrow{AB} \cdot \overrightarrow{AD}$ ii) $\overrightarrow{CB} \cdot \overrightarrow{CD}$ iii) $\overrightarrow{BA} \cdot \overrightarrow{BC}$ iv) $\overrightarrow{DA} \cdot \overrightarrow{DC}$

b) Describe how the dot products in part a are related.

c) Explain why this relationship applies to all parallelograms.

d) What special case results if the parallelogram is a rectangle?

12. Application

  a) Describe how you could use dot products of vectors to determine whether three given points are the vertices of a right triangle.

  b) Test your method using each set of points.
  i) A(−5, 5), B(−2, 1), C(7, 8)   **ii)** J(−3, −4), K(5, 0), L(2, 6)

13. a) Describe how you could use dot products of vectors to determine whether three given points are collinear.

  b) Test your method using each set of points.
  i) D(−4, 7), E(2, 3), F(8, −1)   **ii)** R(7, 2), S(4, 1), T(−4, −2)

14. The vector [5, 2] represents one side of a square. Write vectors to represent the other three sides.

15. The length of a rectangle is double its width. The vector [4, 2] represents one side of this rectangle. Write all possible vectors that could represent the other sides of this rectangle.

16. Thinking/Inquiry/Problem Solving The dot product has a geometric interpretation as an area. Let $\vec{a} = \overrightarrow{OA}$ and $\vec{b} = \overrightarrow{OB}$ be any two vectors forming an angle θ. Then $\vec{a} \cdot \vec{b}$ can be expressed as $|\vec{a}||\vec{b}| \cos \theta$.

  a) Assume that $0° \le \theta < 90°$. On the diagram below, point C was constructed so that $\angle OCB = 90°$. Then point D was constructed so that OD = OC. Segments OA and OD form adjacent sides of rectangle OAED. Show that $\vec{a} \cdot \vec{b}$ represents the area of this rectangle.

  b) Describe what happens to the rectangle when $\theta = 90°$, and when $\theta = 0°$.

  c) What special case occurs when $\theta = 45°$? Explain.

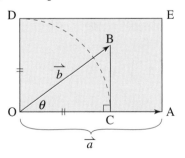

17. Let $\vec{u} = [2, 0]$, $\vec{v} = [2, 1]$, and $\vec{w} = [1, 2]$.

  a) Graph $\vec{u}$, $\vec{v}$, and $\vec{w}$ on a grid.

  b) Determine each of the following:
  i) $(\vec{u} \cdot \vec{v})\vec{w}$ **ii)** $(\vec{v} \cdot \vec{w})\vec{u}$ **iii)** $(\vec{w} \cdot \vec{u})\vec{v}$

  c) Explain what the expressions in part b represent. Illustrate on a diagram.

18. Determine the value of k such that each pair of vectors is perpendicular.

    a) $\vec{a} = [k, -2]$, $\vec{b} = [-1, 2]$ **b)** $\vec{a} = [-3, 4]$, $\vec{b} = [5, k]$

19. Let $\vec{a} = [2, -3]$, $\vec{b} = [-1, 4]$, and $\vec{c} = [5, 2]$. Determine each dot product.

    a) $\vec{a} \bullet (\vec{b} + \vec{c})$ **b)** $(\vec{a} + \vec{b}) \bullet \vec{c}$

    c) $(\vec{a} + \vec{b}) \bullet (\vec{a} + \vec{c})$ **d)** $(2\vec{a} + 3\vec{b}) \bullet (5\vec{a} - 2\vec{b})$

20. In physics, if a constant force is applied to an object and moves it from point A to point B, the *work* done is the product of the magnitude of the displacement and the magnitude of the force in the direction of the displacement. In the diagram, the vector $\vec{d}$ represents the displacement of an object when a force $\vec{F}$ is applied to it at an angle θ to the direction of the displacement.

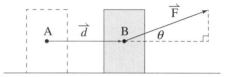

    a) Write an expression for the magnitude of the force in the direction of the displacement.

    b) Show that the work done is $\vec{F} \bullet \vec{d}$.

21. A child pulls a wagon with a constant force of 30 N. How much work is done in moving the wagon 100 m if the handle makes an angle of 30° with the ground? The unit of work is a newton metre, also called a *joule*.

C

22. Refer to exercise 16. Draw a diagram to represent the situation when θ is an obtuse angle.

23. Refer to exercise 16. Draw vectors $\vec{a}$ and $\vec{b}$ as they are in the given diagram.

    a) Construct a different rectangle whose area equals the dot product $\vec{a} \bullet \vec{b}$.

    b) Repeat parts b and c of exercise 16 for your rectangle.

1.8 Properties of the Dot Product and Projections

In Section 1.7 we defined the dot product of the vectors $\vec{a}$ and $\vec{b}$ to be the product of their magnitudes and the cosine of the angle between them:

$$\vec{a} \cdot \vec{b} = |\vec{a}||\vec{b}| \cos \theta$$

Then we showed that for Cartesian vectors $\vec{a} = [a_1, a_2]$ and $\vec{b} = [b_1, b_2]$:

$$\vec{a} \cdot \vec{b} = a_1 b_1 + a_2 b_2$$

To say that $\vec{a} \cdot \vec{b}$ is a product, we need to ensure that it has properties that correspond to properties of products in arithmetic and algebra.

The Commutative Law

Products in arithmetic and algebra satisfy the *commutative law of multiplication,* $xy = yx$. We would expect that the dot product also satisfies this law, but we cannot assume that this is so. To prove this, we can use either the definition of the dot product or Cartesian vectors.

Proof that $\vec{a} \cdot \vec{b} = \vec{b} \cdot \vec{a}$

Using the definition   *Using Cartesian vectors*

$$\vec{a} \cdot \vec{b} = |\vec{a}||\vec{b}| \cos \theta \qquad\qquad \vec{a} \cdot \vec{b} = a_1 b_1 + a_2 b_2$$
$$= |\vec{b}||\vec{a}| \cos \theta \qquad\qquad\qquad = b_1 a_1 + b_2 a_2$$
$$= \vec{b} \cdot \vec{a} \qquad\qquad\qquad\qquad = \vec{b} \cdot \vec{a}$$

Both proofs use the fact that multiplication of real numbers is commutative. However, we cannot assume from this that all properties of multiplication of real numbers carry over to dot products. We have already seen an example of one that does not. The product of two real numbers is a real number, but the dot product of two vectors is *not* a vector. See exercises 3 and 5 for two other properties of products in arithmetic that are not properties of dot products.

Something to Think About

- When writing a dot product, we must always use the dot. The expression $\vec{a} \times \vec{b}$ is not defined for 2-dimensional vectors. The expressions $\vec{a}\,\vec{b}$ and $(\vec{a})(\vec{b})$ are not defined for any vectors.

The Distributive Law

Operations in arithmetic satisfy the distributive law. We saw in Section 1.4 that scalar multiplication is distributive over vector addition: $m(\vec{a} + \vec{b}) = m\vec{a} + m\vec{b}$. The corresponding property for dot products is $\vec{a} \cdot (\vec{b} + \vec{c}) = \vec{a} \cdot \vec{b} + \vec{a} \cdot \vec{c}$.

The proof of this property using the definition is not as straightforward as the proof of the commutative law. However, we can prove it easily using Cartesian vectors.

Proof that $\vec{a} \cdot (\vec{b} + \vec{c}) = \vec{a} \cdot \vec{b} + \vec{a} \cdot \vec{c}$

Let $\vec{a} = [a_1, a_2]$, $\vec{b} = [b_1, b_2]$, and $\vec{c} = [c_1, c_2]$.

$$\text{Then } \vec{b} + \vec{c} = [b_1, b_2] + [c_1, c_2]$$
$$= [b_1 + c_1, b_2 + c_2]$$

$$\vec{a} \cdot (\vec{b} + \vec{c}) = [a_1, a_2] \cdot [b_1 + c_1, b_2 + c_2]$$
$$= a_1(b_1 + c_1) + a_2(b_2 + c_2)$$
$$= a_1 b_1 + a_1 c_1 + a_2 b_2 + a_2 c_2$$

$$\vec{a} \cdot \vec{b} + \vec{a} \cdot \vec{c} = [a_1, a_2] \cdot [b_1, b_2] + [a_1, a_2] \cdot [c_1, c_2]$$
$$= a_1 b_1 + a_2 b_2 + a_1 c_1 + a_2 c_2$$

Since the results are equal, we conclude that:

$$\vec{a} \cdot (\vec{b} + \vec{c}) = \vec{a} \cdot \vec{b} + \vec{a} \cdot \vec{c}$$

Hence, the dot product is distributive over vector addition.

In algebra, the distributive law, $x(y + z) = xy + xz$, is important because it is the basis for expanding products of polynomials, such as $(x + 2)(x + 3) = x^2 + 5x + 6$ and $(x + y)^2 = x^2 + 2xy + y^2$. Since the dot product is distributive over vector addition, we expect that we can do similar calculations with expressions involving dot products. This is true, but with certain differences that take into account that we are working with vectors and not real numbers.

For example, we can write the following equation:

$$(\vec{a} + \vec{b}) \cdot (\vec{a} + \vec{b}) = \vec{a} \cdot \vec{a} + 2\vec{a} \cdot \vec{b} + \vec{b} \cdot \vec{b} \qquad ①$$

This can be proved using the distributive and commutative laws proved above (see exercise 8). Notice that we do not write $(\vec{a} + \vec{b}) \cdot (\vec{a} + \vec{b})$, $\vec{a} \cdot \vec{a}$, and $\vec{b} \cdot \vec{b}$ as squares because we have not defined the square of a vector.

Equation ① contains two terms that are the dot product of a vector with itself. Let us consider one of these terms.

$$\vec{a} \cdot \vec{a} = [a_1, a_2] \cdot [a_1, a_2]$$

$$\vec{a} \cdot \vec{a} = a_1{}^2 + a_2{}^2$$

$$\vec{a} \cdot \vec{a} = |\vec{a}|^2$$

This important result shows that the dot product of a vector with itself is the square of its magnitude.

We can use this property to write equation ① in a different form:

$$|\vec{a} + \vec{b}|^2 = |\vec{a}|^2 + 2\vec{a} \cdot \vec{b} + |\vec{b}|^2$$

Use the definition of $\vec{a} \cdot \vec{b}$ to obtain:

$$|\vec{a} + \vec{b}|^2 = |\vec{a}|^2 + 2|\vec{a}||\vec{b}| \cos \theta + |\vec{b}|^2 \qquad ②$$

Equation ② corresponds to the equation $(x + y)^2 = x^2 + 2xy + y^2$ in algebra. It relates the magnitude of the sum, $\vec{a} + \vec{b}$, to the magnitudes of the vectors $\vec{a}$ and $\vec{b}$. The reason why $\cos \theta$ appears in the equation can be explained geometrically.

Example 1

Expand and simplify: $(2\vec{u} + \vec{v}) \cdot (\vec{u} - 2\vec{v})$

Solution

Use the rules of algebra, but write dot products.

$$(2\vec{u} + \vec{v}) \cdot (\vec{u} - 2\vec{v}) = (2\vec{u}) \cdot (\vec{u}) + (2\vec{u}) \cdot (-2\vec{v}) + \vec{v} \cdot (\vec{u}) + \vec{v} \cdot (-2\vec{v})$$

$$= 2\vec{u} \cdot \vec{u} - 4\vec{u} \cdot \vec{v} + \vec{u} \cdot \vec{v} - 2\vec{v} \cdot \vec{v}$$

$$= 2\vec{u} \cdot \vec{u} - 3\vec{u} \cdot \vec{v} - 2\vec{v} \cdot \vec{v}$$

Take Note

Properties of the Dot Product

Let $\vec{a}$, $\vec{b}$, and $\vec{c}$ be three non-zero, non-collinear vectors arranged tail-to-tail.

$$\vec{a} \cdot \vec{b} = \vec{b} \cdot \vec{a}$$

$$\vec{a} \cdot (\vec{b} + \vec{c}) = \vec{a} \cdot \vec{b} + \vec{a} \cdot \vec{c}$$

$$\vec{a} \cdot \vec{a} = |\vec{a}|^2$$

$$\vec{a} \cdot \vec{0} = 0$$

$\vec{a} \cdot \vec{u} = |\vec{a}|$ where $\vec{u}$ is a unit vector in the same direction as $\vec{a}$

If $\vec{a} \cdot \vec{b} = 0$, then $\vec{a}$ and $\vec{b}$ are perpendicular.

Vectors are used in computer animation to determine the length of a shadow projected onto a flat surface. We use this idea to define the projection of a vector on a vector.

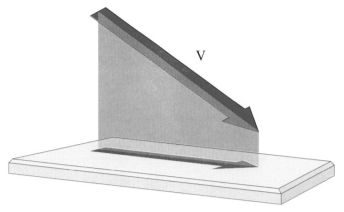

Let $\vec{a} = \overrightarrow{OA}$ and $\vec{b} = \overrightarrow{OB}$ be any two vectors ($\vec{b} \neq \vec{0}$) forming an angle θ. Let N be the point on the line OB such that AN is perpendicular to OB. Then we define the *projection* of $\vec{a}$ on $\vec{b}$ to be the vector $\overrightarrow{ON}$. We think of this as the shadow of $\vec{a}$ on $\vec{b}$.

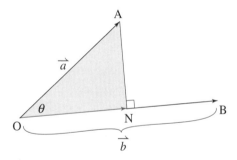

Since $\overrightarrow{ON}$ is a scalar multiple of $\vec{b}$, let $\overrightarrow{ON} = k\vec{b}$. To determine k, we calculate the magnitude of $\overrightarrow{ON}$ in two ways. In the following, we assume that $0° \leq \theta \leq 90°$. The development for $90° < \theta \leq 180°$ is similar, except that the direction of the projection is opposite to the direction of $\vec{b}$.

The magnitude of $\overrightarrow{ON}$ is k times the magnitude of $\vec{b}$. Therefore:

$$\left|\overrightarrow{ON}\right| = k\left|\vec{b}\right| \qquad ③$$

In $\triangle AON$,

$$\left|\overrightarrow{ON}\right| = \left|\vec{a}\right|\cos\theta$$

$$= \left|\vec{a}\right| \times \frac{\vec{a} \cdot \vec{b}}{\left|\vec{a}\right|\left|\vec{b}\right|}$$

$$= \frac{\vec{a} \cdot \vec{b}}{\left|\vec{b}\right|} \qquad ④$$

Compare ③ and ④:

$$k\left|\vec{b}\right| = \frac{\vec{a} \cdot \vec{b}}{\left|\vec{b}\right|}$$

$$k = \frac{\vec{a} \cdot \vec{b}}{\left|\vec{b}\right|^2}$$

$$k = \frac{\vec{a} \cdot \vec{b}}{\vec{b} \cdot \vec{b}}$$

Therefore, the projection of $\vec{a}$ on $\vec{b}$ is $\overrightarrow{ON} = \left(\dfrac{\vec{a} \cdot \vec{b}}{\vec{b} \cdot \vec{b}}\right)\vec{b}$. The projection is a scalar multiple of $\vec{b}$, and the scalar is equal to $\dfrac{\vec{a} \cdot \vec{b}}{\vec{b} \cdot \vec{b}}$.

There is no standard symbol for the projection of $\vec{a}$ on $\vec{b}$. In this book, we will use the symbol $\vec{a} \downarrow \vec{b}$.

Take Note

Projection of a Vector

The projection of $\vec{a}$ on $\vec{b}$ is:

$$\vec{a} \downarrow \vec{b} = \left(\frac{\vec{a} \cdot \vec{b}}{\vec{b} \cdot \vec{b}}\right)\vec{b}$$

where $\vec{b} \neq \vec{0}$

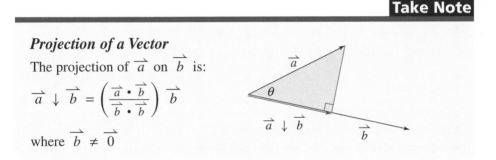

Example 2

If $\vec{u} = [-4, 1]$ and $\vec{v} = [4, 3]$, determine $\vec{u} \downarrow \vec{v}$. Illustrate the result on a diagram.

Solution

$\vec{u} = [-4, 1]$, $\vec{v} = [4, 3]$

$\vec{u} \downarrow \vec{v}$ is a scalar multiple of $\vec{v}$.

The scalar is:

$$\frac{\vec{u} \cdot \vec{v}}{\vec{v} \cdot \vec{v}} = \frac{(-4)(4) + (1)(3)}{4^2 + 3^2}$$

$$= -\frac{13}{25}$$

$$= -0.52$$

Hence,

$$\vec{u} \downarrow \vec{v} = -0.52\vec{v}$$

$$= -0.52[4, 3]$$

$$= [-2.08, -1.56]$$

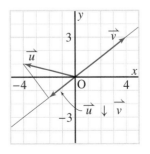

In *Example 2*, notice that $\vec{u} \cdot \vec{v}$ is negative. Hence, the angle between $\vec{u}$ and $\vec{v}$ is obtuse. The projection $\vec{u} \downarrow \vec{v}$ is collinear with $\vec{v}$, but has the opposite direction.

Just like addition, subtraction, and the dot product, vector projection is an operation on two vectors. You will discover some properties of this operation in the exercises (exercises 9, 10, 15–17).

1.8 Exercises

B

1. Expand and simplify.

a) $\vec{a} \cdot (\vec{b} + \vec{c})$

b) $\vec{a} \cdot (\vec{a} + \vec{b})$

c) $\vec{u} \cdot (\vec{u} + 2\vec{v})$

d) $3\vec{u} \cdot (2\vec{u} - 3\vec{v})$

2. Expand and simplify.

a) $(\vec{a} + \vec{b}) \cdot (\vec{a} - \vec{b})$

b) $(\vec{a} - \vec{b}) \cdot (\vec{a} + 2\vec{b})$

c) $(4\vec{a} + \vec{b}) \cdot (\vec{a} + 2\vec{b})$

d) $(2\vec{a} + 3\vec{b}) \cdot (3\vec{a} - 2\vec{b})$

3. Knowledge/Understanding

a) Products in arithmetic and algebra satisfy the *associative law*: $(xy)z = x(yz)$. This law states that more than two numbers can be multiplied together in any order. Does the dot product of vectors satisfy the associative law? Explain.

b) Can any meaning be given to the expression $\vec{a} \cdot \vec{b} \cdot \vec{c}$? Explain.

4. Two properties of multiplication in arithmetic and algebra are:

Multiplying by 0: $0x = 0$

Multiplying by 1: $1x = x$

The corresponding properties of the dot product of vectors are: $\vec{a} \cdot \vec{0} = 0$ and $\vec{a} \cdot \vec{u} = |\vec{a}|$ (where $\vec{u}$ is a unit vector in the same direction as $\vec{a}$). Prove each property using either the definition of the dot product or Cartesian vectors.

5. a) If $\vec{a} \cdot \vec{c} = \vec{b} \cdot \vec{c}$ does it follow that $\vec{a} = \vec{b}$? Draw a diagram to support your explanation.

b) Explain why $\dfrac{\vec{a} \cdot \vec{c}}{\vec{b} \cdot \vec{c}}$ cannot be written as $\dfrac{\vec{a}}{\vec{b}}$.

6. Application OABC is a parallelogram with $\vec{a} = \overrightarrow{OA}$ and $\vec{c} = \overrightarrow{OC}$.

a) Express $\overrightarrow{OB}$ and $\overrightarrow{AC}$ in terms of $\vec{a}$ and $\vec{b}$.

b) What special case of a parallelogram results if $(\vec{c} + \vec{a}) \cdot (\vec{c} - \vec{a}) = 0$? Explain.

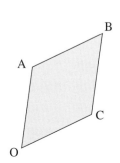

7. **Communication** The term *dot product of vectors* implies that we are multiplying two vectors. List several properties of dot products and illustrate how they resemble corresponding properties of products of real numbers. List two properties of multiplication of real numbers that do not correspond to dot products.

8. a) Use the distributive and commutative laws to prove that:
$$(\vec{a} + \vec{b}) \cdot (\vec{a} + \vec{b}) = \vec{a} \cdot \vec{a} + 2\vec{a} \cdot \vec{b} + \vec{b} \cdot \vec{b}$$

   b) Show that the equation in part a can be written as:
   $$|\vec{a} + \vec{b}|^2 = |\vec{a}|^2 + 2|\vec{a}||\vec{b}| \cos \theta + |\vec{b}|^2$$

   c) What special case results if $\vec{a}$ and $\vec{b}$ are perpendicular?

9. Show that $\vec{a} \downarrow \vec{a} = \vec{a}$. Use a diagram to explain why this is reasonable.

10. Given $\vec{a} = [6, 4]$ and $\vec{b} = [8, -4]$:
    a) Determine $\vec{a} \downarrow \vec{b}$.
    b) Determine $\vec{b} \downarrow \vec{a}$.
    c) Illustrate the results of parts a and b on a diagram.
    d) Does vector projection satisfy the commutative law? Explain.

11. Determine the projection of $\vec{a}$ on $\vec{b}$. Draw a diagram to illustrate each result.
    a) $\vec{a} = [3, 0]$, $\vec{b} = [2, 3]$
    b) $\vec{a} = [4, 5]$, $\vec{b} = [-5, 4]$
    c) $\vec{a} = [-4, -2]$, $\vec{b} = [3, 1]$
    d) $\vec{a} = 2\vec{i} - 3\vec{j}$, $\vec{b} = 6\vec{i} + 2\vec{j}$

12. Triangle PQR has vertices P(-4, 0), Q(-1, 6), and R(3, 4).
    a) Graph $\triangle$PQR.
    b) Determine each projection. Illustrate the result on your graph.
    i) $\overrightarrow{PR} \downarrow \overrightarrow{PQ}$ ii) $\overrightarrow{RP} \downarrow \overrightarrow{RQ}$ iii) $\overrightarrow{PQ} \downarrow \overrightarrow{PR}$ iv) $\overrightarrow{QR} \downarrow \overrightarrow{PR}$
    c) Explain what $\overrightarrow{PQ} \downarrow \overrightarrow{PR} + \overrightarrow{QR} \downarrow \overrightarrow{PR}$ represents.

13. Vectors $\vec{a}$ and $\vec{b}$ are such that $|\vec{a}| = 4$, $|\vec{b}| = 7$, and the angle between them is 60°.
    a) Determine $\vec{a} \downarrow \vec{b}$.
    b) Draw a diagram to illustrate these vectors.

14. Vectors $\vec{u}$ and $\vec{v}$ are such that $|\vec{u}| = 8$, $|\vec{v}| = 11$, and the angle between them is 135°.

 a) Determine $\vec{u} \cdot \vec{v}$.

 b) Draw a diagram to illustrate these vectors.

15. Draw a diagram to illustrate your answer to each question.

 a) Is it possible to have $\vec{a} \cdot \vec{b} = \vec{0}$?

 b) Is it possible for $\vec{a} \cdot \vec{b}$ to be undefined?

16. **Thinking/Inquiry/Problem Solving** Use a diagram to explain what each expression represents.

 a) $(\vec{a} \cdot \vec{b}) \cdot \vec{b}$

 b) $\vec{b} \cdot (\vec{a} \cdot \vec{b})$

 c) $(\vec{a} \cdot \vec{b}) \cdot \vec{a}$

 d) $\vec{a} \cdot (\vec{a} \cdot \vec{b})$

17. Suppose $\vec{a}$, $\vec{b}$, and $\vec{c}$ are non-zero vectors.

 a) Is it possible to have $\vec{a} \cdot \vec{b} = \vec{b} \cdot \vec{a}$?

 b) Explain why $\vec{a} \cdot (\vec{b} \cdot \vec{c}) = \vec{a} \cdot \vec{c}$.

C

18. Find two perpendicular vectors $\vec{u}$ and $\vec{v}$ such that one of these vectors is twice as long as the other, and their sum is the vector [6, 8].

19. a) Show that $\vec{a} \cdot \vec{b} = \frac{1}{4}|\vec{a} + \vec{b}|^2 - \frac{1}{4}|\vec{a} - \vec{b}|^2$.

 b) Write a similar equation for the product xy in algebra. Show that your equation is correct.

A vector quantity has magnitude and direction.

A geometric vector is represented by a directed line segment $\overrightarrow{AB}$ whose length, $\left|\overrightarrow{AB}\right|$, represents the magnitude of the vector, and whose direction shows the direction of the vector.

Equal vectors have the same magnitude and direction.
Opposite vectors have the same magnitude but opposite directions.

Addition and Subtraction of Vectors

Geometric vectors can be added using either:

Triangle Law of Vector Addition   or   Parallelogram Law of Vector Addition

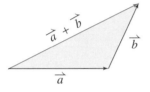 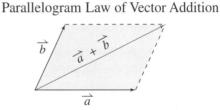

The zero vector, $\overrightarrow{0}$, has zero length and no specified direction.

A geometric vectors may be subtracted by adding its opposite, for example, $\overrightarrow{a} - \overrightarrow{b} = \overrightarrow{a} + (-\overrightarrow{b})$, or arranging the vectors tail-to-tail as shown below.

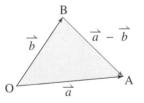

Scalar Multiples of Vectors

A vector $\overrightarrow{v}$ may be multiplied by a scalar k to produce a vector $k\overrightarrow{v}$ whose magnitude is $|k|$ times that of $\overrightarrow{v}$, and whose direction is either the same as that of $\overrightarrow{v}$, if $k > 0$, or opposite, if $k < 0$.

Two vectors are collinear if one vector is a scalar multiple of the other. If $\overrightarrow{a}$ and $\overrightarrow{b}$ are non-zero, non-collinear vectors, then any vector $\overrightarrow{OP}$ in the plane containing $\overrightarrow{a}$ and $\overrightarrow{b}$ can be expressed as a linear combination of $\overrightarrow{a}$ and $\overrightarrow{b}$.

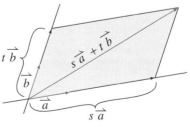

Cartesian Vectors

Vectors can be represented on a coordinate grid. If $A(x_1, y_1)$ and $B(x_2, y_2)$ are two points on a coordinate grid, the components of the vector $\overrightarrow{AB}$ are $[x_2 - x_1, y_2 - y_1]$.

The magnitude of $\overrightarrow{AB}$ is equal to $\sqrt{(x_2 - x_1)^2 + (y_2 - y_1)^2}$. If a non-zero vector $\overrightarrow{v}$ makes an angle θ with the positive x-axis, the components of $\overrightarrow{v}$ are $[\,|\overrightarrow{v}|\cos\theta, \ |\overrightarrow{v}|\sin\theta\,]$.

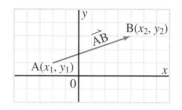

Operations on Cartesian Vectors

If $\overrightarrow{u} = [x_1, y_1]$ and $\overrightarrow{v} = [x_2, y_2]$, then $\overrightarrow{u} + \overrightarrow{v} = [x_1 + x_2, y_1 + y_2]$
$$\overrightarrow{u} - \overrightarrow{v} = [x_1 - x_2, y_1 - y_2]$$
$$k\overrightarrow{u} = [kx_1, ky_1]$$

The Dot Product of Two Vectors

If $\overrightarrow{a}$ and $\overrightarrow{b}$ are two vectors arranged tail-to-tail forming an angle θ, where $0° \le \theta \le 180°$, then the dot product of these vectors is defined to be $\overrightarrow{a} \cdot \overrightarrow{b} = |\overrightarrow{a}||\overrightarrow{b}|\cos\theta$ and $\overrightarrow{a} \cdot \overrightarrow{b}$ is a real number.

So, $\cos\theta = \dfrac{\overrightarrow{a} \cdot \overrightarrow{b}}{|\overrightarrow{a}||\overrightarrow{b}|}$

If $\overrightarrow{a} = [a_1, a_2]$ and $\overrightarrow{b} = [b_1, b_2]$, then $\overrightarrow{a} \cdot \overrightarrow{b} = a_1b_1 + a_2b_2$

Properties of the dot product:
$$\overrightarrow{a} \cdot \overrightarrow{b} = \overrightarrow{b} \cdot \overrightarrow{a}$$
$$\overrightarrow{a} \cdot (\overrightarrow{b} + \overrightarrow{c}) = \overrightarrow{a} \cdot \overrightarrow{b} + \overrightarrow{a} \cdot \overrightarrow{c}$$
$$\overrightarrow{a} \cdot \overrightarrow{a} = |\overrightarrow{a}|^2$$

If $\overrightarrow{a} \cdot \overrightarrow{b} = 0$ for two non-zero, non-collinear vectors $\overrightarrow{a}$ and $\overrightarrow{b}$, then $\theta = 90°$.

Projection of a Vector

The projection of $\overrightarrow{a}$ on $\overrightarrow{b}$ is:
$$\overrightarrow{a} \downarrow \overrightarrow{b} = \left(\frac{\overrightarrow{a} \cdot \overrightarrow{b}}{\overrightarrow{b} \cdot \overrightarrow{b}}\right)\overrightarrow{b}$$

where $\overrightarrow{b} \ne \overrightarrow{0}$.

1. State three examples of scalar quantities and three examples of vector quantities.

2. Construct a scale drawing of each vector. The direction of each vector is given in square brackets.

   a) 20 N [east]   b) 24 m/s [135°]

3. ABCD is a square (below left).

   a) List all pairs of equal vectors.

   b) List all pairs of opposite vectors.

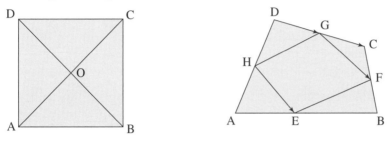

4. Use the diagram above right. Express each vector as the sum of two other vectors.

   a) $\overrightarrow{HE}$ b) $\overrightarrow{GF}$ c) $\overrightarrow{DG}$ d) $\overrightarrow{DC}$

5. In the diagram below, there are 5 congruent rectangles. Express each sum as a single vector.

   a) $\overrightarrow{PG} + \overrightarrow{PR}$ b) $\overrightarrow{RA} + \overrightarrow{RQ}$ c) $\overrightarrow{CD} + \overrightarrow{RS} - \overrightarrow{EF}$ d) $\overrightarrow{DR} + \overrightarrow{QB} - \overrightarrow{FS}$

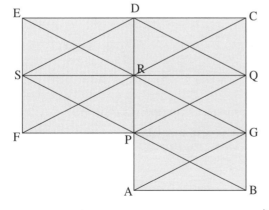

6. In any rectangle ABCD, determine the sum $\overrightarrow{AB} + \overrightarrow{BC} + \overrightarrow{CD} + \overrightarrow{DA}$.

7. Copy each pair of vectors, then draw $\vec{u} - \vec{v}$.

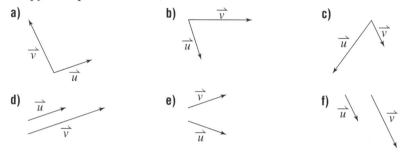

a)

b)

c)

d)

e)

f)

8. In the diagram at the right, $\triangle ABC$ is equilateral and D, E, and F are the midpoints of its sides. Express each vector as the difference of two other vectors.

a) $\overrightarrow{FD}$ b) $\overrightarrow{EB}$

c) $\overrightarrow{CB}$ d) $\overrightarrow{AE}$

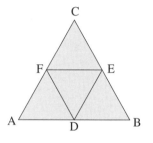

9. Draw any two non-collinear vectors $\vec{u}$ and $\vec{v}$ tail-to-tail. Draw each of the following on the same diagram.

a) $2\vec{u} + 3\vec{v}$ b) $4\vec{u} - 2\vec{v}$

c) $-3\vec{u} + 4\vec{v}$ d) $-\vec{u} - \vec{v}$

10. BCDE is a parallelogram (below left). B is the midpoint of AC, $\overrightarrow{ED} = \vec{u}$, and $\overrightarrow{CD} = \vec{v}$. Express each vector in terms of $\vec{u}$ and/or $\vec{v}$.

a) $\overrightarrow{AC}$ b) $\overrightarrow{AD}$ c) $\overrightarrow{EA}$

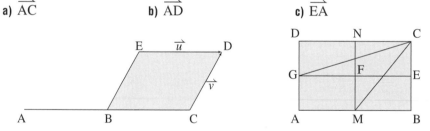

11. ABCD is a rectangle (above right). M, N, E, and G are the midpoints of its sides. Express $\overrightarrow{CG}$ and $\overrightarrow{CM}$ as linear combinations of $\overrightarrow{CD}$ and $\overrightarrow{CB}$.

12. Suppose $\vec{u} = [-1, 2]$.

a) Determine each vector.

   i) $3\vec{u}$ ii) $2\vec{u}$ iii) $-\vec{u}$ iv) $-4\vec{u}$

b) Determine the length of each vector in part a.

13. A triangle has vertices A(3, 2), B(7, 4), and C(–1, 10).

　　a) Determine $\overrightarrow{AB}$, $\overrightarrow{BC}$ and $\overrightarrow{CA}$.

　　b) What kind of triangle is ABC? Justify your answer.

14. Consider the vectors $\overrightarrow{u}$ = [0, 2] and $\overrightarrow{v}$ = [1, –3].

　　a) Express the vector $\overrightarrow{w}$ = [4, 8] as a linear combination of $\overrightarrow{u}$ and $\overrightarrow{v}$.

　　b) Illustrate the results of part a on a diagram.

15. Two forces of 90 N act on an object. The forces make an angle of 48° to each other. Calculate the resultant force and the force that must be applied to the object to create equilibrium.

16. A plane flies on a heading of 120° at a constant speed of 550 km/h. If the velocity of the wind is 50 km/h on a bearing 220°, what is the velocity of the plane with respect to the ground?

17. A boat travels at a speed of 5 m/s in still water. The boat moves directly across a river that is 70 m wide. The water in the river flows at a speed of 2 m/s. How long does it take the boat to cross the river? In what direction is the boat headed when it starts the crossing?

18. Calculate the angle between the given vectors.

　　a) $\overrightarrow{a}$ = [2, 0], $\overrightarrow{b}$ = [4, 3]　　　　**b)** $\overrightarrow{a}$ = [–2, 1], $\overrightarrow{b}$ = [3, 5]

　　c) $\overrightarrow{a}$ = [4, –2], $\overrightarrow{b}$ = [–1, –3]　　**d)** $\overrightarrow{a}$ = [2, 6], $\overrightarrow{b}$ = [–2, –1]

19. Calculate the angles of $\triangle$ABC with vertices A(–3, 5), B(8, 1), and C(–2, –1).

20. Suppose $\overrightarrow{a}$ = [–1, 3], $\overrightarrow{b}$ = [4, 2], and $\overrightarrow{c}$ = [–2, –1]. Determine each product.

　　a) $\overrightarrow{a} \cdot (\overrightarrow{b} + \overrightarrow{c})$　　　　**b)** $(\overrightarrow{a} - \overrightarrow{b}) \cdot \overrightarrow{c}$　　　　**c)** $(2\overrightarrow{a} + \overrightarrow{c}) \cdot (\overrightarrow{a} - 3\overrightarrow{b})$

21. Verify your answers to exercise 20 by first expanding each product.

22. Expand and simplify.

　　a) $(\overrightarrow{u} + 3\overrightarrow{v}) \cdot (2\overrightarrow{u} + \overrightarrow{v})$　　　　**b)** $(3\overrightarrow{a} - 4\overrightarrow{b}) \cdot (3\overrightarrow{a} + 4\overrightarrow{b})$

23. Vectors $\overrightarrow{a}$ and $\overrightarrow{b}$ are such that $|\overrightarrow{a}|$ = 5, $|\overrightarrow{b}|$ = 3, and the angle between them is 150°.

　　a) Draw a diagram to illustrate these vectors.

　　b) Determine $\overrightarrow{a} \downarrow \overrightarrow{b}$ and $\overrightarrow{b} \downarrow \overrightarrow{a}$.

Self-Test

1. **Knowledge/Understanding** ABCD is a parallelogram. Find a single vector that is equivalent to each vector.

   a) $\overrightarrow{CD} - \overrightarrow{DA}$

   b) $\overrightarrow{AD} + \overrightarrow{DC} + \overrightarrow{CP} + \overrightarrow{PB}$

   c) $\overrightarrow{DC} - \overrightarrow{CB}$

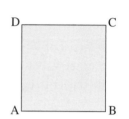

2. ABCD is a square. Determine $\overrightarrow{AB} - \overrightarrow{BC} + \overrightarrow{CD} - \overrightarrow{DA}$.

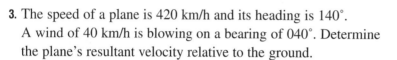

3. The speed of a plane is 420 km/h and its heading is 140°. A wind of 40 km/h is blowing on a bearing of 040°. Determine the plane's resultant velocity relative to the ground.

4. **Application** Suppose $\overrightarrow{a} = [4, 6]$ and $\overrightarrow{b} = [1, 2]$. Determine:

   a) A vector with unit length in the opposite direction to $\overrightarrow{b}$.

   b) The components of a vector with the same magnitude as $\overrightarrow{a}$ making an angle of 60° with the positive x-axis.

   c) $\overrightarrow{a} \downarrow \overrightarrow{b}$

5. If $\overrightarrow{a} = [k, 2]$ and $\overrightarrow{b} = [7, 6]$, where k is a real number, determine all values of k such that $\left| \overrightarrow{a} - \overrightarrow{b} \right| = 5$.

6. **Thinking/Inquiry/Problem Solving** ABCDEF is a hexagon with three pairs of opposite sides parallel. If $\overrightarrow{AB} = \overrightarrow{a}$ and $\overrightarrow{BC} = \overrightarrow{b}$, explain why $\overrightarrow{ED}$, $\overrightarrow{FE}$, and $\overrightarrow{FA}$ can be written as scalar multiples, $k\overrightarrow{a}$ and $l\overrightarrow{b}$, of these vectors. Express the vectors represented by $\overrightarrow{AC}$ and $\overrightarrow{FD}$ in terms of $\overrightarrow{a}$ and $\overrightarrow{b}$. If AC is parallel to FD, determine a relationship between k and l.

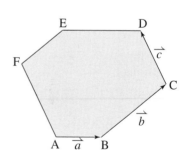

7. **Communication** Draw a large diagram of any two non-collinear vectors $\overrightarrow{a}$ and $\overrightarrow{b}$ tail-to-tail.

   a) Draw each linear combination on the same diagram.

   i) $\frac{1}{4}\overrightarrow{a} + \frac{3}{4}\overrightarrow{b}$ ii) $\frac{1}{2}\overrightarrow{a} + \frac{1}{2}\overrightarrow{b}$ iii) $\frac{3}{4}\overrightarrow{a} + \frac{1}{4}\overrightarrow{b}$

   b) Describe the pattern formed by the vectors $\overrightarrow{a}$, $\overrightarrow{b}$, and the vectors in part a.

Curriculum Expectations

By the end of this chapter, you will:

- Represent Cartesian vectors in three-space as ordered triples.

- Perform the operations of addition, subtraction, scalar multiplication, dot product, and cross product on Cartesian vectors.

- Determine and interpret the dot product and cross product of geometric vectors.

- Determine … the projection of a geometric vector.

In Chapter 1, we limited our work with Cartesian vectors to vectors in the *xy*-plane. These vectors are represented by ordered pairs in a 2-dimensional coordinate system called *2-space*, or R^2. In this chapter and in Chapter 3, we will work with Cartesian vectors in three dimensions. These vectors are represented by ordered triples in a 3-dimensional coordinate system called *3-space*, or R^3.

To work with vectors in 3-space, you need to be able to visualize a 3-dimensional coordinate system that is drawn on a 2-dimensional piece of paper. This investigation is designed to help you do this. Work with a partner to complete the investigation.

Investigation

Introduction to 3-space

The diagram below is a 2-dimensional representation of a 3-dimensional classroom. The classroom has length 10 m, width 8 m, and height 4 m. Use this diagram as a reference for all of the exercises in the investigation.

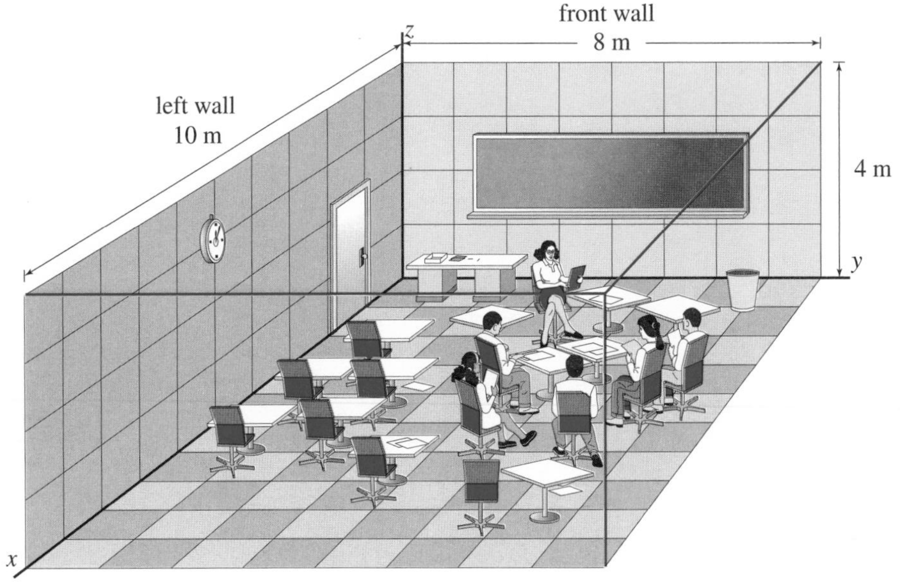

1. We need three coordinate axes to describe the positions of points in 3-space.

   a) Which axis runs along the intersection of the floor and the left wall?

   b) Which axis runs along the intersection of the floor and the front wall?

c) Which axis runs along the intersection of the front wall and the left wall?

d) What point does the front left corner on the floor of the classroom represent?

e) What angle do the three axes make with each other?

2. The three coordinate axes taken in pairs determine three planes called *coordinate planes*. For example, the *xy*-plane is the plane that contains the *x*- and *y*-axes. Which plane do each of these represent?

a) the floor

b) the front wall

c) the left wall

3. The three coordinate planes divide 3-space into 8 regions called *octants*. The octant where *x*, *y*, and *z* are all positive is called the first octant. On the diagram, visualize the negative *x*-, *y*-, and *z*-axes and imagine 7 other rooms situated in the other 7 octants.

a) How many of these rooms are located on the same floor as the classroom? Describe the location of each room, and state the signs of *x*, *y*, and *z* in that room.

b) How many rooms are located on a different floor than the classroom? Describe the location of each room, and state the signs of *x*, *y*, and *z* in that room.

c) Which corner point do all 8 rooms share in common?

4. Points in 3-space are represented by an ordered triple of real numbers (*x*, *y*, *z*). To locate the point (*x*, *y*, *z*) start at the origin. Move *x* units along the *x*-axis, then *y* units parallel to the *y*-axis, then *z* units parallel to the *z*-axis. Determine the coordinates of each point as accurately as you can.

a) the 8 corners of the room

b) the centre of the classroom clock

c) the top left corner of the blackboard

d) the top of the teacher's head

5. **a)** What are the *y*- and *z*-coordinates of every point on the *x*-axis?

   b) What are the *x*- and *z*-coordinates of every point on the *y*-axis?

   c) What are the *x*- and *y*-coordinates of every point on the *z*-axis?

6. a) What is the z-coordinate of every point on the xy-plane?

   b) What is the y-coordinate of every point on the xz-plane?

   c) What is the x-coordinate of every point on the yz-plane?

7. What condition is satisfied by the coordinates of every point on the plane:

   a) containing the back wall?

   b) containing the ceiling?

   c) containing the right wall?

8. The diagram below shows the same classroom. Vector $\overrightarrow{OP}$ is drawn from the origin to the point P(10, 8, 4) on the ceiling that is farthest from the origin. Determine $\left|\overrightarrow{OP}\right|$.

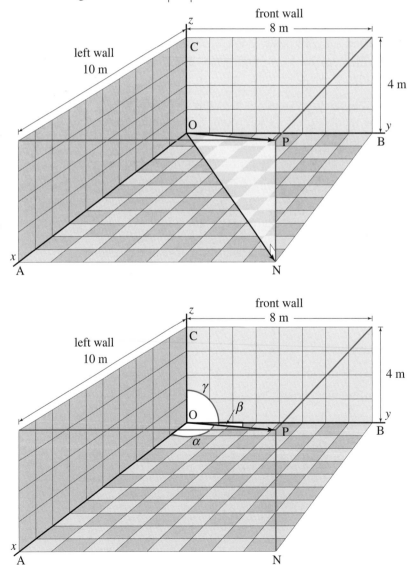

9. Use the diagram at the bottom of the previous page. The three angles $\alpha = \angle POA$, $\beta = \angle POB$, and $\gamma = \angle POC$ formed by $\overrightarrow{OP}$ and the positive x-, y-, and z-axes respectively are called the *direction angles* of $\overrightarrow{OP}$.

   a) Determine each cosine. These are called the *direction cosines* of $\overrightarrow{OP}$.

   i) $\cos \alpha$ **ii)** $\cos \beta$ **iii)** $\cos \gamma$

   b) Use the results of part a to determine the three direction angles α, β, and γ.

   c) Determine $\cos^2 \alpha + \cos^2 \beta + \cos^2 \gamma$.

We plot a point $P(x, y, z)$ in 3-space as shown below. It is customary to draw the x-axis as though it were coming out of the paper towards the viewer, the y-axis to the right, and the z-axis upwards.

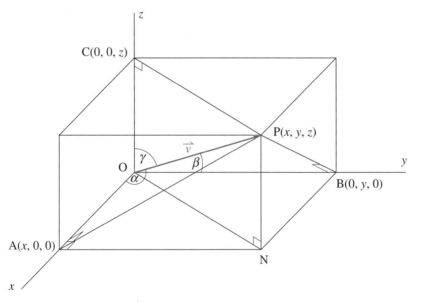

On this diagram, let $\overrightarrow{v} = [x, y, z]$.

To determine the magnitude of $\overrightarrow{v}$, we apply the Pythagorean Theorem to $\triangle ONP$ and $\triangle OAN$.

$$OP^2 = ON^2 + NP^2$$
$$= OA^2 + AN^2 + NP^2$$
$$= OA^2 + OB^2 + OC^2$$
$$= x^2 + y^2 + z^2$$

Therefore, $|\overrightarrow{v}| = \sqrt{x^2 + y^2 + z^2}$.

To describe the direction of $\overrightarrow{v}$, we use its direction angles:
$\alpha = \angle POA$, $\beta = \angle POB$, $\gamma = \angle POC$.

In $\triangle$POA,   In $\triangle$POB,   In $\triangle$POC,

$\angle OAP = 90°$ $\angle OBP = 90°$ $\angle OCP = 90°$

$\cos\alpha = \dfrac{x}{|\vec{v}|}$ $\cos\beta = \dfrac{y}{|\vec{v}|}$ $\cos\gamma = \dfrac{z}{|\vec{v}|}$

We can determine the direction angles from the values of the direction cosines.

Take Note

Magnitude and Direction of Cartesian Vectors in 3-space

Let $\vec{v} = [x, y, z]$ be any non-zero vector.

The magnitude of $\vec{v}$ is $|\vec{v}| = \sqrt{x^2 + y^2 + z^2}$.

The direction of $\vec{v}$ is specified by its direction angles α, β, and γ. These are the angles formed by $\vec{v}$ and the positive x-, y-, and z-axes respectively. Therefore, $0° \le \alpha \le 180°$, $0° \le \beta \le 180°$, and $0° \le \gamma \le 180°$.

To determine the direction angles, use the direction cosines of $\vec{v}$:

$\cos\alpha = \dfrac{x}{|\vec{v}|}$ $\cos\beta = \dfrac{y}{|\vec{v}|}$ $\cos\gamma = \dfrac{z}{|\vec{v}|}$

The direction cosines satisfy the following condition (see exercise 16).

$$\cos^2\alpha + \cos^2\beta + \cos^2\gamma = 1$$

Example 1

The vector $\vec{u} = [3, 5, -2]$ is given.

a) Determine the magnitude of $\vec{u}$.

b) Determine the direction angles of $\vec{u}$.

Solution

a) $\vec{u} = [3, 5, -2]$

$|\vec{u}| = \sqrt{3^2 + 5^2 + (-2)^2}$

$|\vec{u}| = \sqrt{38}$

The magnitude of $\vec{u}$ is $\sqrt{38}$.

b) $\vec{u} = [3, 5, -2]$ and $|\vec{u}| = \sqrt{38}$

$\cos\alpha = \dfrac{3}{\sqrt{38}}$ $\cos\beta = \dfrac{5}{\sqrt{38}}$ $\cos\gamma = \dfrac{-2}{\sqrt{38}}$

$\doteq 0.487$ $\doteq 0.811$ $\doteq -0.324$

$\alpha \doteq 61°$ $\beta \doteq 36°$ $\gamma \doteq 109°$

The direction angles of $\vec{u}$ are approximately 61°, 36°, and 109°.

In R^2, we found the components of a vector whose tail is not at the origin by subtracting the coordinates of its tail from the coordinates of its head. This procedure also applies to vectors in R^3.

The Vector in 3-space with Given Head and Tail

If $A(a_1, a_2, a_3)$ and $B(b_1, b_2, b_3)$ are any two points, then:

$$\overrightarrow{AB} = [b_1 - a_1, b_2 - a_2, b_3 - a_3]$$

The magnitude of this vector is:

$$\left|\overrightarrow{AB}\right| = \sqrt{(b_1 - a_1)^2 + (b_2 - a_2)^2 + (b_3 - a_3)^2}$$

We can use vectors to solve problems involving figures that we visualize on a coordinate grid in 3-space. In many of these problems a diagram is useful, but it is not necessary to plot the points accurately on a grid.

Example 2

Quadrilateral ABCD has vertices A(−3, 4, −1), B(5, 0, 3), C(12, −2, −2), and D(4, 2, −6). Show that ABCD is a parallelogram.

Solution

Sketch the quadrilateral.

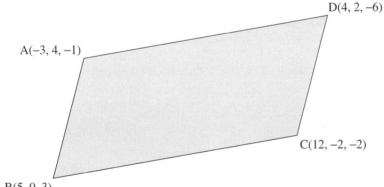

Determine the vectors forming the sides of the quadrilateral.

$\overrightarrow{AB} = [5 - (-3), 0 - 4, 3 - (-1)]$
     $= [8, -4, 4]$

$\overrightarrow{DC} = [12 - 4, -2 - 2, -2 - (-6)]$
     $= [8, -4, 4]$

Therefore, sides AB and DC are parallel.

$$\overrightarrow{AD} = [4 - (-3), 2 - 4, -6 - (-1)]$$
$$= [7, -2, -5]$$
$$\overrightarrow{BC} = [12 - 5, -2 - 0, -2 - 3]$$
$$= [7, -2, -5]$$

Therefore, sides AD and BC are parallel.

Since both pairs of opposite sides are parallel, quadrilateral ABCD is a parallelogram.

Something to Think About

- Why is a diagram needed to solve this problem?
- Why is it not necessary to draw the diagram on a 3-dimensional grid?
- Can this problem be solved in a different way?

Alternate representation of Cartesian vectors

As in 2-space, we can represent Cartesian vectors in 3-space using the unit vectors $\overrightarrow{i} = [1, 0, 0]$, $\overrightarrow{j} = [0, 1, 0]$, and $\overrightarrow{k} = [0, 0, 1]$ along the coordinate axes. For example, the vector $\overrightarrow{u}$ in *Example 1* can be written as:
$$\overrightarrow{u} = 3\overrightarrow{i} + 5\overrightarrow{j} - 2\overrightarrow{k}.$$

2.1 Exercises

B

1. Suppose you start at the origin, move along the *x*-axis a distance of 4 units in the positive direction, and then move downwards a distance of 3 units.

   a) Draw a diagram to represent this situation. What are the coordinates of your position?

   b) Write a vector to represent your position relative to the origin.

   c) Determine the length of the vector in part b.

   d) Determine the direction cosines of the vector in part b.

   e) Determine the direction angles of the vector.

2. Consider these points: P(2, 3, 7), Q(–5, 1, –2), R(0, –3, 0), and S(0, 5, 3). Explain your answer to each question.

a) Which point lies on the *y*-axis?

b) Which point lies on the *yz*-plane?

c) Which point lies below the *xy*-plane?

d) Which point is closest to the *xz*-plane?

e) What is the distance from P to the *xy*-plane?

3. Knowledge/Understanding We can draw the point P(3, 5, 4) as one corner of a box with one corner at O(0, 0, 0) and P at the diagonally opposite corner (below left). The faces of the box are parallel to the coordinate planes. Draw the diagram. Use your diagram to determine:

a) $|\overrightarrow{OP}|$

b) The direction cosines of $\overrightarrow{OP}$.

c) The direction angles of $\overrightarrow{OP}$.

d) Choose one of the coordinate planes. Let N be the corner of the box that lies on the plane you chose. Repeat parts a, b, and c for the vector $\overrightarrow{ON}$.

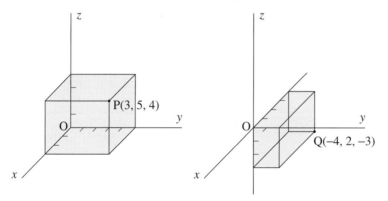

4. The diagram above right shows the point Q(–4, 2, –3) as the corner of a box. The faces of the box are parallel to the coordinate planes. Draw the diagram. Use your diagram to determine:

a) $|\overrightarrow{OQ}|$

b) The direction cosines of $\overrightarrow{OQ}$.

c) The direction angles of $\overrightarrow{OQ}$.

d) Choose one of the coordinate planes. Let N be the corner of the box that lies on the plane you chose. Repeat parts a, b, and c for the vector $\overrightarrow{ON}$.

5. Communication For every point in space, is it possible to draw a box like the ones in exercises 3 and 4? Use diagrams to explain your answer.

6. Graph each vector. Determine its length, its direction cosines, and its direction angles.

a) $\vec{a} = [1, 2, 3]$

b) $\vec{b} = [0, 1, -2]$

c) $\vec{c} = [2, -2, 0]$

d) $\vec{d} = [-4, 0, 0]$

e) $\vec{e} = 3\vec{i} - 4\vec{j} - \vec{k}$

f) $\vec{f} = -2\vec{i} + 2\vec{j} - 2\vec{k}$

7. The coordinates of the head and tail of a vector, $\overrightarrow{PQ}$, are given. Represent $\overrightarrow{PQ}$ as an ordered triple and determine $|\overrightarrow{PQ}|$.

a) P(2, -1, 4), Q(1, -1, 2)

b) P(4, -2, 3), Q(2, 4, -1)

c) P(2, 3, -1), Q(4, 0, 2)

d) P(3, 0, -4), Q(1, 1, 1)

8. The vector $\overrightarrow{AB} = [3, 2, -1]$ has its tail at the point A(6, 9, -2). Determine the coordinates of B.

9. The vector $\overrightarrow{PQ} = [7, 6, -3]$ has its head at the point Q(-2, 1, 3). Determine the coordinates of P.

10. Triangle ABC has vertices A(1, 2, 3), B(4, 0, 5) and C(3, 6, 4).

a) Calculate the lengths of the sides of △ABC.

b) Show that △ABC is a right triangle.

11. Show that △ABC with vertices A(1, 2, 3), B(1, 3, 4), and C(0, 3, 3) is equilateral.

12. **Thinking/Inquiry/Problem Solving**

a) The points A(1, -2, 4), B(3, 5, 7), C(4, 6, 8) are three vertices of parallelogram ABCD. Determine the coordinates of vertex D.

b) Three vertices of a parallelogram have coordinates (2, -5, 1), (4, 1, -2), and (0, 3, 7). Determine all possible coordinates for the fourth vertex.

c) Explain why there is only one answer in part a but three possible answers in part b.

13. Suppose point P lies on the x-axis. What are the direction angles of $\overrightarrow{OP}$?

14. Suppose point P lies on the xy-plane. State as much as you can about the direction angles of $\overrightarrow{OP}$.

15. **Application** In 2-space, the direction of a vector is described using a single angle, such as a bearing or a rotation angle. Explain how direction angles could also be used to describe the direction of a vector in 2-space. Use some examples to illustrate your explanation.

16. Let $\overrightarrow{OP}$ be any vector with direction angles α, β, and γ.

   a) Prove that $\cos^2 \alpha + \cos^2 \beta + \cos^2 \gamma = 1$.

   b) If you know two direction angles of a vector, explain how you could determine the third direction angle. Use an example to illustrate your explanation.

17. Suppose the direction angles of the vector $\overrightarrow{OP}$ are all equal.

   a) Determine the direction angles of $\overrightarrow{OP}$.

   b) Draw a diagram to illustrate the situation.

18. Use the method on pages 36 and 37 in Section 1.5 to prove that $\overrightarrow{AB} = [b_1 - a_1, b_2 - a_2, b_3 - a_3]$ given that $A(a_1, a_2, a_3)$ and $B(b_1, b_2, b_3)$ are two points in 3-space.

C

19. Determine the head of a vector with length 3, and in the same direction as $\overrightarrow{a} = [-3, -4, 12]$.

20. The vector $\overrightarrow{v}$ has length 10, positive and equal x- and y-components, and a z-component of 4. Determine $\overrightarrow{v}$.

21. Determine the coordinates of the point P on the y-axis that is equidistant from $A(1, 6, -5)$ and $B(5, 4, -7)$.

22. Vectors $\overrightarrow{OP}$ and $\overrightarrow{OQ}$ are not collinear. The sum of the direction angles of each vector is $180°$. Draw diagrams to illustrate possible positions of P and Q.

23. Let $\overrightarrow{OP}$ be any vector with direction angles α, β, and γ. Then $\sin \alpha$, $\sin \beta$, and $\sin \gamma$ can be called the *direction sines* of $\overrightarrow{OP}$.

   a) Determine $\sin^2 \alpha + \sin^2 \beta + \sin^2 \gamma$.

   b) Explain why the direction sines are not used for describing the direction of a vector.

Sofia Kovalevskaya (1850–1891)
Born: Moscow, Russia

It is rumoured that Kovalevskaya's nursery walls were papered with notes on differential and integral analysis—her introduction to calculus. Kovalevskaya encountered many obstacles in her pursuit of an education and a career in mathematics. After receiving her PhD, she was refused a university position in Russia, but accepted one in Stockholm. In 1886, Kovalevskaya received a prestigious French prize for her work on the rotation of a solid body about a fixed point. This inspired the Russian Imperial Academy of Sciences to change their rules regarding women, and elect Kovalevskaya a member.

2.2 Operations on Cartesian Vectors in 3-space

In Chapter 1 we defined a vector as a quantity that has both magnitude and direction. We represented vectors in the plane, or 2-space, using ordered pairs, and we developed the operations of addition, subtraction, scalar multiplication, and dot products on these vectors. It is reasonable to expect that these operations can be extended to vectors in 3-space, which are represented by ordered triples. The operations are the same as in 2-space, except there are 3 components to be considered instead of 2.

Take Note

Operations on Cartesian Vectors

If $\vec{u} = [x_1, y_1, z_1]$ and $\vec{v} = [x_2, y_2, z_2]$, then:

$$\vec{u} + \vec{v} = [x_1 + x_2, y_1 + y_2, z_1 + z_2]$$
$$\vec{u} - \vec{v} = [x_1 - x_2, y_1 - y_2, z_1 - z_2]$$
$$k\vec{u} = [kx_1, ky_1, kz_1]$$

Example 1

Given the vectors $\vec{u} = [1, 3, -2]$ and $\vec{v} = [3, -1, 4]$, determine:

a) $\vec{u} + \vec{v}$

b) $2\vec{u} - 3\vec{v}$

Solution

a) $\vec{u} + \vec{v} = [1, 3, -2] + [3, -1, 4]$
$= [1 + 3, 3 - 1, -2 + 4]$
$= [4, 2, 2]$

b) $2\vec{u} - 3\vec{v} = 2[1, 3, -2] - 3[3, -1, 4]$
$= [2, 6, -4] + [-9, 3, -12]$
$= [-7, 9, -16]$

Testing if two vectors are collinear

Two vectors are defined to be collinear if one is a scalar multiple of the other. We can often determine this by inspection. For example, the vectors $\vec{a} = [4, -3, 2]$ and $\vec{b} = [8, -6, 4]$ are collinear because each component of $\vec{b}$ is 2 times the corresponding component of $\vec{a}$. Hence $\vec{b} = 2\vec{a}$, which shows that $\vec{a}$ and $\vec{b}$ are collinear.

Example 2

Determine if the vectors $\vec{a} = [6, -21, 9]$ and $\vec{b} = [-10, 35, -15]$ are collinear.

Solution

Method 1

Attempt to express one of the vectors as a scalar multiple of the other.

Choose either vector, say $\vec{b}$.

Let $\vec{b} = s\vec{a}$ ①

$[-10, 35, -15] = s[6, -21, 9]$

$[-10, 35, -15] = [6s, -21s, 9s]$

Since these vectors are equal, their components are equal.

$6s = -10 \qquad -21s = 35 \qquad 9s = -15$

$s = -\dfrac{5}{3} \qquad\quad s = -\dfrac{5}{3} \qquad\quad s = -\dfrac{5}{3}$

Since the solutions of these equations are all $-\dfrac{5}{3}$, then $\vec{b} = -\dfrac{5}{3}\vec{a}$.

Therefore, $\vec{a}$ and $\vec{b}$ are collinear.

Method 2

The components of each vector have a common factor. Hence,

$$\vec{a} = 3[2, -7, 3]$$
$$\vec{b} = 5[-2, 7, -3]$$
$$\vec{b} = -5[2, -7, 3]$$

Since $\vec{a}$ and $\vec{b}$ are both multiples of the same vector, $[2, -7, 3]$, they are both collinear with this vector, and with each other.

Method 3

Form the ratios of the corresponding components of $\vec{a}$ and $\vec{b}$.

$\vec{a} = [6, -21, 9]$ and $\vec{b} = [-10, 35, -15]$

$\dfrac{6}{-10} = -\dfrac{3}{5} \qquad \dfrac{-21}{35} = -\dfrac{3}{5} \qquad \dfrac{9}{-15} = -\dfrac{3}{5}$

Since each ratio equals $-\dfrac{3}{5}$, therefore $\vec{b} = -\dfrac{5}{3}\vec{a}$.

Therefore, $\vec{a}$ and $\vec{b}$ are collinear.

Something to Think About

- Method 1 is a direct application of the definition of collinear vectors, and will be extended in the next example. Methods 2 and 3 are more efficient methods.

Testing if three vectors are coplanar

In *Example 1*, we determined a linear combination of the vectors $\vec{u} = [1, 3, -2]$ and $\vec{v} = [3, -1, 4]$. Any two non-collinear vectors in $\mathbf{R}^3$ determine a plane, and all linear combinations of these vectors lie on this plane (see exercise 6). There are many other vectors in 3-space that do not lie on this plane. An important problem is to determine whether or not three given vectors lie on the same plane. If they do, they are called *coplanar*.

To determine if three non-collinear vectors are coplanar, we try to express any one of them as a linear combination of the other two.

The problem of determining if three vectors are coplanar will have great significance in Chapter 3.

Example 3

Determine if the vectors $\vec{a} = [1, 2, 3]$, $\vec{b} = [2, -1, 3]$, and $\vec{c} = [8, 1, 15]$ are coplanar.

Solution

Attempt to express one of the vectors as a linear combination of the other two vectors. Choose any one of the vectors, say, $\vec{c}$.

Let $\vec{c} = s\vec{a} + t\vec{b}$ ①

$[8, 1, 15] = s[1, 2, 3] + t[2, -1, 3]$

$[8, 1, 15] = [s + 2t, 2s - t, 3s + 3t]$

Since these vectors are equal, their components are equal.

$$s + 2t = 8 \qquad ②$$
$$2s - t = 1 \qquad ③$$
$$3s + 3t = 15$$
$$\text{or} \qquad s + t = 5 \qquad ④$$

Something to Think About

- Equations ②, ③, and ④ form a system of 3 linear equations in 2 variables. Such a system may or may not have a solution. If there is a solution, we say that the system is *consistent*. If there is no solution, the system is *inconsistent*.

Choose any two of these equations and solve for s and t. Then check to see if the solution satisfies the third equation. Choose equations ② and ③.

$$s + 2t = 8 \qquad ②$$
$$2s - t = 1 \qquad ③$$

Copy ②: $s + 2t = 8$
③ × 2: $\underline{4s - 2t = 2}$
Add: $5s = 10$
                        $s = 2$
Substitute $s = 2$ in ②:
                $2 + 2t = 8$
                    $t = 3$

The solution of the system formed by equations ② and ③ is $s = 2, t = 3$.
If the vectors $\vec{a}$, $\vec{b}$, and $\vec{c}$ are coplanar, these values of s and t will satisfy equation ④.

Substitute $s = 2$ and $t = 3$ in ④:
L.S. $= s + t$ R.S. $= 5$
        $= 2 + 3$
        $= 5$

Since the values of s and t that satisfy equations ② and ③ also satisfy equation ④, substitute these values in equation ① to obtain:

$\vec{c} = 2\vec{a} + 3\vec{b}$

Therefore, $\vec{c}$ is a linear combination of $\vec{a}$ and $\vec{b}$, so the vectors $\vec{a}$, $\vec{b}$, and $\vec{c}$ are coplanar.

The diagram below shows the situation in *Example 3*. The vectors $\vec{a} = [1, 2, 3]$, $\vec{b} = [2, -1, 3]$, and $\vec{c} = [8, 1, 15]$ lie on a plane containing a grid of parallelograms determined by $\vec{a}$ and $\vec{b}$. Their heads are the points A(1, 2, 3), B(2, -1, 3), and C(8, 1, 15). Point C can be reached by starting at the origin and going in the direction of $\vec{a}$ and 2 times its length to M, then going in the direction of $\vec{b}$ and 3 times its length to C.

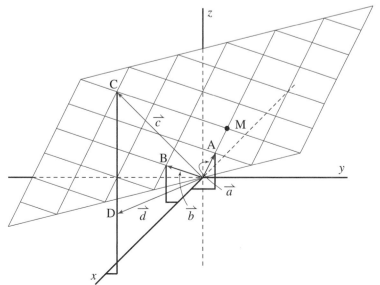

In *Example 3*, suppose the third vector had been $\vec{d} = [8, 1, 5]$. Then equation ④ would have been $3s + 3t = 5$. The values of s and t found by solving equations ② and ③ do not satisfy this equation. This means that $\vec{d}$ cannot be expressed as a linear combination of $\vec{a}$ and $\vec{b}$, so the vectors $\vec{a}$, $\vec{b}$, and $\vec{d}$ are not coplanar. This situation is also shown on the diagram on the previous page. The head of $\vec{d} = [8, 1, 5]$ is D(8, 1, 5), which does not lie on the plane determined by $\vec{a}$ and $\vec{b}$.

Linear dependence and independence

In *Example 2*, we showed that $\vec{b} = -\frac{5}{3}\vec{a}$, which means that $\vec{a}$ and $\vec{b}$ are collinear. In *Example 3*, we showed that $\vec{c} = 2\vec{a} + 3\vec{b}$, which means that $\vec{a}$, $\vec{b}$, and $\vec{c}$ are coplanar. In both examples, we say that the vectors are *linearly dependent*. This is a general term that means "collinear" in R^2 and "coplanar" in R^3. Algebraically, it means that there is a simple equation that relates the vectors (having the form $\vec{b} = s\vec{a}$ in R^2 and $\vec{c} = s\vec{a} + t\vec{b}$ in R^3).

Vectors that are not linearly dependent are *linearly independent*.

2.2) Exercises

A

1. Given $\vec{u} = [5, -1, 3]$ and $\vec{v} = [-1, 2, -4]$, determine:

   a) $\vec{u} + \vec{v}$ b) $\vec{u} - \vec{v}$ c) $-\vec{u}$

   d) $2\vec{u}$ e) $\vec{u} + 2\vec{v}$ f) $3\vec{u} - 2\vec{v}$

2. If $\vec{a} = [2, 3, -2]$ and $\vec{b} = [6, 4, -1]$, determine:

   a) $\vec{a} + \vec{b}$ b) $\vec{a} - \vec{b}$ c) $-2\vec{a}$

   d) $0.5\vec{b}$ e) $-\vec{a} - \vec{b}$ f) $4\vec{a} - 3\vec{b}$

3. If $\vec{u} = 3\vec{i} + \vec{j} - 2\vec{k}$ and $\vec{v} = -\vec{i} + 2\vec{j} + 3\vec{k}$, determine:

   a) $\vec{u} + \vec{v}$ b) $\vec{u} - \vec{v}$ c) $2\vec{u} + \vec{v}$

   d) $\vec{u} - 2\vec{v}$ e) $5\vec{u} + 4\vec{v}$ f) $-2\vec{u} + 3\vec{v}$

4. **Thinking/Inquiry/Problem Solving** Let $\vec{u} = [1, -2, 3]$ and $\vec{v} = [2, 2, 2]$. Suppose you were to graph the following vectors in R^3 with their tails at the origin.

   $\ldots, \vec{u} - 3\vec{v}, \vec{u} - 2\vec{v}, \vec{u} - \vec{v}, \vec{u}, \vec{u} + \vec{v}, \vec{u} + 2\vec{v}, \vec{u} + 3\vec{v}, \ldots$

   Describe how the heads of the vectors would be related.

5. In *Example 3*, we chose $\vec{c}$ and let $\vec{c} = s\vec{a} + t\vec{b}$. Then we found that $\vec{c} = 2\vec{a} + 3\vec{b}$. What result would we have obtained if we had chosen:

   a) $\vec{b}$ instead of $\vec{c}$?

   b) $\vec{a}$ instead of $\vec{c}$?

6. a) How can we be certain that any two non-collinear vectors determine a plane?

   b) How do we know that all linear combinations of these vectors lie in this plane?

B

7. Find a vector that has the same direction as $\vec{a} = [2, -2, 1]$ and:

   a) is 4 times as long as $\vec{a}$.

   b) is half as long as $\vec{a}$.

   c) has length 6.

   d) has length 1.

8. Determine the direction angles of the vectors in exercise 7.

9. Find two different vectors that are collinear with $\vec{u} = [3, 2, -1]$ and:

   a) are twice as long as $\vec{u}$.

   b) have length 1.

10. Any vector that has length 1 is called a *unit vector*. Find two different unit vectors that are collinear with each vector.

    a) $\vec{u} = [4, 3, 0]$ b) $\vec{u} = [-4, 2, 4]$

    c) $\vec{u} = [-1, 4, 1]$ d) $\vec{u} = [2, -3, 5]$

11. Determine if the given vectors are collinear.

    a) $\vec{a} = [2, 5, -3]$, $\vec{b} = [-4, -10, -6]$

    b) $\vec{a} = [-14, -21, 35]$, $\vec{b} = [-6, -9, 15]$

    c) $\vec{a} = [8, 12, -6]$, $\vec{b} = [-12, -18, 9]$

12. Refer to exercise 11. Determine the direction angles of the vectors that are collinear.

13. a) Describe how you can determine if three given points are collinear.

    b) Test these points for collinearity.

       i) P(2, 1, -3), Q(-4, 5, -1), R(5, -1, -4)
       ii) J(2, 6, 2), K(-1, 3, 0), L(8, 1, -2)
       iii) A(0, 2, -1), B(2, 0, -5), C(-3, 5, 5)

14. a) Express the vector $\vec{w} = [8, -9, 3]$ as a linear combination of the vectors $\vec{u} = [1, 3, 0]$ and $\vec{v} = [-2, 5, -1]$.

b) Express $\vec{u}$ as a linear combination of $\vec{v}$ and $\vec{w}$.

c) Express $\vec{v}$ as a linear combination of $\vec{u}$ and $\vec{w}$.

15. Knowledge/Understanding Determine if the following vectors are coplanar.

a) $\vec{a} = [3, -1, 4]$, $\vec{b} = [-2, 3, 1]$, $\vec{c} = [8, 2, 18]$

b) $\vec{a} = [5, 0, -6]$, $\vec{b} = [3, -2, 0]$, $\vec{c} = [6, 1, -9]$

c) $\vec{a} = [2, 7, -1]$, $\vec{b} = [5, -3, 2]$, $\vec{c} = [9, 11, 2]$

16. Communication

a) Explain what it means for three vectors in 3-space to be coplanar.

b) Explain why three given vectors in 3-space may or may not be coplanar.

c) Describe how you can determine if three given vectors in 3-space are coplanar. Make up an example (different from those in this section) to illustrate your method.

17. Determine if the following vectors are linearly dependent.

a) $\vec{u} = [4, 1, 0]$, $\vec{v} = [-8, 5, 2]$, $\vec{w} = [0, 7, 2]$

b) $\vec{u} = [-1, 3, 4]$, $\vec{v} = [2, 1, 5]$, $\vec{w} = [6, -3, 2]$

c) $\vec{u} = [6, 1, -2]$, $\vec{v} = [-2, 5, 3]$, $\vec{w} = [30, -11, -17]$

18. Application In general, four points in 3-space may or may not lie on the same plane.

a) Describe how you could use vectors to determine if four given points are coplanar.

b) Use your method to determine if the following points are coplanar.

i) A(3, 1, 0), B(2, -3, 1), C(-1, 0, 4), D(5, -6, -2)
ii) P(-2, 3, 0), Q(0, 2, 1), R(-1, 0, 3), S(2, 6, -3)
iii) J(4, 1, 3), K(5, 3, 5), L(7, -3, 2), M(-1, 1, 1)

C

19. Let $\vec{a}$ and $\vec{m}$ be non-collinear vectors in R^3. Suppose you were to graph vectors of the form $\vec{p} = \vec{a} + t\vec{m}$ with their tails at the origin, where t is any scalar. What common property would the heads of these vectors have? Explain.

20. Let $\vec{a}$, $\vec{m}$, and $\vec{n}$ be non-collinear vectors in R^3, where $\vec{m}$ and $\vec{n}$ are not collinear. Suppose you were to graph vectors of the form $\vec{p} = \vec{a} + s\vec{m} + t\vec{n}$ with their tails at the origin, where s and t are any scalars. What common property would the heads of these vectors have? Explain.

2.3 The Dot Product in 3-space

In Section 1.7, we defined the dot product of two vectors $\vec{a}$ and $\vec{b}$ as $\vec{a} \cdot \vec{b} = |\vec{a}||\vec{b}|\cos\theta$, where θ is the angle between $\vec{a}$ and $\vec{b}$. Since this definition was given for geometric vectors, we can use it for vectors in 3-space.

In Section 1.7, we also showed that for the vectors $\vec{a} = [a_1, a_2]$ and $\vec{b} = [b_1, b_2]$ in 2-space, $\vec{a} \cdot \vec{b} = a_1b_1 + a_2b_2$. Therefore, we expect that for the vectors $\vec{a} = [a_1, a_2, a_3]$ and $\vec{b} = [b_1, b_2, b_3]$ in 3-space:
$$\vec{a} \cdot \vec{b} = a_1b_1 + a_2b_2 + a_3b_3$$

This result can be derived the same way as the corresponding result in 2-space was derived in Chapter 1 (see exercise 20 on page 98).

Take Note

Dot Products in 3-Space

Let $\vec{a} = [a_1, a_2, a_3]$ and $\vec{b} = [b_1, b_2, b_3]$ be any two non-zero vectors in 3-space arranged tail-to-tail. Let θ represent the angle between $\vec{a}$ and $\vec{b}$.

$$\vec{a} \cdot \vec{b} = |\vec{a}||\vec{b}|\cos\theta$$

$$\vec{a} \cdot \vec{b} = a_1b_1 + a_2b_2 + a_3b_3$$

$\vec{a} \cdot \vec{b}$ is a real number.

We can use dot products to calculate the angle between any two non-zero vectors in 3-space.

Example 1

The vectors $\vec{u} = [-3, 4, 2]$ and $\vec{v} = [2, -1, 3]$ are given.

a) Determine $\vec{u} \cdot \vec{v}$.

b) Calculate the angle between $\vec{u}$ and $\vec{v}$.

Solution

a) $\vec{u} \cdot \vec{v} = [-3, 4, 2] \cdot [2, -1, 3]$
$= (-3)(2) + 4(-1) + 2(3)$
$= -6 - 4 + 6$
$= -4$

b) Use the formula $\vec{u} \cdot \vec{v} = |\vec{u}||\vec{v}| \cos \theta$.

$$\cos \theta = \frac{\vec{u} \cdot \vec{v}}{|\vec{u}||\vec{v}|}$$

$$= \frac{-4}{\sqrt{(-3)^2 + 4^2 + 2^2}\sqrt{2^2 + (-1)^2 + 3^2}}$$

$$= \frac{-4}{\sqrt{29}\sqrt{14}}$$

$$\doteq -0.199$$

$$\theta \doteq 101°$$

The angle between $\vec{u}$ and $\vec{v}$ is approximately $101°$.

Example 2

Triangle ABC has vertices A(2, 3, 1), B(4, 0, −2) and C(3, 6, −4). Calculate ∠B.

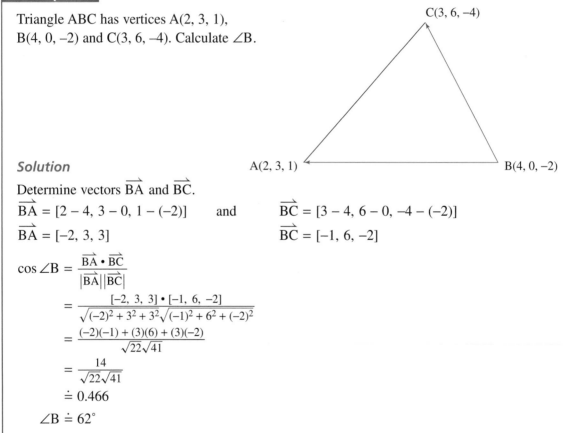

Solution

Determine vectors $\overrightarrow{BA}$ and $\overrightarrow{BC}$.

$\overrightarrow{BA} = [2 - 4, 3 - 0, 1 - (-2)]$ and $\overrightarrow{BC} = [3 - 4, 6 - 0, -4 - (-2)]$

$\overrightarrow{BA} = [-2, 3, 3]$ $\overrightarrow{BC} = [-1, 6, -2]$

$$\cos \angle B = \frac{\overrightarrow{BA} \cdot \overrightarrow{BC}}{|\overrightarrow{BA}||\overrightarrow{BC}|}$$

$$= \frac{[-2, 3, 3] \cdot [-1, 6, -2]}{\sqrt{(-2)^2 + 3^2 + 3^2}\sqrt{(-1)^2 + 6^2 + (-2)^2}}$$

$$= \frac{(-2)(-1) + (3)(6) + (3)(-2)}{\sqrt{22}\sqrt{41}}$$

$$= \frac{14}{\sqrt{22}\sqrt{41}}$$

$$\doteq 0.466$$

$$\angle B \doteq 62°$$

Something to Think About

- Why is a diagram useful for solving the problem in *Example 2*?

In Section 1.8, we defined the projection of a vector on a vector, and showed that the projection of $\vec{a}$ on $\vec{b}$ is:

$$\vec{a} \downarrow \vec{b} = \left(\frac{\vec{a} \cdot \vec{b}}{\vec{b} \cdot \vec{b}}\right) \vec{b} \text{ where } \vec{b} \neq 0$$

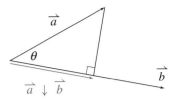

Since we derived this formula using geometric vectors, we can use it for vectors in 3-space.

Example 3

Given $\vec{u} = [3, -2, 4]$ and $\vec{v} = [-1, 5, 2]$:

a) Determine $\vec{u} \downarrow \vec{v}$, and illustrate the result on a diagram.

b) Determine $|\vec{u} \downarrow \vec{v}|$.

Solution

a) $\vec{u} \downarrow \vec{v}$ is a scalar multiple of $\vec{v}$. The scalar is:

$$\frac{\vec{u} \cdot \vec{v}}{\vec{v} \cdot \vec{v}} = \frac{[3, -2, 4] \cdot [-1, 5, 2]}{[-1, 5, 2] \cdot [-1, 5, 2]}$$

$$= \frac{(3)(-1) + (-2)(5) + (4)(2)}{(-1)^2 + 5^2 + 2^2}$$

$$= -\frac{1}{6}$$

Since the result is negative, the direction of $\vec{u} \downarrow \vec{v}$ is opposite to the direction of $\vec{v}$.

$$\vec{u} \downarrow \vec{v} = \left(\frac{\vec{u} \cdot \vec{v}}{\vec{v} \cdot \vec{v}}\right) \vec{v}$$

$$= -\frac{1}{6}[-1, 5, 2]$$

$$= \left[\frac{1}{6}, -\frac{5}{6}, -\frac{1}{3}\right]$$

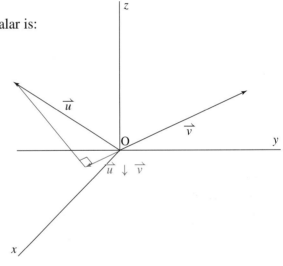

b) $|\vec{u} \downarrow \vec{v}|$ represents the magnitude of $\vec{u} \downarrow \vec{v}$. Use the result of part a to determine this magnitude.

$$|\vec{u} \downarrow \vec{v}| = \sqrt{\left(\frac{1}{6}\right)^2 + \left(-\frac{5}{6}\right)^2 + \left(-\frac{1}{3}\right)^2}$$

$$|\vec{u} \downarrow \vec{v}| = \sqrt{\frac{5}{6}}$$

Something to Think About

- There is another way to calculate the magnitude of $|\vec{u} \downarrow \vec{v}|$ (see exercise 17).

Two non-collinear vectors in 3-space define a plane. An important problem is to find a vector that is perpendicular to the plane. There are infinitely many such vectors, but they are all scalar multiples of one another, as illustrated in the diagram.

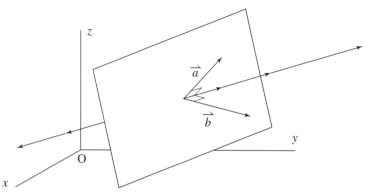

In many problems, it is sufficient to find only one vector that is perpendicular to the plane determined by two non-collinear vectors. The method for finding such a vector is illustrated in the following example.

Example 4

The vectors $\vec{a} = [2, 1, -1]$ and $\vec{b} = [1, 2, -3]$ are given. Determine a vector that is perpendicular to both $\vec{a}$ and $\vec{b}$. Check the result.

Solution

Let $\vec{n} = [x, y, z]$ represent a vector that is perpendicular to both $\vec{a}$ and $\vec{b}$. Then the dot products $\vec{a} \bullet \vec{n}$ and $\vec{b} \bullet \vec{n}$ are both equal to 0.

$\vec{a} \bullet \vec{n} = [2, 1, -1] \bullet [x, y, z]$ and $\vec{b} \bullet \vec{n} = [1, 2, -3] \bullet [x, y, z]$
$\vec{a} \bullet \vec{n} = 2x + y - z$ $\qquad\qquad\qquad \vec{b} \bullet \vec{n} = x + 2y - 3z$

Therefore, $2x + y - z = 0$ $\qquad\qquad$ Therefore, $x + 2y - 3z = 0$

Find values of x, y, and z such that:
$\qquad 2x + y - z = 0 \qquad\qquad$ ①
$\qquad x + 2y - 3z = 0 \qquad\quad$ ②

Something to Think About

- Equations ① and ② form a system of 2 linear equations in 3 variables. Such a system usually has infinitely many solutions. We will determine all of these solutions in Chapter 3. Here, we only require one of the solutions.

Each set of values of x, y, and z that satisfies these two equations corresponds to one of the vectors that is perpendicular to both $\vec{a}$ and $\vec{b}$. Only one set of values is required, and it does not matter how these values are found.

If $z = 1$, then:

$$2x + y = 1 \qquad \text{③}$$
$$x + 2y = 3 \qquad \text{④}$$

Solve the system.

③ × 2:	$4x + 2y = 2$	Copy ③:	$2x + y = 1$
Copy ④:	$x + 2y = 3$	④ × 2:	$2x + 4y = 6$
Subtract:	$3x = -1$	Subtract:	$-3y = -5$
	$x = -\dfrac{1}{3}$		$y = \dfrac{5}{3}$

A vector that is perpendicular to both $\vec{a} = [2, 1, -1]$ and $\vec{b} = [1, 2, -3]$ is $\vec{n} = \left[-\dfrac{1}{3}, \dfrac{5}{3}, 1\right]$.

Check

$$\vec{n} \cdot \vec{a} = \left[-\frac{1}{3}, \frac{5}{3}, 1\right] \cdot [2, 1, -1] \quad \text{and} \quad \vec{n} \cdot \vec{b} = \left[-\frac{1}{3}, \frac{5}{3}, 1\right] \cdot [1, 2, -3]$$

$$= -\frac{2}{3} + \frac{5}{3} - 1 \qquad\qquad\qquad\qquad = -\frac{1}{3} + \frac{10}{3} - 3$$

$$= 0 \qquad\qquad\qquad\qquad\qquad\qquad\qquad = 0$$

Therefore, the vector $\left[-\dfrac{1}{3}, \dfrac{5}{3}, 1\right]$ is perpendicular to both $\vec{a} = [2, 1, -1]$ and $\vec{b} = [1, 2, -3]$.

In *Example 4*, we could have avoided fractions in the *Check* by using the vector $[-1, 5, 3]$, which is 3 times as long as $\vec{n}$.

2.3 Exercises

A

1. Calculate the dot product of each pair of vectors.

a) $\vec{u} = [3, 5, -2]$, $\vec{v} = [4, -1, 2]$

b) $\vec{u} = [3, -1, 5]$, $\vec{v} = [2, 1, -1]$

c) $\vec{a} = [2, 2, 3]$, $\vec{b} = [-1, 0, 3]$

d) $\vec{a} = [-1, 6, 4]$, $\vec{b} = [-5, -3, 1]$

2. The vectors $\vec{i} = [1, 0, 0]$, $\vec{j} = [0, 1, 0]$, and $\vec{k} = [0, 0, 1]$ define the unit cube shown in the diagram. Determine each dot product in two different ways.

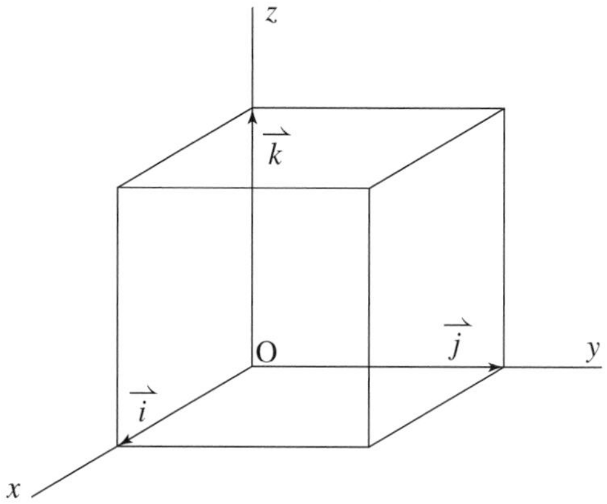

a) $\vec{i} \cdot \vec{i}$ b) $\vec{j} \cdot \vec{j}$

c) $\vec{k} \cdot \vec{k}$ d) $\vec{i} \cdot \vec{j}$

e) $\vec{j} \cdot \vec{k}$ f) $\vec{k} \cdot \vec{i}$

B

3. Calculate the angle between the given vectors.

a) $\vec{a} = [1, 0, -1]$, $\vec{b} = [1, 1, 1]$

b) $\vec{a} = [2, 2, 3]$, $\vec{b} = [-1, 0, 3]$

c) $\vec{a} = [1, 4, 1]$, $\vec{b} = [5, 0, 5]$

d) $\vec{a} = [6, 2, -1]$, $\vec{b} = [-2, -4, 1]$

4. Calculate the angles in each triangle with the given vertices.

a) A(−3, 1, 0), B(−3, 5, −4), C(−1, 3, −4)

b) P(2, 3, 11), Q(5, −1, −1), R(−2, 3, 8)

c) R(−1, 0, 2), S(2, 1, −1), T(1, −2, 2)

5. Only one of the vectors below is perpendicular to the vector [8, 3, −2]. Which vector is it? Explain.

[−2, 1, 3]   [−1, 6, 5]   [1, −1, 3]

6. Determine any vector that is perpendicular to each vector.

a) [1, 2, 3]   b) [2, 2, 2]

c) [4, −5, 2]   d) [0, 3, −4]

7. Determine any vector that is perpendicular to both given vectors. Check each result.

a) $\vec{u} = [0, 2, 1]$, $\vec{v} = [1, -1, 3]$

b) $\vec{u} = [3, -1, 4]$, $\vec{v} = [1, 0, -1]$

c) $\vec{u} = [1, 1, 1]$, $\vec{v} = [1, 2, 3]$

d) $\vec{u} = [-2, 3, 1]$, $\vec{v} = [1, -2, 4]$

8. Knowledge/Understanding Check your results in each part.

a) Determine any vector that is perpendicular to the vector $\vec{u} = [-2, 6, 1]$.

b) Determine any vector that is perpendicular to the vector $\vec{u} = [3, 0, 2]$ and to the vector $\vec{v} = [1, -1, 3]$.

9. Quadrilateral ABCD has vertices A(2, 4, –1), B(7, 3, –8), C(6, 10, –13), and D(1, 11, –6).

Student Reference

Rhombus

a) Show that the quadrilateral is a rhombus.

b) Determine the interior angles of the quadrilateral.

c) Show that the diagonals AC and BD are perpendicular.

10. Points O(0, 0, 0), A(2, 2, 0), B(6, –2, –3) and C(4, –4, –3) are the vertices of a quadrilateral.

a) Determine the angle at each vertex.

b) Use the result of part a to identify the quadrilateral.

11. Find the value(s) of k so that the vectors in each pair are perpendicular.

a) $\vec{a} = [0, k, -2]$, $\vec{b} = [2, -1, 2]$

b) $\vec{a} = [-1, -3, k]$, $\vec{b} = [5, k, 1]$

c) $\vec{a} = [k, -3, 2]$, $\vec{b} = [k, k, -5]$

12. Determine x and y so that $\vec{a} = [x, y, 1]$ is perpendicular to both $\vec{b} = [3, 1, 2]$ and $\vec{c} = [1, 2, 3]$.

13. **Communication** Refer to *Example 4*. To find a set of values of x, y, and z that satisfy equations ① and ②, we began by letting $z = 1$.

a) Find other sets of values of x, y, and z that satisfy these equations by letting:

i) $x = 1$ ii) $y = 1$ iii) $z = 3$ iv) $z = 6$

b) How are the sets of values you found related? Explain.

c) What happens if you let $z = 0$? Explain.

14. If $\vec{a} = [1, 2, 3]$ and $\vec{b} = [4, -1, 2]$, evaluate:

a) $\vec{a} \cdot \vec{b}$

b) $\vec{a} \cdot (\vec{a} + \vec{b})$

c) $(\vec{a} + \vec{b}) \cdot (\vec{a} - \vec{b})$

d) $4\vec{a} \cdot (2\vec{a} + 3\vec{b})$

15. Let $\vec{a} = [3, -1, 1]$, $\vec{b} = [2, -3, 0]$, and $\vec{c} = [-5, 4, 7]$. Determine:

a) $\vec{a} \cdot (\vec{b} + \vec{c})$

b) $(\vec{a} + \vec{b}) \cdot \vec{c}$

c) $(\vec{a} + \vec{b}) \cdot (\vec{a} + \vec{c})$

d) $(\vec{a} + \vec{b}) \cdot (\vec{a} - \vec{b})$

16. The rectangular box shown at the right has dimensions 2 units by 1 unit by 1 unit.

a) Determine $\angle CAB$.

b) Determine $|\vec{AB} \downarrow \vec{AC}|$.

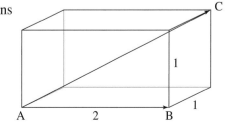

17. Application

    a) In the diagram at the right, θ is acute. Show that
$$|\overrightarrow{u} \downarrow \overrightarrow{v}| = \frac{\overrightarrow{u} \cdot \overrightarrow{v}}{|\overrightarrow{v}|}.$$

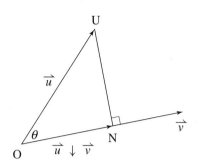

    b) Show how to modify the formula in part a so that it also applies if θ is obtuse.

    c) The vectors $\overrightarrow{u} = [3, -2, 4]$ and $\overrightarrow{v} = [-1, 5, 2]$ are given. Use the formula in part a to calculate $|\overrightarrow{u} \downarrow \overrightarrow{v}|$. Compare your answer with the answer in *Example 3*, and show that the two answers are equal.

18. Determine $\overrightarrow{u} \downarrow \overrightarrow{v}$ and $|\overrightarrow{u} \downarrow \overrightarrow{v}|$ for each of the following.

    a) $\overrightarrow{u} = [1, 1, -4]$, $\overrightarrow{v} = [2, -1, 3]$

    b) $\overrightarrow{u} = [-4, 1, 3]$, $\overrightarrow{v} = [1, -2, 2]$

    c) $\overrightarrow{u} = [1, 2, 2]$, $\overrightarrow{v} = [-1, 3, 2]$

    d) $\overrightarrow{u} = [-1, 1, 1]$, $\overrightarrow{v} = [-2, 1, -1]$

19. The points P(-2, 1, 6), Q(3, 1, -2), R(-3, 1, 4), and S(2, -1, 2) are given. Determine the projection of $\overrightarrow{PQ}$ on $\overrightarrow{RS}$.

20. The vectors $\overrightarrow{u} = [x_1, y_1, z_1]$ and $\overrightarrow{v} = [x_2, y_2, z_2]$ are given. The dot product $\overrightarrow{u} \cdot \overrightarrow{v}$ is defined as $\overrightarrow{u} \cdot \overrightarrow{v} = |\overrightarrow{u}||\overrightarrow{v}| \cos \theta$ where θ is the angle between $\overrightarrow{u}$ and $\overrightarrow{v}$. Use the method on page 53 in Section 1.7 to show that $\overrightarrow{u} \cdot \overrightarrow{v} = x_1 x_2 + y_1 y_2 + z_1 z_2$.

21. Thinking/Inquiry/Problem Solving The vector $\overrightarrow{u} = [1, -2, 1]$ is given.

    a) Determine three different non-collinear vectors that are perpendicular to $\overrightarrow{u}$.

    b) Show that the three vectors you determined in part a are coplanar.

22. Quadrilateral ABCD has vertices A(3, -1, 4), B(-2, 3, 2), C(-5, 9, -1), and D(0, 5, 1).

    a) Prove that this quadrilateral is a parallelogram.

    b) Determine the angle of intersection of the diagonals of the parallelogram.

C

23. Refer to *Example 4*. To find a set of values of x, y, and z that satisfied equations ① and ②, we began by letting $z = 1$. Would it ever be possible to have two equations like these that you could not solve by starting with $z = 1$? Use an example to explain your answer.

2.4 The Cross Product

In Section 1.7, we stated that there are two products of vectors that have great significance in mathematics and science. In that section, we introduced the dot product which is a scalar quantity. Now we will introduce the other product, which is a vector. This product is called the *cross product*, and it has important applications to problems involving rotation (see exercises 17 and 18) and electromagnetic fields.

Let $\vec{a}$ and $\vec{b}$ be two non-collinear vectors in 3-space arranged tail-to-tail forming an angle θ, where $0° < \theta < 180°$. The cross product, $\vec{a} \times \vec{b}$, is defined to be a vector. The direction and the magnitude of this vector are defined as follows.

> In Section 2.5, we will extend this definition to include collinear vectors, so that $0° \leq \theta \leq 180°$.

Defining the direction of $\vec{a} \times \vec{b}$

The direction of $\vec{a} \times \vec{b}$ is perpendicular to the plane containing $\vec{a}$ and $\vec{b}$ so that $\vec{a}$, $\vec{b}$, and $\vec{a} \times \vec{b}$ satisfy the *right-hand rule*: when the fingers of the right hand point in the direction of $\vec{a}$ and curl towards $\vec{b}$, the thumb points in the direction of $\vec{a} \times \vec{b}$.

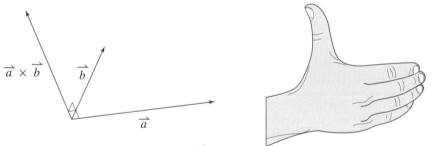

Defining the magnitude of $\vec{a} \times \vec{b}$

The magnitude of $\vec{a} \times \vec{b}$ is equal to the area of the parallelogram determined by $\vec{a}$ and $\vec{b}$.

Area of parallelogram = (base)(height)

$$= \left(|\vec{a}|\right)\left(|\vec{b}|\sin\theta\right)$$

$$= |\vec{a}||\vec{b}|\sin\theta$$

The magnitude of $\vec{a} \times \vec{b}$ is defined to be $|\vec{a} \times \vec{b}| = |\vec{a}||\vec{b}|\sin\theta$.

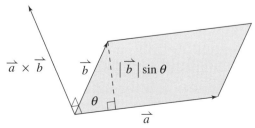

Something to Think About

- The number of linear units in the magnitude of $\vec{a} \times \vec{b}$ equals the number of square units in the area of the parallelogram. We say that they are *numerically equal*.

Unlike the dot product, the cross product is defined only for three-dimensional vectors. It is not possible to form cross products of two-dimensional vectors.

Example 1

Visualize this page in three dimensions on your desk or table. In the diagram, $|\vec{a}| = 3$, $|\vec{b}| = 2$, and $\theta = 30°$. Determine the magnitude of each cross product. Then state whether the cross product vector is directed up towards the ceiling or down towards the floor.

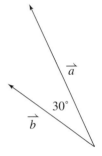

a) $\vec{a} \times \vec{b}$

b) $\vec{b} \times \vec{a}$

Solution

a) The magnitude of $\vec{a} \times \vec{b}$ is:

$$|\vec{a} \times \vec{b}| = |\vec{a}||\vec{b}|\sin\theta$$

$$|\vec{a} \times \vec{b}| = (3)(2)(\sin 30°)$$

$$|\vec{a} \times \vec{b}| = 3$$

Place your right hand on the page with the fingers pointing in the direction of $\vec{a}$ and curling towards $\vec{b}$. Your thumb points in the direction of the cross product. Hence, $\vec{a} \times \vec{b}$ is directed up towards the ceiling.

b) The magnitude of $\vec{b} \times \vec{a}$ is:

$$|\vec{b} \times \vec{a}| = |\vec{b}||\vec{a}|\sin\theta$$

$$|\vec{b} \times \vec{a}| = (2)(3)(\sin 30°)$$

$$|\vec{b} \times \vec{a}| = 3$$

This time you will have to turn your right fist upside down so that the fingers point in the direction of $\vec{b}$ and curl towards $\vec{a}$. Your thumb points in the direction of the cross product. Hence, $\vec{b} \times \vec{a}$ is directed down towards the floor.

Example 1 shows that $\vec{a} \times \vec{b}$ and $\vec{b} \times \vec{a}$ have the same magnitude, but opposite directions. Hence, $\vec{a} \times \vec{b}$ and $\vec{b} \times \vec{a}$ are not equal. In general, $\vec{a} \times \vec{b} = -(\vec{b} \times \vec{a})$.

Notice that the cross product was not drawn on the diagram in *Example 1*. The reason is that it is not possible to tell the direction of the cross product without additional information. To see why, compare the diagram in *Example 1* with the diagrams below which show two triangular prisms viewed from different positions. On all three diagrams, the arrows representing $\vec{a}$ and $\vec{b}$ are congruent and in the same position. On the diagrams below, the cross product $\vec{a} \times \vec{b}$ was drawn according to the right-hand rule. If we remove the additional information and show only the vectors $\vec{a}$ and $\vec{b}$ (as in *Example 1*), the cross product could be in either of two possible directions.

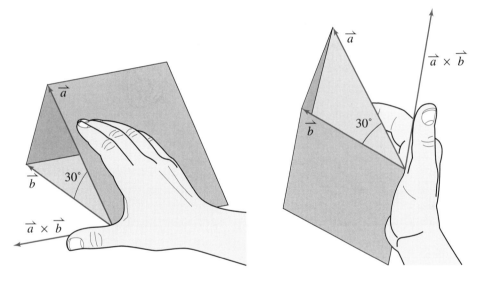

Definition of the Cross Product

Suppose $\vec{a}$ and $\vec{b}$ are two non-collinear, non-zero vectors arranged tail-to-tail forming an angle θ, where $0° < \theta < 180°$. The *cross product*, $\vec{a} \times \vec{b}$, is defined as follows:

$\vec{a} \times \vec{b} \perp \vec{a}$ and $\vec{a} \times \vec{b} \perp \vec{b}$

$\vec{a}$, $\vec{b}$, and $\vec{a} \times \vec{b}$ satisfy the right-hand rule

$|\vec{a} \times \vec{b}| = |\vec{a}||\vec{b}| \sin\theta$

Cross Product of Cartesian Vectors

We will often need to determine the cross product of vectors in Cartesian form. For example, consider the vectors $\vec{a} = [2, 1, -1]$ and $\vec{b} = [1, 2, -3]$. By definition, the cross product, $\vec{a} \times \vec{b}$, has magnitude $|\vec{a}||\vec{b}| \sin \theta$, and it is perpendicular to both $\vec{a}$ and $\vec{b}$. The calculation of $\vec{a} \times \vec{b}$ involves several steps. We will outline the method, without showing intermediate calculations.

Step 1: Calculate the magnitude of $\vec{a} \times \vec{b}$

We need to determine $|\vec{a}||\vec{b}| \sin \theta$. We calculate the three factors separately.

Using $\vec{a} = [2, 1, -1]$, we obtain $|\vec{a}| = \sqrt{6}$.

Using $\vec{b} = [1, 2, -3]$, we obtain $|\vec{b}| = \sqrt{14}$.

Using $\cos \theta = \dfrac{\vec{a} \cdot \vec{b}}{|\vec{a}||\vec{b}|}$, we obtain $\cos \theta = \dfrac{7}{\sqrt{84}}$.

Substitute this expression for $\cos \theta$ into the Pythagorean identity $\sin^2 \theta + \cos^2 \theta = 1$, then solve for $\sin \theta$ to obtain:

$$\sin \theta = \pm \sqrt{\frac{5}{12}}$$

Student Reference

Pythagorean identity
Radical

Since $\cos \theta$ is positive, θ is an acute angle and $\sin \theta$ is positive.

$$\sin \theta = \sqrt{\frac{5}{12}}$$

The magnitude of $\vec{a} \times \vec{b}$ is:

$$|\vec{a} \times \vec{b}| = |\vec{a}||\vec{b}| \sin \theta$$

$$|\vec{a} \times \vec{b}| = \sqrt{84}\sqrt{\frac{5}{12}}$$

$$|\vec{a} \times \vec{b}| = \sqrt{35}$$

Step 2: Determine any vector perpendicular to both $\vec{a}$ and $\vec{b}$

The vectors $\vec{a} = [2, 1, -1]$ and $\vec{b} = [1, 2, -3]$ are the ones used in *Example 4* in Section 2.3. In that example, we found that the vector $\vec{n} = \left[-\frac{1}{3}, \frac{5}{3}, 1\right]$ is perpendicular to both $\vec{a}$ and $\vec{b}$. Therefore, $\vec{a} \times \vec{b}$ must be collinear with this vector.

Step 3: Determine the components of $\vec{a} \times \vec{b}$

$\vec{a} \times \vec{b}$ is a scalar multiple of $\vec{n} = \left[-\frac{1}{3}, \frac{5}{3}, 1\right]$. To determine the scalar, we calculate the magnitude of $\vec{n}$. The result is:

$$|\vec{n}| = \frac{\sqrt{35}}{3}$$

From Step 1, the magnitude of $\vec{a} \times \vec{b}$ is $\sqrt{35}$, so $\vec{a} \times \vec{b}$ is 3 times as long as $\vec{n}$. Hence, $\vec{a} \times \vec{b} = [-1, 5, 3]$.

Therefore, if $\vec{a} = [2, 1, -1]$ and $\vec{b} = [1, 2, -3]$, then $\vec{a} \times \vec{b} = [-1, 5, 3]$.

Step 4: Check the orientation of $\vec{a} \times \vec{b}$

To be certain that $\vec{a} \times \vec{b}$ is $[-1, 5, 3]$ and not its opposite, $[1, -5, -3]$, we need to check that $\vec{a}$, $\vec{b}$, and $[-1, 5, 3]$ satisfy the right-hand rule. The diagram below shows these three vectors drawn on a grid in R^3. These vectors satisfy the right-hand rule. Therefore, we know that $\vec{a} \times \vec{b} = [-1, 5, 3]$.

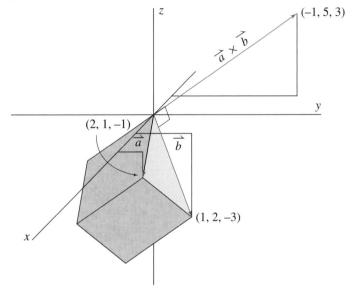

Although many calculations were required to determine $\vec{a} \times \vec{b}$, we obtained a simple result, $\vec{a} \times \vec{b} = [-1, 5, 3]$. This suggests that there should be a formula for determining the cross product of Cartesian vectors. The following formula can be obtained by applying the above method to $\vec{a} = [a_1, a_2, a_3]$ and $\vec{b} = [b_1, b_2, b_3]$. It can be shown that when $\vec{a} \times \vec{b}$ is calculated using this formula, the vectors $\vec{a}$, $\vec{b}$, and $\vec{a} \times \vec{b}$ will always satisfy the right-hand rule.

Take Note

Cross Product of Cartesian Vectors

If $\vec{a} = [a_1, a_2, a_3]$ and $\vec{b} = [b_1, b_2, b_3]$, then

$$\vec{a} \times \vec{b} = [a_2b_3 - b_2a_3, a_3b_1 - b_3a_1, a_1b_2 - b_1a_2]$$

This formula is a pattern involving the components of the vectors $\vec{a}$ and $\vec{b}$. Instead of memorizing the formula, it is easier to apply the following procedure. We will demonstrate the procedure using the vectors $\vec{a} = [2, 1, -1]$ and $\vec{b} = [1, 2, -3]$.

Write the components of the first vector in a row, *starting with the second component and repeating it at the end*:

1   −1   2   1

Below this, do the same with the components of the second vector:

1   −1   2   1
2   −3   1   2

Visualize three squares of numbers from left to right. Take the downward product *minus* the upward product in each square.

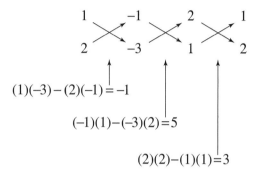

$$(1)(-3) - (2)(-1) = -1$$
$$(-1)(1) - (-3)(2) = 5$$
$$(2)(2) - (1)(1) = 3$$

The results are −1, 5, and 3, respectively. These are the components of the cross product. Therefore, $\vec{a} \times \vec{b} = [-1, 5, 3]$.

Example 2

If $\vec{u} = [0, 2, 1]$ and $\vec{v} = [1, -1, 3]$, calculate:

a) $\vec{u} \times \vec{v}$

b) $\vec{v} \times \vec{u}$

Solution

a) Write the components of $\vec{u}$ in a row, starting with the second component and repeating it at the end. Do the same for $\vec{v}$ in the second row.

2   1   0   2
−1   3   1   −1

The components of $\vec{u} \times \vec{v}$ are:

$(2)(3) - (-1)(1) = 7$

$(1)(1) - (3)(0) = 1$

$(0)(-1) - (1)(2) = -2$

Therefore, $\vec{u} \times \vec{v} = [7, 1, -2]$.

b)

$$\begin{array}{cccc} -1 & 3 & 1 & -1 \\ \times & \times & \times \\ 2 & 1 & 0 & 2 \end{array}$$

The components of $\vec{v} \times \vec{u}$ are:

$(-1)(1) - (2)(3) = -7$

$(3)(0) - (1)(1) = -1$

$(1)(2) - (0)(-1) = 2$

Therefore, $\vec{v} \times \vec{u} = [-7, -1, 2]$.

To check the calculation of a cross product, we can verify that the result is perpendicular to both given vectors. In *Example 2a*:

$(\vec{u} \times \vec{v}) \bullet \vec{u} = [7, 1, -2] \bullet [0, 2, 1]$ and $(\vec{u} \times \vec{v}) \bullet \vec{v} = [7, 1, -2] \bullet [1, -1, 3]$

$\qquad\qquad\qquad = 0 + 2 - 2 \qquad\qquad\qquad\qquad\qquad\qquad = 7 - 1 - 6$

$\qquad\qquad\qquad = 0 \qquad\qquad\qquad\qquad\qquad\qquad\qquad\quad = 0$

Therefore, $\vec{u} \times \vec{v}$ is perpendicular to both $\vec{u}$ and $\vec{v}$.

Since the magnitude of the cross product of two vectors equals the area of a parallelogram, we can use cross products to calculate areas of parallelograms and triangles in $\boldsymbol{R}^3$.

Example 3

Determine the area of $\triangle PQR$ with vertices $P(2, -1, 4)$, $Q(3, 1, -1)$, and $R(1, 0, 2)$.

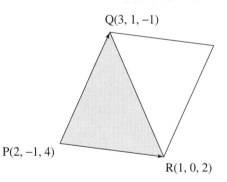

Solution

Two adjacent sides of the triangle are $\overrightarrow{PQ}$ and $\overrightarrow{PR}$. The area of $\triangle PQR$ is half the area of the parallelogram determined by $\overrightarrow{PQ}$ and $\overrightarrow{PR}$.

$\overrightarrow{PQ} = [3 - 2, 1 - (-1), -1 - 4]$

$\overrightarrow{PQ} = [1, 2, -5]$

$\overrightarrow{PR} = [1 - 2, 0 - (-1), 2 - 4]$

$\overrightarrow{PR} = [-1, 1, -2]$

Determine the cross product, $\overrightarrow{PQ} \times \overrightarrow{PR}$.

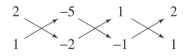

The components of $\overrightarrow{PQ} \times \overrightarrow{PR}$ are:

$(2)(-2) - (1)(-5) = 1$
$(-5)(-1) - (-2)(1) = 7$
$(1)(1) - (-1)(2) = 3$

Therefore, $\quad \overrightarrow{PQ} \times \overrightarrow{PR} = [1, 7, 3]$

$$|\overrightarrow{PQ} \times \overrightarrow{PR}| = \sqrt{1^2 + 7^2 + 3^2}$$
$$= \sqrt{59}$$

The area of the parallelogram determined by $\overrightarrow{PQ}$ and $\overrightarrow{PR}$ is $\sqrt{59}$ square units. Hence, the area of $\triangle PQR$ is $\frac{1}{2}\sqrt{59}$ square units.

Something to Think About

- We calculated the area of $\triangle PQR$ using sides PQ and PR. Could we have used other pairs of sides to calculate the area? Explain.

2.4 Exercises

A

1. In the definition of $\overrightarrow{a} \times \overrightarrow{b}$ on page 101, why are $\overrightarrow{a}$ and $\overrightarrow{b}$ non-collinear vectors?

2. Visualize this page in three dimensions on your desk or table. For each pair of vectors, calculate $|\overrightarrow{u} \times \overrightarrow{v}|$. Then state whether $\overrightarrow{u} \times \overrightarrow{v}$ is directed up towards the ceiling or down towards the floor.

a) $|\overrightarrow{u}| = 15, |\overrightarrow{v}| = 10$ b) $|\overrightarrow{u}| = 10, |\overrightarrow{v}| = 12$

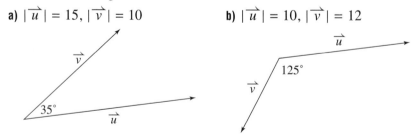

3. In general, if a drawing of two vectors in 3-space is given, it is not possible to tell the direction of the cross product without additional information. What additional information is present in these diagrams?

a) The diagram on page 74.

b) The diagrams on page 99.

c) The diagrams in exercise 2 above.

4. Use the diagram on page 74. Verify that the positive directions of the coordinate axes satisfy the right-hand rule when they are taken in their usual order: x-axis, y-axis, z-axis.

B

5. The vectors $\vec{u} = [x_1, y_1, z_1]$ and $\vec{v} = [x_2, y_2, z_2]$ are given.

a) Use the procedure described on page 104 to verify that
$$\vec{u} \times \vec{v} = [y_1z_2 - y_2z_1, z_1x_2 - z_2x_1, x_1y_2 - x_2y_1].$$

b) Verify that $\vec{u} \times \vec{v}$ is perpendicular to both $\vec{u}$ and $\vec{v}$.

6. Calculate $\vec{u} \times \vec{v}$ for each pair of vectors. Check each result.

a) $\vec{u} = [0, -1, 1]$, $\vec{v} = [1, -1, 0]$

b) $\vec{u} = [1, 2, 3]$, $\vec{v} = [-2, 1, -3]$

c) $\vec{u} = [3, -5, 2]$, $\vec{v} = [7, 0, -1]$

d) $\vec{u} = [4, -3, 1]$, $\vec{v} = [8, -2, 5]$

7. To check the calculation of the cross product of two vectors, we can show that the result is perpendicular to both given vectors. Is it possible for the result to be perpendicular to both given vectors and still not be the cross product of those vectors? Explain.

8. Calculate the area of the parallelogram determined by each pair of vectors.

a) $\vec{a} = [1, 1, 0]$, $\vec{b} = [3, 2, 2]$

b) $\vec{a} = [-1, 1, 2]$, $\vec{b} = [0, 3, 4]$

c) $\vec{a} = [1, 4, 3]$, $\vec{b} = [2, 0, -1]$

d) $\vec{a} = [2, -1, 2]$, $\vec{b} = [3, 1, -1]$

9. Knowledge/Understanding The vectors $\vec{a} = [0, 2, -3]$ and $\vec{b} = [1, 1, 5]$ are given.

a) Calculate $\vec{a} \times \vec{b}$.

b) Verify that $\vec{a} \times \vec{b}$ is perpendicular to both $\vec{a}$ and $\vec{b}$.

c) Calculate the area of the parallelogram determined by vectors $\vec{a}$ and $\vec{b}$.

d) Illustrate the results on a diagram, showing vectors $\vec{a}$, $\vec{b}$, $\vec{a} \times \vec{b}$, and the parallelogram.

10. Find a vector that is perpendicular to both given vectors.

a) $\vec{u} = [1, 2, 3]$, $\vec{v} = [3, 2, 1]$

b) $\vec{u} = [5, -3, 2]$, $\vec{v} = [1, -2, -4]$

c) $\vec{u} = [0, 2, -1]$, $\vec{v} = [2, -2, -1]$

d) $\vec{u} = [6, 2, 1]$, $\vec{v} = [-3, -1, 2]$

11. The vectors $\vec{i} = [1, 0, 0]$, $\vec{j} = [0, 1, 0]$, and $\vec{k} = [0, 0, 1]$ define the unit cube shown in the diagram. Determine each cross product.

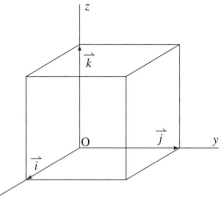

a) $\vec{i} \times \vec{i}$ **b)** $\vec{j} \times \vec{j}$ **c)** $\vec{k} \times \vec{k}$

d) $\vec{i} \times \vec{j}$ **e)** $\vec{j} \times \vec{i}$ **f)** $\vec{j} \times \vec{k}$

g) $\vec{k} \times \vec{j}$ **h)** $\vec{k} \times \vec{i}$ **i)** $\vec{i} \times \vec{k}$

12. **Thinking/Inquiry/Problem Solving** The vectors $\vec{u} = \overrightarrow{OU}$ and $\vec{v} = \overrightarrow{OV}$ are any two non-collinear, non-zero vectors in 3-space forming an angle θ. Point N is the foot of the perpendicular from U to the line containing $\overrightarrow{OV}$.

a) Prove that:

i) The length of segment ON is $\dfrac{|\vec{u} \cdot \vec{v}|}{|\vec{v}|}$.

ii) The length of segment UN is $\dfrac{|\vec{u} \times \vec{v}|}{|\vec{v}|}$.

b) Draw a diagram to illustrate what the expressions $\dfrac{|\vec{u} \cdot \vec{v}|}{|\vec{u}|}$ and $\dfrac{|\vec{u} \times \vec{v}|}{|\vec{u}|}$ represent.

13. Find the area of the parallelogram with the given vertices.

a) P(3, −1, 1), Q(1, 2, −1), R(0, 3, 0), S(−2, 6, −2)

b) D(0, 3, 1), E(2, −2, 4), F(−1, 3, 2), G(1, −2, 5)

14. Find the area of the triangle with the given vertices.

a) A(0, 2, 3), B(2, −1, −1), C(4, −2, −3)

b) P(2, −1, 4), Q(3, −3, 7), R(−1, 0, 1)

15. The points A(1, −2, 0), B(3, 1, 4), and C(−1, 0, 3) are given.

a) Determine $\overrightarrow{AB}$, $\overrightarrow{BC}$, and $\overrightarrow{CA}$. Then show that $\overrightarrow{AB} + \overrightarrow{BC} + \overrightarrow{CA} = \vec{0}$.

b) Determine each cross product.

i) $\overrightarrow{AB} \times \overrightarrow{BC}$
ii) $\overrightarrow{BC} \times \overrightarrow{CA}$
iii) $\overrightarrow{CA} \times \overrightarrow{AB}$

c) Explain why the cross products in part b are all equal.

16. Communication Vectors $\vec{a}$ and $\vec{b}$ are non-collinear such that $|\vec{a}| = 4$, $|\vec{b}| = 3$, and $|\vec{a} \times \vec{b}| = 6$.

a) Determine the angle θ between $\vec{a}$ and $\vec{b}$.

b) Draw a diagram to illustrate this situation.

c) Explain why there are two possible angles in part a.

Exercises 17 and 18 involve a concept from physics called *torque*. Torque is a measure of how much a force acting on an object causes that object to rotate, and it is a vector. The torque vector, $\vec{\tau}$, is defined as:

$$\vec{\tau} = \vec{r} \times \vec{F}$$

where $\vec{r}$ is the radius vector from the centre of rotation to the point where the force, $\vec{F}$, is applied.

17. When we use a wrench to tighten a bolt, three vectors are involved (see diagram below).

- $\vec{r}$ has its tail at the centre of the bolt and its head at the point where we apply the force that turns the wrench.
- $\vec{F}$ represents the force we apply to the wrench. Its direction is not necessarily perpendicular to the wrench. Let θ represent the angle between $\vec{F}$ and $\vec{r}$ (when they are arranged tail-to-tail).
- $\vec{\tau}$ represents the torque vector.

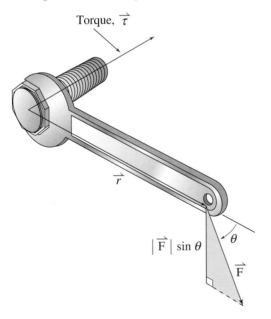

a) Explain why the magnitude of the torque vector is $|\vec{r}||\vec{F}| \sin \theta$.

b) Check that the direction of the torque vector in the diagram is correct.

18. **Application** Suppose you apply a force of 50 N at a point on a door that is 0.7 m from its hinges. The direction of the force makes an angle of 60° with the door (below left).

a) Calculate the magnitude of the torque vector (the units are newton metres).

b) Suppose you apply the same force at the same distance from the hinges, but at an angle of 120° (below right). Explain why the magnitude of the torque vector is the same as in part a.

c) Describe the direction of the torque vector.

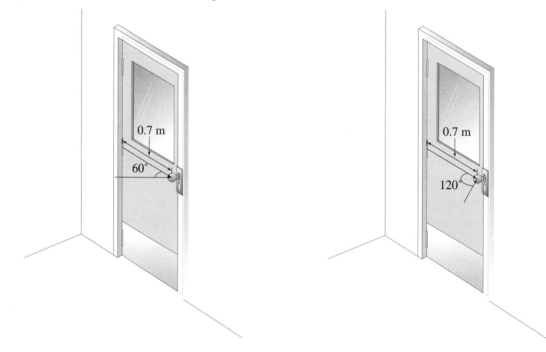

C

19. The Sine Law states that in any $\triangle ABC$, $\frac{\sin A}{a} = \frac{\sin B}{b} = \frac{\sin C}{c}$. Use cross products to prove the Sine Law.

2.5 Properties of the Cross Product

In Section 2.2, we stated that the problem of determining if three vectors are coplanar will have great significance in Chapter 3. It is so significant that we need to develop a more efficient method of determining if three vectors are coplanar. This method involves using both the cross and dot products together in the same expression.

The product $\vec{u} \bullet \vec{v} \times \vec{w}$

Since the cross product of two vectors is a vector, we can calculate a dot product such as $\vec{u} \bullet (\vec{v} \times \vec{w})$, or $\vec{u} \bullet \vec{v} \times \vec{w}$. We do not need to use brackets in this expression because $\vec{u} \bullet \vec{v}$ is a scalar. Therefore, $\vec{u} \bullet \vec{v} \times \vec{w}$ cannot mean $(\vec{u} \bullet \vec{v}) \times \vec{w}$ because this expression is not defined.

Example 1

The vectors $\vec{u} = [2, -1, 5]$, $\vec{v} = [-3, 2, 2]$, and $\vec{w} = [1, 4, -6]$ are given.

a) Calculate $\vec{u} \bullet \vec{v} \times \vec{w}$.

b) Determine if the vectors $\vec{u}$, $\vec{v}$, and $\vec{w}$ are coplanar.

Solution

a) First, calculate $\vec{v} \times \vec{w}$.

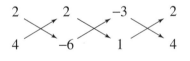

The components of $\vec{v} \times \vec{w}$ are:
$(2)(-6) - (4)(2) = -20$
$(2)(1) - (-6)(-3) = -16$
$(-3)(4) - (1)(2) = -14$

Therefore, $\vec{v} \times \vec{w} = [-20, -16, -14]$
$$\begin{aligned} \vec{u} \bullet \vec{v} \times \vec{w} &= [2, -1, 5] \bullet [-20, -16, -14] \\ &= -40 + 16 - 70 \\ &= -94 \end{aligned}$$

b) The vectors $\vec{v}$ and $\vec{w}$ are both perpendicular to $\vec{v} \times \vec{w}$. Since $\vec{u} \bullet \vec{v} \times \vec{w} \neq 0$, we know that $\vec{u}$ is not perpendicular to $\vec{v} \times \vec{w}$. Therefore, the vectors $\vec{u}$, $\vec{v}$, and $\vec{w}$ are not coplanar.

Example 1b is significant because it is the basis of a simple test for coplanar vectors. Let $\vec{u}$, $\vec{v}$, and $\vec{w}$ be vectors in three dimensions drawn tail-to-tail. Then either $\vec{u} \cdot \vec{v} \times \vec{w} = 0$ or $\vec{u} \cdot \vec{v} \times \vec{w} \neq 0$.

An expression of the form $\vec{u} \cdot \vec{v} \times \vec{w}$ is called a scalar triple product.

Suppose $\vec{u} \cdot \vec{v} \times \vec{w} = 0$

Then $\vec{v}$ and $\vec{w}$ are both perpendicular to $\vec{v} \times \vec{w}$, and $\vec{u}$ is perpendicular to $\vec{v} \times \vec{w}$.

Hence, $\vec{u}$, $\vec{v}$, and $\vec{w}$ are coplanar.

Suppose $\vec{u} \cdot \vec{v} \times \vec{w} \neq 0$.

Then $\vec{u}$ is not perpendicular to $\vec{v} \times \vec{w}$, so $\vec{u}$ does not lie on the plane determined by $\vec{v}$ and $\vec{w}$.

Hence, $\vec{u}$, $\vec{v}$, and $\vec{w}$ are not coplanar.

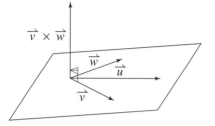
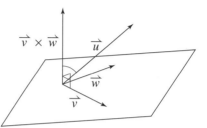

Take Note

Test for Coplanar Vectors

Let $\vec{u}$, $\vec{v}$, and $\vec{w}$ be vectors in three dimensions. To determine if the vectors are coplanar, calculate $\vec{u} \cdot \vec{v} \times \vec{w}$.

- If $\vec{u} \cdot \vec{v} \times \vec{w} = 0$, then $\vec{u}$, $\vec{v}$, and $\vec{w}$ are coplanar.
- If $\vec{u} \cdot \vec{v} \times \vec{w} \neq 0$, then $\vec{u}$, $\vec{v}$, and $\vec{w}$ are not coplanar.

Instead of $\vec{u} \cdot \vec{v} \times \vec{w}$, we can use $\vec{v} \cdot \vec{u} \times \vec{w}$ or $\vec{w} \cdot \vec{u} \times \vec{v}$.

Example 2

Determine if the vectors $\vec{a} = [1, 2, 3]$, $\vec{b} = [2, -1, 3]$, and $\vec{c} = [8, 1, 15]$ are coplanar.

Solution

Calculate the cross product of any two of the vectors, say, $\vec{a} \times \vec{b}$.

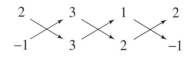

The components of $\vec{a} \times \vec{b}$ are:

$(2)(3) - (-1)(3) = 9$

$(3)(2) - (3)(1) = 3$

$(1)(-1) - (2)(2) = -5$

Hence, $\vec{a} \times \vec{b} = [9, 3, -5]$

Now calculate $\vec{c} \bullet \vec{a} \times \vec{b}$.

$$\begin{aligned} \vec{c} \bullet \vec{a} \times \vec{b} &= [8, 1, 15] \bullet [9, 3, -5] \\ &= 72 + 3 - 75 \\ &= 0 \end{aligned}$$

Therefore, the vectors $\vec{a}$, $\vec{b}$, and $\vec{c}$ are coplanar.

Compare *Example 2* with *Example 3* on page 86. In the earlier example, we showed that the vectors are coplanar by showing that $\vec{c} = 2\vec{a} + 3\vec{b}$. The example above illustrates a more efficient method, but it does not give as much information.

Other properties of the cross product

In Section 2.4 we defined the cross product of two vectors $\vec{a}$ and $\vec{b}$ in $\mathbf{R}^3$ to be the vector $\vec{a} \times \vec{b}$ with magnitude equal to the area of the parallelogram determined by $\vec{a}$ and $\vec{b}$, or $|\vec{a}||\vec{b}| \sin \theta$, and direction perpendicular to the plane containing $\vec{a}$ and $\vec{b}$ so that $\vec{a}$, $\vec{b}$, and $\vec{a} \times \vec{b}$ satisfy the right-hand rule.

For Cartesian vectors $\vec{a} = [a_1, a_2, a_3]$ and $\vec{b} = [b_1, b_2, b_3]$, the cross product is $\vec{a} \times \vec{b} = [a_2b_3 - b_2a_3, a_3b_1 - b_3a_1, a_1b_2 - b_1a_2]$. This is best determined using the procedure shown on page 104 in Section 2.4.

To say that $\vec{a} \times \vec{b}$ is a product, we would expect it to have some properties that correspond to properties of products in arithmetic and algebra. We have already seen a property that it does *not* have. In Section 2.4, we found that the cross product does not satisfy the commutative law. Instead, $\vec{a} \times \vec{b} = -(\vec{b} \times \vec{a})$.

We saw in Chapter 1 that the dot product is distributive over addition: $\vec{a} \bullet (\vec{b} + \vec{c}) = \vec{a} \bullet \vec{b} + \vec{a} \bullet \vec{c}$. The corresponding property for cross products is $\vec{a} \times (\vec{b} + \vec{c}) = \vec{a} \times \vec{b} + \vec{a} \times \vec{c}$. In the exercises, you will verify this property using a specific example (see exercise 9). This property can be proved using Cartesian vectors (exercise 19). It can also be proved using the definition of the cross product, but the proof is beyond the scope of this book.

In arithmetic and algebra, the product of a number and itself is its square. Using $\times$ for ordinary multiplication, we write $y \times y = y^2$.

In Section 1.8, we found the dot product of a vector with itself. The result is the square of its magnitude: $\vec{a} \cdot \vec{a} = |\vec{a}|^2$.

In the definition of the cross product $\vec{a} \times \vec{b}$ on page 101, the vectors $\vec{a}$ and $\vec{b}$ are not collinear, and the angle θ between them satisfies $0° < \theta < 180°$. Since this requires $\vec{a}$ and $\vec{b}$ to have different directions, it is not possible according to this definition to create the cross product $\vec{a} \times \vec{a}$.

However, we can extend the definition to include the case where $\vec{a}$ and $\vec{b}$ are collinear, and $\theta = 0°$ or $\theta = 180°$. Since $\sin \theta = 0$ for these values of θ, the magnitude of $\vec{a} \times \vec{b}$ is 0. Hence, $\vec{a} \times \vec{b}$ is the zero vector and has no specified direction. That is, if $\vec{a}$ and $\vec{b}$ are collinear, then $\vec{a} \times \vec{b} = \vec{0}$. This means that $\vec{a} \times \vec{a} = \vec{0}$.

Take Note

Properties of the Cross Product

Let $\vec{a}$, $\vec{b}$, and $\vec{c}$ be three non-zero, non-collinear vectors arranged tail-to-tail.

$$\vec{a} \times \vec{b} = -(\vec{b} \times \vec{a})$$

$$\vec{a} \times (\vec{b} + \vec{c}) = \vec{a} \times \vec{b} + \vec{a} \times \vec{c}$$

$$\vec{a} \times \vec{a} = \vec{0}$$

2.5) Exercises

A

1. In *Example 2*, we determined that the vectors $\vec{a}$, $\vec{b}$, and $\vec{c}$ were coplanar by showing that $\vec{c} \cdot \vec{a} \times \vec{b} = 0$. Show that these vectors are coplanar by calculating:

   a) $\vec{a} \cdot \vec{b} \times \vec{c}$ b) $\vec{b} \cdot \vec{a} \times \vec{c}$

2. a) Explain why $\vec{a} \cdot \vec{a} \times \vec{b} = 0$ and $\vec{b} \cdot \vec{a} \times \vec{b} = 0$.

   b) Explain why brackets are not needed in the expressions in part a.

3. a) What is the cross product of a vector with itself?

   b) What is the cross product of a vector with its opposite?

B

4. **Knowledge/Understanding** Determine if the vectors are coplanar.

a) $\vec{a} = [4, -1, 5]$, $\vec{b} = [1, 2, 6]$, $\vec{c} = [10, -7, 4]$

b) $\vec{p} = [-2, 7, 1]$, $\vec{q} = [-4, 1, 1]$, $\vec{r} = [-3, 4, 1]$

c) $\vec{u} = [0, 8, -3]$, $\vec{v} = [2, -4, 1]$, $\vec{w} = [1, 10, -3]$

5. Determine if the points are coplanar.

a) A(-1, 2, 1), B(3, -1, 2), C(1, 4, -3), D(7, 2, 1)

b) J(5, 7, -2), K(8, 3, 0), L(4, 10, 1), M(9, 0, -3)

c) P(-3, 5, 4), Q(2, 3, 1), R(8, 4, 0), S(3, -1, 2)

6. **Communication** When we test if three vectors $\vec{u}$, $\vec{v}$, and $\vec{w}$ are coplanar, explain why it doesn't matter whether we calculate $\vec{u} \cdot \vec{v} \times \vec{w}$, $\vec{v} \cdot \vec{u} \times \vec{w}$, or $\vec{w} \cdot \vec{u} \times \vec{v}$.

7. Let $\vec{a} = [-1, 4, 5]$ and $\vec{b} = [3, 1, -2]$. Determine each of the following.

a) $(2\vec{a}) \times \vec{b}$ b) $\vec{a} \times (2\vec{b})$ c) $2(\vec{a} \times \vec{b})$

8. Let k be any scalar. Use the definition of the cross product to explain why $(k\vec{a}) \times \vec{b} = \vec{a} \times (k\vec{b}) = k(\vec{a} \times \vec{b})$.

9. Let $\vec{a} = [2, -1, 3]$, $\vec{b} = [4, 2, -1]$, and $\vec{c} = [-3, 0, 2]$. Show that $\vec{a} \times (\vec{b} + \vec{c}) = \vec{a} \times \vec{b} + \vec{a} \times \vec{c}$.

10. Let $\vec{a} = [1, 3, -4]$ and $\vec{b} = [2, -3, 1]$. Determine each of the following, and compare the results.

a) $(2\vec{a}) \times \vec{b}$ b) $(3\vec{a}) \times \vec{b}$ c) $(5\vec{a}) \times \vec{b}$

11. Let r and s be any positive scalars. Use the definition of the cross product to explain why $(r\vec{a}) \times \vec{b} + (s\vec{a}) \times \vec{b} = [(r + s)\vec{a}] \times \vec{b}$.

12. **Thinking/Inquiry/Problem Solving** The identity below is significant because it relates 3 different kinds of products— a cross product and a dot product of two vectors on the left side, and the product of two real numbers on the right side.

Student Reference

Identity

$$\left| \vec{a} \times \vec{b} \right|^2 + (\vec{a} \cdot \vec{b})^2 = \left| \vec{a} \right|^2 \left| \vec{b} \right|^2$$

a) Use the definitions of $\vec{a} \times \vec{b}$ and $\vec{a} \cdot \vec{b}$ to prove the identity.

b) Explain why the identity is equivalent to the Pythagorean identity.

13. If $\vec{a} + \vec{b} + \vec{c} = \vec{0}$, explain why $\vec{a} \times \vec{b} = \vec{b} \times \vec{c} = \vec{c} \times \vec{a}$.

14. **Application** When we multiply more than two numbers in arithmetic, it does not matter which ones we multiply first: $(xy)z = x(yz)$. This property is called the *associative law of multiplication*. Explain why the cross product does *not* satisfy the associative law. That is, $(\vec{a} \times \vec{b}) \times \vec{c} \neq \vec{a} \times (\vec{b} \times \vec{c})$.

15. Explain your answer to each question.

    a) A property of multiplication in arithmetic is that multiplying a number by 1 does not change the number. For example, $5 \times 1 = 5$. Is there a corresponding property for cross products?

    b) Another property of multiplication in arithmetic is that multiplying a number by 0 gives a product of 0. For example, $5 \times 0 = 0$. Is there a corresponding property for cross products?

16. If $\vec{a} \times \vec{c} = \vec{b} \times \vec{c}$, does it follow that $\vec{a} = \vec{b}$? Draw a diagram to illustrate your explanation.

17. In exercise 5 in Section 1.8 (page 64), you showed that if $\vec{a} \cdot \vec{c} = \vec{b} \cdot \vec{c}$ it does not follow that $\vec{a} = \vec{b}$. In exercise 16, you showed that if $\vec{a} \times \vec{c} = \vec{b} \times \vec{c}$ it does not follow that $\vec{a} = \vec{b}$. Prove that if *both* $\vec{a} \cdot \vec{c} = \vec{b} \cdot \vec{c}$ and $\vec{a} \times \vec{c} = \vec{b} \times \vec{c}$, with $\vec{c} \neq 0$, then it does follow that $\vec{a} = \vec{b}$.

C

18. Given that $\vec{a} \times (\vec{b} + \vec{c}) = \vec{a} \times \vec{b} + \vec{a} \times \vec{c}$, prove that $(\vec{b} + \vec{c}) \times \vec{a} = \vec{b} \times \vec{a} + \vec{c} \times \vec{a}$.

19. Given that $\vec{a} = [a_1, a_2, a_3]$, $\vec{b} = [b_1, b_2, b_3]$, and $\vec{c} = [c_1, c_2, c_3]$, prove that $\vec{a} \times (\vec{b} + \vec{c}) = \vec{a} \times \vec{b} + \vec{a} \times \vec{c}$.

20. Given that $\vec{u} = s\vec{v} + t\vec{w}$, prove algebraically that $\vec{u} \cdot \vec{v} \times \vec{w} = 0$.

Cartesian vectors in 3-space, or R^3, are ordered triples. By convention, points O(0, 0, 0), P(x, y, z), and vector $\vec{v}$ = [x, y, z] in R^3 are plotted on a grid like the one shown below.

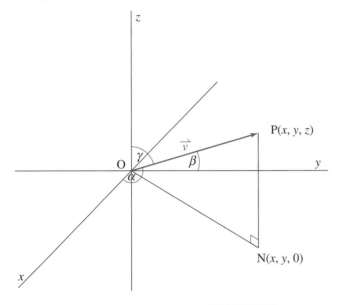

The magnitude of $\vec{v}$ is $|\vec{v}| = \sqrt{x^2 + y^2 + z^2}$.

To determine the direction angles α, β, and γ, use the direction cosines of $\vec{v}$:

$$\cos \alpha = \frac{x}{|\vec{v}|} \qquad \cos \beta = \frac{y}{|\vec{v}|} \qquad \cos \gamma = \frac{z}{|\vec{v}|}$$

Also, $\cos^2 \alpha + \cos^2 \beta + \cos^2 \gamma = 1$

If A(a_1, a_2, a_3) and B(b_1, b_2, b_3) are any two points, then:

$$\vec{AB} = [b_1 - a_1, b_2 - a_2, b_3 - a_3]$$

The magnitude of this vector is:

$$|\vec{AB}| = \sqrt{(b_1 - a_1)^2 + (b_2 - a_2)^2 + (b_3 - a_3)^2}$$

Operations on Cartesian Vectors

If $\vec{u}$ = [x_1, y_1, z_1] and $\vec{v}$ = [x_2, y_2, z_2], then:

$$\vec{u} + \vec{v} = [x_1 + x_2, y_1 + y_2, z_1 + z_2]$$
$$\vec{u} - \vec{v} = [x_1 - x_2, y_1 - y_2, z_1 - z_2]$$
$$k\vec{u} = [kx_1, ky_1, kz_1]$$

Test for Collinear Vectors

If $\vec{a}$ and $\vec{b}$ are given vectors and a scalar s can be found such that $\vec{b} = s\vec{a}$, then $\vec{a}$ and $\vec{b}$ are collinear.

Test for Coplanar Vectors

If $\vec{a}$, $\vec{b}$ and $\vec{c}$ are given vectors and scalars s and t can be found such that $\vec{c} = s\vec{a} + t\vec{b}$, then $\vec{a}$, $\vec{b}$, and $\vec{c}$ are coplanar.

See the last item in this toolkit for a different test for coplanar vectors.

The Dot Product of Two Vectors

If $\vec{a}$ and $\vec{b}$ are any two vectors forming an angle θ, then their dot product is defined to be $\vec{a} \cdot \vec{b} = |\vec{a}||\vec{b}| \cos \theta$. This definition applies to both R^2 and R^3.

For Cartesian vectors $\vec{a} = [a_1, a_2, a_3]$ and $\vec{b} = [b_1, b_2, b_3]$,
$\vec{a} \cdot \vec{b} = a_1b_1 + a_2b_2 + a_3b_3$

To calculate the angle between two vectors, use $\cos \theta = \dfrac{\vec{a} \cdot \vec{b}}{|\vec{a}||\vec{b}|}$.

Test for Perpendicular Vectors

If two vectors are perpendicular, then their dot product is 0.

The Cross Product of Two Vectors

If $\vec{a}$ and $\vec{b}$ are any two vectors in 3-space forming an angle θ, their cross product $\vec{a} \times \vec{b}$ is defined to be a vector having:

- direction perpendicular to the plane containing $\vec{a}$ and $\vec{b}$ such that $\vec{a}$, $\vec{b}$, and $\vec{a} \times \vec{b}$ satisfy the right-hand rule
- magnitude equal to $|\vec{a}||\vec{b}| \sin \theta$, which is the area of the parallelogram determined by $\vec{a}$ and $\vec{b}$.

For Cartesian vectors $\vec{a} = [a_1, a_2, a_3]$ and $\vec{b} = [b_1, b_2, b_3]$ the cross product is calculated using the following procedure. Write the components of the vectors in two rows, starting with the second component and repeating it at the end. Then calculate each downward product minus the upward product as indicated.

$$
\begin{array}{cccc}
a_2 & a_3 & a_1 & a_2 \\
b_2 & b_3 & b_1 & b_2
\end{array}
$$

Properties of the cross product:
$$\vec{a} \times \vec{b} = -(\vec{b} \times \vec{a})$$
$$\vec{a} \times (\vec{b} + \vec{c}) = \vec{a} \times \vec{b} + \vec{a} \times \vec{c}$$
$$\vec{a} \times \vec{a} = \vec{0}$$

Test for Coplanar Vectors

Let $\vec{a}$, $\vec{b}$ and $\vec{c}$ be vectors in three dimensions. To determine if the vectors are coplanar, calculate $\vec{a} \cdot \vec{b} \times \vec{c}$.

- If $\vec{a} \cdot \vec{b} \times \vec{c} = 0$, then $\vec{a}$, $\vec{b}$ and $\vec{c}$ are coplanar.
- If $\vec{a} \cdot \vec{b} \times \vec{c} \neq 0$, then $\vec{a}$, $\vec{b}$ and $\vec{c}$ are not coplanar.

Instead of $\vec{a} \cdot \vec{b} \times \vec{c}$, we can use $\vec{b} \cdot \vec{a} \times \vec{c}$ or $\vec{c} \cdot \vec{a} \times \vec{b}$.

1. Given the vector $\vec{a} = [4, 1, 2]$, determine its:

   a) magnitude

   b) direction cosines

   c) direction angles

2. Determine the magnitude and the direction angles of $\overrightarrow{AB}$ for the given points.

   a) A(2, –3, 1), B(4, 0, 1)

   b) A(0, –1, 3), B(–3, 2, 6)

3. The vectors $\vec{u} = [3, 1, –2]$ and $\vec{v} = [–1, 4, 2]$ are given. Determine:

   a) $\vec{u} + 2\vec{v}$ b) $3\vec{u} - \vec{v}$ c) $4\vec{u} - 3\vec{v}$

4. Determine if the vectors $\vec{u} = [10, –4, 6]$ and $\vec{v} = [–15, 6, –9]$ are collinear.

5. Determine if the points A(2, –4, 1), B(11, 2, –2), and C(–1, –6, 2) are collinear.

6. Determine if the vectors $\vec{a} = [–2, –1, 4]$, $\vec{b} = [5, –2, 5]$, and $\vec{c} = [3, 0, –1]$ are coplanar.

7. Determine if the points P(3, –2, –7), Q(0, 4, 2), R(–1, 3, –1), and S(5, –1, –3) are coplanar.

8. Determine the value of m so that the vectors $\vec{u} = [4, -2, 6]$ and $\vec{v} = [6, m, 9]$ are:

a) parallel

b) perpendicular

9. Triangle ABC has vertices A(−1, 3, 2), B(−1, 5, 2), and C(1, 5, −2).

a) Show that △ABC is a right triangle.

b) Calculate the measures of the two acute angles.

c) Calculate the projection of $\overrightarrow{AC}$ on $\overrightarrow{AB}$.

10. Let $\vec{a} = [1, 1, -2]$, $\vec{b} = [3, -2, 5]$, $\vec{c} = [0, 5, 2]$, and $\vec{d} = [-2, 1, 3]$. Explain your answer to each question.

a) Does $\vec{a} \bullet \vec{b} = \vec{b} \bullet \vec{a}$?

b) Can any meaning be given to $\vec{a} \bullet \vec{b} \bullet \vec{c}$?

c) Does $\vec{a} \bullet (\vec{b} + \vec{c}) = \vec{a} \bullet \vec{b} + \vec{a} \bullet \vec{c}$?

d) Does $(\vec{a} + \vec{b}) \bullet \vec{c} = \vec{a} \bullet \vec{c} + \vec{b} \bullet \vec{c}$?

e) Does $(\vec{a} + \vec{b}) \bullet (\vec{c} + \vec{d}) = \vec{a} \bullet \vec{c} + \vec{a} \bullet \vec{d} + \vec{b} \bullet \vec{c} + \vec{b} \bullet \vec{d}$?

11. Given $\vec{a} = [2, 3, 3]$ and $\vec{b} = [-1, 0, 3]$, determine:

a) $\vec{a} \downarrow \vec{b}$

b) $|\vec{a} \downarrow \vec{b}|$

c) $\vec{b} \downarrow \vec{a}$

d) $|\vec{b} \downarrow \vec{a}|$

12. Determine a vector perpendicular to both the y-axis and the vector with tail at A(1, 1, 0) and head at B(3, 0, 2).

13. The vector $\vec{a} = [2, -5, 6]$ is given. Determine one vector that is perpendicular to $\vec{a}$.

14. The vectors $\vec{a} = [2, -5, 6]$ and $\vec{b} = [-1, 0, 4]$ are given. Determine one vector that is perpendicular to both $\vec{a}$ and $\vec{b}$.

15. Find two unit vectors each of which is perpendicular to the vectors [1, 1, 0] and [1, 0, 1].

16. If $\vec{a} = [4, -2, 3]$ and $\vec{b} = [-2, 1, -2]$, calculate:

a) $\vec{a} \times \vec{b}$

b) $\vec{b} \times \vec{a}$

c) the area of the parallelogram determined by $\vec{a}$ and $\vec{b}$.

17. Given the points A(1, 2, 0), B(0, 1, 0) and C(1, 0, 2), determine the area of △ABC.

18. Determine x and y if $\vec{a} = [x, y, 1]$, $\vec{b} = [1, 2, 3]$, and $\vec{a} \times \vec{b} = [7, -5, 1]$.

19. Which of the following statements are true? Explain.

a) $\vec{a} \times \vec{b} = \vec{b} \times \vec{a}$

b) $\vec{a} \bullet \vec{b} = \vec{b} \bullet \vec{a}$

c) $\vec{a} \bullet (\vec{b} + \vec{c}) = \vec{a} \bullet \vec{b} + \vec{a} \bullet \vec{c}$

d) $\vec{a} \times (\vec{b} \bullet \vec{c}) = \vec{a} \times \vec{b} \bullet \vec{c}$

e) $\vec{a} \bullet \vec{b} \times \vec{c} = \vec{b} \bullet \vec{c} \times \vec{a}$

f) $\vec{a} \times (\vec{b} + \vec{c}) = \vec{a} \times \vec{b} + \vec{a} \times \vec{c}$

g) $(\vec{a} - \vec{b}) \times (\vec{a} + \vec{b}) = 2\vec{a} \times \vec{b}$

20. a) Refer to exercise 17 on page 109. Describe how the torque would change under the following conditions. Indicate the direction and magnitude of the torque vector.

    i) The magnitude of the radius vector is multiplied by 2.

    ii) The applied force is acting in the opposite direction.

b) At what angle would the applied force create the greatest torque? Explain.

Charles Dodgson (1832–1898)
Born: Daresbury, England

Upon graduating from Christ Church College, Oxford, Dodgson became a lecturer of mathematics there. Dodgson is most famous for writing *Alice's Adventures in Wonderland* and *Through the Looking Glass*, using the pen name Lewis Carroll. He was also an avid photographer and specialized in photographing children.
Dodgson's mathematical works are numerous, but less well known. It is rumoured that Queen Victoria, having said how much she enjoyed *Alice's Adventures in Wonderland* and was looking forward to another work by him, was dismayed to receive *A Syllabus of Plane Algebraical Geometry.*

1. Show that the vectors $\vec{a} = [5, 1, -2]$ and $\vec{b} = [3, -3, 6]$ are perpendicular.

2. Given the vectors $\vec{a} = [4, 1, 2]$ and $\vec{b} = [3, -2, 5]$, determine:

   a) $\vec{a} \cdot \vec{b}$

   b) $\vec{a} \times \vec{b}$

   c) the angle between $\vec{a}$ and $\vec{b}$

   d) $\vec{a} \downarrow \vec{b}$

   e) $|\vec{a} \downarrow \vec{b}|$

3. The vector $\vec{u} = [3, -1, 6]$ is given. Determine two different non-collinear vectors both of which are perpendicular to $\vec{u}$.

4. **Communication** Describe three different methods you could use to show that the triangle with vertices A(3, 1, 2), B(4, 3, 5), and C(7, −4, 4) has a right angle at A.

5. Given $\vec{a} = [3, 4, 3]$ and $\vec{b} = [1, -2, 5]$.

   a) Determine $\vec{a} \cdot \vec{b}$.

   b) Calculate the angle between $\vec{a}$ and $\vec{b}$.

   c) If $\vec{c} = [1, -3, t]$, find t so that $\vec{a}$ and $\vec{c}$ are perpendicular.

   d) Determine $\vec{a} \downarrow \vec{b}$.

   e) Determine $\vec{a} \times \vec{b}$.

6. **Knowledge/Understanding** Determine if the vectors $\vec{a} = [5, 1, -2]$, $\vec{b} = [-2, 3, 1]$, and $\vec{c} = [11, 9, -4]$ are coplanar.

7. **Application** Calculate the area of the parallelogram whose adjacent sides are $\vec{a} = [1, 1, -2]$ and $\vec{b} = [3, 3, -1]$.

8. **Thinking/Inquiry/Problem Solving**

   a) What is the z-component of a vector parallel to the xy-plane? Explain.

   b) Find all unit vectors parallel to the xy-plane and perpendicular to the vector [1, −2, 2].

Equations of Lines and Planes

Curriculum Expectations

By the end of this chapter, you will:

- Determine the vector and parametric equations of lines in two-space and the vector, parametric, and symmetric equations of lines in three-space.

- Determine the intersections of lines in three-space.

- Determine the vector, parametric, and scalar equations of planes.

- Determine the intersection of a line and a plane in three-space.

- Solve systems of linear equations involving up to three unknowns, using row reduction of matrices, with and without the aid of technology.

- Interpret row reduction of matrices as the creation of a new linear system equivalent to the original.

- Determine the intersection of two or three planes by setting up and solving a system of linear equations in three unknowns.

- Interpret a system of two linear equations in two unknowns and a system of three linear equations in three unknowns geometrically, and relate the geometrical properties to the type of solution set the system of equations possesses.

- Solve problems involving the intersections of lines and planes, and present the solutions with clarity and justification.

3.1 Revisiting the Equation of a Line in 2-space

In earlier grades, you learned various forms of the equation of a line in R^2. Consider the line passing through A(-1, 4) with slope $\frac{2}{3}$, as shown in the diagram.

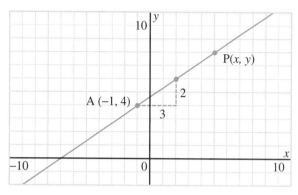

In *slope-point form*, the equation of the line is:

$$y = \frac{2}{3}(x + 1) + 4$$

If we solve this equation for y, we obtain the *slope y-intercept form*:

$$y = \frac{2}{3}x + \frac{14}{3}$$

If we rearrange the terms, we obtain the equation in *standard form*:

$$2x - 3y + 14 = 0$$

The equation of a line is satisfied by the coordinates of all points on the line, and no others. For example, the point (5, 8) is on the line above. These coordinates satisfy all three equations.

In the next section, we will consider the equations of a line in R^3. None of the above forms of equation can be extended to lines in three dimensions. The equations involving slope cannot be extended to R^3 because the concept of slope involves only two quantities. The slope of a line in R^3 is not defined. The standard form can be extended to R^3, but we will see in Section 3.3 that an equation such as $2x - 3y + z + 14 = 0$ does not represent a line (it represents a plane).

In this section, we will establish other forms of the equation of a line in R^2. These are forms that are easily extended to R^3, and we will do that in the next section. These forms involve vectors.

The diagram below shows the same line as on page 124. This line passes through A(−1, 4) and has *direction vector* $\vec{m}$ = [3, 2]. That is, the line is parallel to $\vec{m}$.

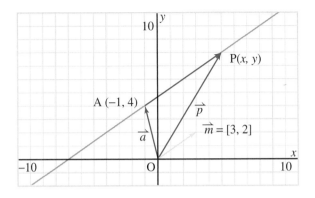

Direction vectors of lines are not unique. Any scalar multiple of [3, 2] is also a direction vector of this line.

We will determine various forms of the equation of this line.

Vector equation

Let P(x, y) be any point on the line. Visualize P moving back and forth along the line. As it moves, points O, A, and P always form a triangle in which the triangle law is satisfied:

$$\overrightarrow{OP} = \overrightarrow{OA} + \overrightarrow{AP}$$

Since $\overrightarrow{AP}$ is collinear with $\vec{m}$, we know that $\overrightarrow{AP} = t\vec{m}$, where t is any scalar. Let $\overrightarrow{OA} = \vec{a}$ and $\overrightarrow{OP} = \vec{p}$. Then we can write the above equation as:

$$\vec{p} = \vec{a} + t\vec{m}$$

or $[x, y] = [−1, 4] + t[3, 2]$ ①

Equation ① is a *vector equation* of the line. Although it is a single equation, it contains information about both the x- and the y-components of any vector with tail [0, 0] and head [x, y]. Vector equations are not unique because any point on the line and any scalar multiple of the direction vector can be used.

We can use equation ① to determine the coordinates of points on the line, simply by substituting values for t. For example:

If $t = 1$, we obtain [−1, 4] + [3, 2] = [2, 6].
If $t = 3$, we obtain [−1, 4] + [9, 6] = [8, 10].
If $t = −2$, we obtain [−1, 4] + [−6, −4] = [−7, 0].

The points (2, 6), (8, 10), and (−7, 0) lie on the line.

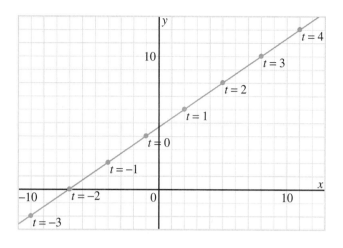

Vector Equation of a Line in 2-space

Let A(a_1, a_2) be a fixed point on a line in R^2 with direction vector $\overrightarrow{m} = [m_1, m_2]$. Let P($x$, y) be any point on the line. The vector equation of the line is:

$$[x, y] = [a_1, a_2] + t[m_1, m_2]$$

where t can be any real number.

Parametric equations

On page 125, we found the coordinates of some points on the line by substituting values of t into equation ① and simplifying the results. It is more efficient to rewrite the equation so that the right side is a single vector before substituting the values.

$$[x, y] = [-1, 4] + t[3, 2]$$
$$[x, y] = [-1, 4] + [3t, 2t]$$
$$[x, y] = [-1 + 3t, 4 + 2t]$$

Since these vectors are equal, the corresponding components are equal.

$$\left. \begin{array}{l} x = -1 + 3t \\ y = 4 + 2t \end{array} \right\} \qquad ②$$

Equations ② are called *parametric equations* of the line. Parametric equations of a line have these properties:

- The constant terms on the right side are the coordinates of a point on the line.
- The coefficients of t are the components of a direction vector of the line.

Parametric equations are formulas for the coordinates of points on the line. For example, if $t = 2$, we obtain (5, 8); if $t = -3$, we obtain (−10, −2), and so on. These points are on the line.

Parametric equations of a line are not unique. In the previous equations, we could replace the constant terms on the right side with the coordinates of any point on the line. We can also replace the coefficients of t with the components of any scalar multiple of the direction vector.

In both the vector equation and the parametric equations, the letter t is called a *parameter*. Coordinates of points on the line are found by substituting different real numbers for t.

Take Note

Parametric Equations of a Line in 2-space

Let A(a_1, a_2) be a fixed point on a line in R^2 with direction vector $\overrightarrow{m} = [m_1, m_2]$. Let P($x$, y) be any point on the line. Parametric equations of the line are:

$$x = a_1 + tm_1$$
$$y = a_2 + tm_2$$

The letter t is a parameter that can represent any real number.

Example 1

A line passes through the points A(−2, 3) and B(5, 2).

a) Write a vector equation of the line.

b) Write parametric equations of the line.

Solution

a) A direction vector for the line is:

$\overrightarrow{AB} = [5 − (−2), 2 − 3]$

$\overrightarrow{AB} = [7, −1]$

A vector equation of the line is:

$[x, y] = [−2, 3] + t[7, −1]$

b) Use the result of part a. Equate corresponding components.
Parametric equations of the line are:

$x = −2 + 7t$

$y = 3 − t$

- What are some other possible vector and parametric equations for the line in *Example 1*?

Symmetric equation

Suppose a line passes through the point A(1, –2) and has direction vector $\overrightarrow{m} = [3, 4]$. Its parametric equations are:

$$x = 1 + 3t$$
$$y = -2 + 4t$$

If we solve each equation for t, we obtain:

$$t = \frac{x-1}{3} \qquad \text{and} \qquad t = \frac{y+2}{4}$$

Since the values of t must be the same in each parametric equation, these two expressions are equal. Hence:

$$\frac{x-1}{3} = \frac{y+2}{4} \qquad \text{or} \qquad \frac{x-1}{3} = \frac{y-(-2)}{4}$$

This equation is a *symmetric equation* of the line.

A symmetric equation of a line has these properties:

- The numbers after the minus signs in the numerators are the coordinates of a point on the line.
- The numbers in the denominators are the components of a direction vector of the line.

Like parametric equations, the symmetric equation of a line is not unique. We can use the coordinates of any point on the line in the numerators of the expressions, and we can use any scalar multiple of the direction vector in the denominators.

A symmetric equation is a convenient way to write the equation of a line through a given point and with a given direction vector.

Take Note

Symmetric Equation of a Line in 2-space

Let $A(a_1, a_2)$ be a fixed point on a line in $\mathbf{R}^2$ with direction vector $\overrightarrow{m} = [m_1, m_2]$. Let $P(x, y)$ be any point on the line. A symmetric equation of the line is:

$$\frac{x - a_1}{m_1} = \frac{y - a_2}{m_2} \qquad \text{where } m_1 \neq 0, \text{ and } m_2 \neq 0$$

When parametric equations of a line are given, we can obtain a symmetric equation by solving each equation for the parameter, as on the previous page. As well, when a symmetric equation is given, we can determine the parametric equations.

Example 2

The symmetric equation of a line is $\frac{x+4}{2} = \frac{y-6}{-3}$.

a) Write parametric equations of the line.

b) Determine the coordinates of three different points on the line.

Solution

a) Let $\frac{x+4}{2} = \frac{y-6}{-3} = t$.

Then,

$$\frac{x+4}{2} = t \qquad \text{and} \qquad \frac{y-6}{-3} = t$$
$$x = -4 + 2t \qquad\qquad\qquad y = 6 - 3t$$

Parametric equations of the line are:

$x = -4 + 2t$
$y = 6 - 3t$

b) Use the parametric equations of the line obtained in part a.

Let $t = 0$ to obtain the point $(-4, 6)$.
Let $t = 1$ to obtain the point $(-2, 3)$.
Let $t = 2$ to obtain the point $(0, 0)$.

These are the coordinates of three different points on the line.

Vector, parametric, and symmetric equations of a line in R^2 represent a different way of thinking about the equation of a line. When we use parametric equations for two different lines in the same problem, we need to use different letters for the parameters of each line.

Example 3

Symmetric equations of two lines are given.

$$L_1: \frac{x+1}{2} = \frac{y-5}{-1} \qquad \text{and} \qquad L_2: \frac{x-3}{3} = \frac{y+2}{1}$$

Find the coordinates of the point of intersection of L_1 and L_2.

Solution

A point on L_1 is $(-1, 5)$ and its direction vector is $[2, -1]$.
Parametric equations of L_1 are:

$$x = -1 + 2t$$
$$y = 5 - t$$

A point on L_2 is $(3, -2)$ and its direction vector is $[3, 1]$.
Parametric equations of L_2 are:

$$x = 3 + 3s$$
$$y = -2 + s$$

The parametric equations of a line give the coordinates of every point on the line. So, at the point of intersection of the lines, the values of x and y are equal.

$$-1 + 2t = 3 + 3s \qquad ①$$
$$5 - t = -2 + s \qquad ②$$

Solve the linear system of equations for s and t.
From ②, $s = 7 - t$.
Substitute this expression for s in ①:

$$-1 + 2t = 3 + 3(7 - t)$$
$$-1 + 2t = 24 - 3t$$
$$t = 5$$

Substitute $t = 5$ into ② to obtain $s = 2$.

To determine the coordinates of the point of intersection, substitute $s = 2$ or $t = 5$ into the parametric equations of the corresponding line. Using L_2:

$$x = 3 + 3s \qquad \text{and} \qquad y = -2 + s$$
$$x = 9 \qquad\qquad\qquad\quad y = 0$$

The lines intersect at the point $(9, 0)$.

Something to Think About

- In the solution of *Example 3*, the values of s and t at the point of intersection are different. This illustrates why we use different letters for the parameters.
- What is another way to solve *Example 3*?

When we are given two lines, not only can we find their point of intersection, if it exists, but also the angle between them.

Example 4

Determine if the lines $L_1: \frac{x-1}{1} = \frac{y-3}{5}$ and $L_2: \frac{x-2}{2} = \frac{1-y}{3}$ intersect, and if so, calculate the angle between them.

Solution

Use the symmetric equation of each line to obtain the direction vectors $\vec{m_1}$ and $\vec{m_2}$, respectively.

$L_1: \frac{x-1}{1} = \frac{y-3}{5}$ has direction vector $\vec{m_1} = [1, 5]$.

$L_2: \frac{x-2}{2} = \frac{y-2}{-3}$ has direction vector $\vec{m_2} = [2, -3]$.

Since $\vec{m_1}$ is not a scalar multiple of $\vec{m_2}$, the lines are not parallel or coincident, and so must intersect.

Use the dot product to determine the angle θ between the direction vectors.

$$\vec{m_1} \bullet \vec{m_2} = |\vec{m_1}||\vec{m_2}| \cos \theta$$

Rearrange. $\quad \cos \theta = \frac{\vec{m_1} \bullet \vec{m_2}}{|\vec{m_1}||\vec{m_2}|}$

$$= \frac{2 - 15}{\sqrt{26}\sqrt{13}}$$

$$= \frac{-13}{13\sqrt{2}}$$

$$= \frac{-1}{\sqrt{2}}$$

Thus, $\quad\quad\quad \theta = 135°$

The acute angle between the lines is $45°$.

3.1 Exercises

A

1. Explain what it means for the coordinates of a point to satisfy the vector equation and the parametric equations of a line.

2. A line has the following vector equation.

$$[x, y] = [2, -3] + t[5, 1]$$

a) State the coordinates of a point on the line.

b) State the coordinates of three other points on the line.

c) Write another vector equation of this line.

3. A line has the following parametric equations.

$$x = -1 + 2t$$
$$y = 5 + t$$

a) State the coordinates of a point on the line.

b) State the coordinates of three other points on the line.

c) Write another set of parametric equations of this line.

4. A line has the following symmetric equation.

$$\frac{x+4}{5} = \frac{y-1}{-2}$$

a) State the coordinates of a point on the line.

b) State the coordinates of three other points on the line.

c) Write another symmetric equation of this line.

5. A line contains the point A(7, –3) and has direction vector $\vec{m} = [-1, 2]$. Determine:

a) a vector equation of the line.

b) parametric equations of the line.

c) a symmetric equation of the line.

6. Write parametric equations for:

a) the x-axis

b) the y-axis

B

7. a) Write parametric equations of the line through A(3, –2) and B(6, 1).

b) Use your parametric equations to determine the coordinates of three other points on the line.

c) Draw a diagram to illustrate the results of part b.

8. Find the coordinates of three different points on each line.

a) $\dfrac{2-x}{-4} = \dfrac{y+1}{3}$

b) $\dfrac{x+3}{2} = \dfrac{3-y}{5}$

9. Knowledge/Understanding Write vector, parametric, and symmetric (if possible) equations of the line determined by each set of conditions.

a) through the point A(4, 1) with direction vector $\vec{m} = [-3, 1]$

b) through the points R(–6, 2) and S(4, –2)

c) through the point K(2, –3) and parallel to the y-axis

10. The equation of a line is $2x - 3y + 12 = 0$. Write the equation of the line in:

a) slope y-intercept form

b) parametric form

c) symmetric form

11. A line passes through the points A(2, –4) and B(5, 2).

    a) Write the equation of the line in:

        i) parametric form.
        ii) symmetric form.
        iii) slope y-intercept form.
        iv) standard form.

    b) Describe the advantages of each form of equation.

12. Communication A line is parallel to one of the coordinate axes. Explain what this tells you about each form of equation. Use examples to illustrate your explanations.

    a) vector equation

    b) parametric equations

    c) symmetric equation

    d) slope y-intercept form

    e) standard form

13. Determine which of the points A(–1, 1), B(–4, 3), C(7, 5), and D(5, –3) are on the line with these parametric equations:

$$x = 2 - 3t$$
$$y = -1 + 2t$$

14. Three sets of parametric equations are given. Do these represent three different lines, two different lines, or only one line? Explain.

Set 1:	**Set 2:**	**Set 3:**
$x = 1 - 3t$	$x = 7 + 9s$	$x = -2 + 3k$
$y = 3 + 2t$	$y = -1 - 6s$	$y = 5 - 2k$

15. Show that the following lines intersect. Find the coordinates of the point of intersection, and the angle of intersection.

    a) L_1: $x = 7 + 2t$ and L_2: $x = -3 + 3s$
             $y = 4 + t$ $y = 4 - s$

    b) L_1: $\frac{x+3}{3} = \frac{y+1}{4}$ and L_2: $\frac{x-6}{3} = \frac{y-2}{-2}$

16. Determine if the two lines intersect. If they do, find the coordinates of the point of intersection.

    a) L_1: $x = -5 + t$ and L_2: $x = 4 - 2s$
             $y = 2 - 3t$ $y = 6s$

    b) L_1: $x = 6 - 2t$ and L_2: $x = 4 + 2s$
             $y = -1 + t$ $y = -8 + s$

17. Determine the coordinates of the point where each line intersects the x- and y-axes.

a) $x = 2 + t$
$y = 5 - t$

b) $\dfrac{x+1}{3} = \dfrac{y-4}{2}$

18. Write vector and parametric equations of each line in R^2.

a) $x = 4$

b) $y = 3$

c) $y = 3x - 2$

d) $x + 2y + 4 = 0$

19. A symmetric equation of a line is given. Write a set of parametric equations of the line.

a) $\dfrac{5-x}{4} = \dfrac{2-y}{3}$

b) $\dfrac{x}{2} = \dfrac{y-1}{-1}$

20. Determine the angle between the lines $y = 4x + 2$ and $y = -x + 3$.

21. Write the equation $[x, y] = [2, 3] + s[1, -2]$ in the form $y = mx + b$.

22. **Thinking/Inquiry/Problem Solving** The direction angles and direction cosines of a line are defined to be the direction angles and direction cosines of its direction vector. Determine the direction angles of each line.

a) $\dfrac{x-2}{1} = \dfrac{y+3}{1}$

b) $\dfrac{x+4}{3} = \dfrac{y-1}{4}$

23. **Application** The line segment joining A(2, 3) to B(9, 2) is the hypotenuse of a right triangle. The third vertex, C, lies on the line with these parametric equations:

$$x = 2 + 2t$$
$$y = 8 - t$$

Determine the coordinates of C. Illustrate with a diagram.

24. Repeat exercise 23 for each situation.

a) Line segment AC is the hypotenuse of the right triangle.

b) Line segment BC is the hypotenuse of the right triangle.

C

25. A line passes through the point A(0, 4). Its first direction angle is 60°.

a) What possible second direction angles can it have?

b) Find parametric equations of the line for each set of direction angles.

c) Draw a diagram illustrating the lines in part b.

26. Given the vectors $\vec{a} = \overrightarrow{OA}$ and $\vec{b} = \overrightarrow{OB}$, show that the vector equation of the line containing the points A and B has the form $\vec{p} = s\vec{a} + t\vec{b}$, where $s + t = 1$.

3.2 The Equation of a Line in 3-space

The methods that were used in Section 3.1 to write the vector, parametric, and symmetric equations of a line in R^2 extend to lines in R^3. For example, the diagram below shows the line passing through the point A(−2, 5, 3) with direction vector $\overrightarrow{m} = [2, 4, 1]$. The direction vector is shown with its tail at the origin. The line is parallel to this vector.

We will determine various forms of the equation(s) of this line.

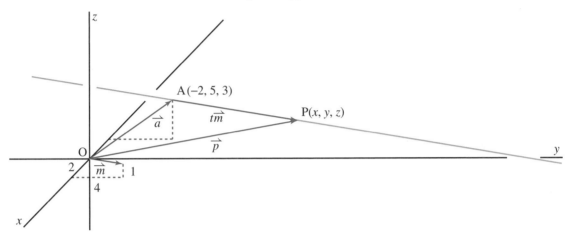

Vector equation

Let P(x, y, z) be any point on this line. Visualize P moving back and forth along the line. As it moves, points O, A, and P always form a triangle in which the triangle law is satisfied:

$$\overrightarrow{OP} = \overrightarrow{OA} + \overrightarrow{AP}$$

Since $\overrightarrow{AP}$ is collinear with $\overrightarrow{m}$, we know that $\overrightarrow{AP} = t\overrightarrow{m}$, where t is any scalar. Let $\overrightarrow{OA} = \overrightarrow{a}$ and $\overrightarrow{OP} = \overrightarrow{p}$. Then we can write the above equation as:

$$\overrightarrow{p} = \overrightarrow{a} + t\overrightarrow{m}$$

or $[x, y, z] = [-2, 5, 3] + t[2, 4, 1]$ ①

Equation ① is a *vector equation* of the line. Vector equations are not unique because any point on the line and any scalar multiple of its direction vector can be used.

Parametric equations

On the right side of equation ①, we can expand the scalar multiple and add the two vectors to obtain:

$$[x, y, z] = [-2 + 2t, 5 + 4t, 3 + t]$$

Since these vectors are equal, corresponding components are equal.

$$\left.\begin{array}{l} x = -2 + 2t \\ y = 5 + 4t \\ z = 3 + t \end{array}\right\} \qquad ②$$

Equations ② are *parametric equations* of the line. As in $\mathbf{R}^2$, parametric equations of a line have these properties:

- The constant terms on the right side are the coordinates of a point on the line.
- The coefficients of t are the components of a direction vector of the line.

Parametric equations are very useful because they are formulas for the coordinates of points on the line. For example, if $t = 1$, we obtain $(0, 9, 4)$; if $t = 2$, we obtain $(2, 13, 5)$; if $t = -1$, we obtain $(-4, 1, 2)$, and so on. All these points are on the line.

As with lines in $\mathbf{R}^2$, parametric equations of a line in $\mathbf{R}^3$ are not unique. In the above equations, we could replace the constant terms on the right side with the coordinates of any point on the line. We can also replace the coefficients of t with the components of any scalar multiple of the direction vector.

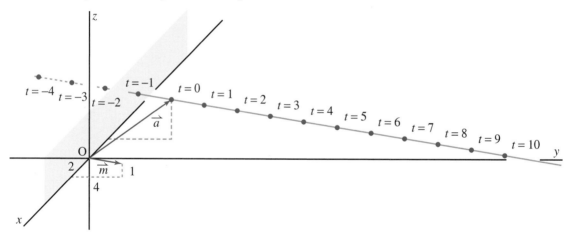

We can obtain additional information about the line from its parametric equations. For example, we can determine where it intersects the coordinate planes. For points on the xz-plane, $y = 0$. Substitute this value of y into the second parametric equation to obtain $0 = 5 + 4t$, so $t = -\frac{5}{4}$. Substitute this value of t into the other two parametric equations to obtain $x = -\frac{9}{2}$ and $z = \frac{7}{4}$. Hence, the line intersects the xz-plane at $\left(-\frac{9}{2}, 0, \frac{7}{4}\right)$.

Symmetric equations

If we solve each of the three parametric equations for t, the results will all be equal. We obtain these *symmetric equations* of the line:

$$\frac{x + 2}{2} = \frac{y - 5}{4} = \frac{z - 3}{1} \qquad ③ \qquad \text{or} \qquad \frac{x - (-2)}{2} = \frac{y - 5}{4} = \frac{z - 3}{1}$$

As in R^2, symmetric equations of a line have these properties:

- The numbers after the minus signs in the numerators are the coordinates of a point on the line.
- The numbers in the denominators are the components of a direction vector of the line.

Like parametric equations, symmetric equations of a line are not unique. We can use the coordinates of any point on the line in the numerators of the expressions, and we can use any scalar multiple of the direction vector in the denominators.

Symmetric equations are a convenient way to write the equations of a line. However, parametric equations are more useful in many problems.

Example 1

Symmetric equations of a line are given.
$$\frac{x-3}{2} = \frac{y+4}{-1} = \frac{z-1}{3}$$

a) Write parametric equations of the line.

b) Determine the coordinates of three different points on the line.

Solution

a) Let $\frac{x-3}{2} = \frac{y+4}{-1} = \frac{z-1}{3} = t$.

Then,

$$\frac{x-3}{2} = t \qquad \text{and} \qquad \frac{y+4}{-1} = t \qquad \text{and} \qquad \frac{z-1}{3} = t$$
$$x = 3 + 2t \qquad\qquad y = -4 - t \qquad\qquad z = 1 + 3t$$

Parametric equations of the line are:

$$x = 3 + 2t$$
$$y = -4 - t$$
$$z = 1 + 3t$$

b) Use the parametric equations from part a.

Let $t = 0$ to obtain the point $(3, -4, 1)$.
Let $t = 1$ to obtain the point $(5, -5, 4)$.
Let $t = 2$ to obtain the point $(7, -6, 7)$.

These are the coordinates of three different points on the line.

Something to Think About

- Although there are three expressions in symmetric equations of a line, there are actually only two equations. For example, the symmetric equations in *Example 1* could be written as:

$$\frac{x-3}{2} = \frac{y+4}{-1} \quad \text{and} \quad \frac{y+4}{-1} = \frac{z-1}{3}$$

Since we can use these equations to show that $\frac{x-3}{2} = \frac{z-1}{3}$, this is not considered to be a third equation.

In the diagram on page 135, suppose the direction vector had been $\vec{m} = [2, 4, 0]$. The z-component, 0, tells us that the line is parallel to the xy-plane and 3 units above it. The parametric equations of the line are:

$$x = -2 + 2t$$
$$y = 5 + 4t$$
$$z = 3$$

Although we can write parametric equations of this line, we cannot write symmetric equations because one of the denominators would be 0. Instead we write:

$$\frac{x+2}{2} = \frac{y-5}{4}, \ z = 3$$

Although these are not symmetric equations, we can still say that they are equations of the line.

Take Note

Equations of a Line in 3-space

Let A(a_1, a_2, a_3) be a fixed point on a line in $\mathbf{R}^3$ with direction vector $\vec{m} = [m_1, m_2, m_3]$. Let P($x$, y, z) be any point on the line. The equations of the line can be written in the following forms.

Vector equation

$$[x, y, z] = [a_1, a_2, a_3] + t[m_1, m_2, m_3]$$

Parametric equations

$$x = a_1 + tm_1$$
$$y = a_2 + tm_2$$
$$z = a_3 + tm_3$$

Symmetric equations

$$\frac{x - a_1}{m_1} = \frac{y - a_2}{m_2} = \frac{z - a_3}{m_3} \quad \text{where } m_1 \neq 0, m_2 \neq 0, \text{ and } m_3 \neq 0$$

In three dimensions, there are three intersection possibilities for two distinct lines.

The lines may intersect.

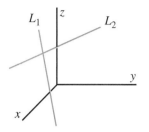

The lines may be parallel.

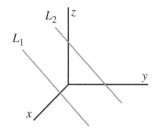

The line may neither intersect nor be parallel. These are called *skew lines*.

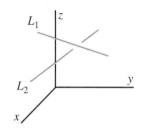

Example 2

Symmetric equations of two lines are given. Show that the lines are parallel.

L_1: $\dfrac{x-2}{1} = \dfrac{y+3}{2} = \dfrac{z-4}{-3}$ and L_2: $\dfrac{x+1}{-2} = \dfrac{y-5}{-4} = \dfrac{z}{6}$

Solution

A direction vector of L_1 is $[1, 2, -3]$ and of L_2 is $[-2, -4, 6]$. These are collinear since $[-2, -4, 6] = -2[1, 2, -3]$. Therefore, the lines are either parallel or they coincide. To show that they do not coincide, show that a point on one of the lines is not on the other line.

From the symmetric equations, the coordinates of a point on L_1 are $(2, -3, 4)$. Substitute these coordinates into the expressions of the symmetric equations of L_2:

$t = \dfrac{x+1}{-2} = \dfrac{2+1}{-2}$ $t = \dfrac{y-5}{-4} = \dfrac{-3-5}{-4}$ $t = \dfrac{z}{6} = \dfrac{4}{6}$

$t = -\dfrac{3}{2}$ $t = 2$ $t = \dfrac{2}{3}$

For this point to lie on L_2, and for both lines to coincide, all these results must be equal. Since they are not, L_1 and L_2 are parallel.

Example 3

Symmetric equations of two lines are given.

L_1: $\dfrac{x-3}{1} = \dfrac{y+7}{-2} = \dfrac{z-5}{4}$ and L_2: $\dfrac{x+7}{3} = \dfrac{y+8}{1} = \dfrac{z-4}{-1}$

a) Show that the lines intersect, and determine the coordinates of the point of intersection.

b) Write symmetric equations of another line L_3 such that L_1 and L_3 are skew lines. Explain why they are skew lines.

Solution

a) Direction vectors of the lines are $[1, -2, 4]$ and $[3, 1, -1]$. Since these are not collinear, the lines either intersect or they are skew lines. Write the equations of L_1 and L_2 in parametric form, using different parameters for each line.

L_1: $x = 3 + s$ and L_2: $x = -7 + 3t$
       $y = -7 - 2s$ $y = -8 + t$
       $z = 5 + 4s$ $z = 4 - t$

At a point of intersection, the values of x are equal, and similarly for the values of y, and z.

     $3 + s = -7 + 3t$ ①
     $-7 - 2s = -8 + t$ ②
     $5 + 4s = 4 - t$ ③

These equations form a linear system that can be solved in different ways.

Solve ② and ③, and determine if the solution satisfies ①.
Add ② and ③ to obtain $-2 + 2s = -4$, so $s = -1$.
Substitute $s = -1$ into ② to obtain $-5 = -8 + t$, so $t = 3$.
The solution of equations ② and ③ is $s = -1$, $t = 3$.

Substitute these values of s and t in ①:

L.S. $= 3 + s$ R.S. $= -7 + 3t$
     $= 3 + (-1)$ $= -7 + 9$
     $= 2$ $= 2$

Since these values are equal, the equations ①, ②, and ③ have a solution, and the lines L_1 and L_2 intersect. To determine the coordinates of the point of intersection, substitute $s = -1$ or $t = 3$ into the parametric equations of the corresponding line. Using L_1:

$x = 3 + s$ $y = -7 - 2s$ $z = 5 + 4s$
   $= 3 - 1$ $= -7 - 2(-1)$ $= 5 + 4(-1)$
   $= 2$ $= -5$ $= 1$

The lines intersect at the point $(2, -5, 1)$.

b) Consider the line with the following symmetric equations:

L_3: $\dfrac{x}{3} = \dfrac{y + 8}{1} = \dfrac{z - 4}{-1}$

These equations are the same as those of L_2, except for the numerator in the first expression. If the solution in part a was repeated, the only difference would occur when $s = -1$, $t = 3$ are substituted into equation ①. This time, that equation would be $3 + s = 3t$, and the equation is not satisfied. This indicates that equations ①, ②, and ③ have no solution, and the lines L_1 and L_3 do not intersect. They are skew lines.

A

1. A line has the following vector equation.

$$[x, y, z] = [5, -4, 1] + t[3, 2, -1]$$

a) State the coordinates of a point on the line.

b) State the coordinates of three other points on the line.

c) Write another vector equation of this line.

2. A line has the following parametric equations.

$$x = 2 + t$$
$$y = -3 + 2t$$
$$z = 4 - 3t$$

a) State the coordinates of a point on the line.

b) State the coordinates of three other points on the line.

c) Write another set of parametric equations of this line.

3. A line has the following symmetric equations.

$$\frac{x-4}{2} = \frac{3-y}{1} = \frac{z+2}{3}$$

a) State the coordinates of a point on the line.

b) State the coordinates of three other points on the line.

c) Write other symmetric equations of this line.

4. Does the point D(1, −2, 6) lie on the line with symmetric equations $\frac{x-4}{3} = \frac{y+2}{1} = \frac{z-6}{2}$? Explain.

5. A line contains the point A(3, −2, 5) and has direction vector $\vec{m} = [-1, 4, -3]$. Determine:

a) a vector equation of the line.

b) parametric equations of the line.

c) symmetric equations of the line.

6. Write parametric equations for:

a) the x-axis   b) the y-axis   c) the z-axis

7. Visualize your classroom as a large rectangular box. Identify two edges of the box that illustrate skew lines.

B

8. a) Write parametric equations of the line through A(5, 1, –3) and B(4, 5, –1).

   b) Use your parametric equations to determine the coordinates of three other points on the line.

9. Find the coordinates of three different points on each line.

a) $\dfrac{x-2}{1} = \dfrac{3-y}{2} = \dfrac{z+1}{-1}$

b) $\dfrac{x-1}{3} = \dfrac{y}{1} = \dfrac{1-z}{2}$

c) $\dfrac{x+3}{-2} = \dfrac{y-5}{1}$, $z = 2$

d) $x = -4$, $\dfrac{y+2}{3} = \dfrac{z-3}{4}$

10. Refer to exercise 9. Explain what the following tell you about the position of the line in R^3.

   a) In part c, $z = 2$.

   b) In part d, $x = -4$.

11. Knowledge/Understanding Write vector, parametric, and symmetric equations of the line determined by each set of conditions.

   a) through A(2, –1, 3) with direction vector $\overrightarrow{m} = [-1, 3, 5]$

   b) through A(4, –2, 1) and B(–1, 0, 3)

   c) through C(5, –1, 0) and D(5, 3, –4)

   d) through M(3, –1, –1) and parallel to the x-axis

   e) through N(–2, 0, 5) and parallel to the y-axis

12. Determine which of the points A(–5, 2, 7), B(3, 0, –1), C(–1, –1, –2), and D(4, –2, 3) are on the line with symmetric equations $\dfrac{x+3}{-2} = \dfrac{y}{1} = \dfrac{z-1}{3}$.

13. Three sets of parametric equations are given. Do these represent three different lines, two different lines, or only one line? Explain.

Set 1:	**Set 2:**	**Set 3:**
$x = 1 + 2t$	$x = -5 - 2s$	$x = 5 + 4k$
$y = 3 - t$	$y = 6 + s$	$y = 1 - 2k$
$z = 7 + 4t$	$z = -5 - 4s$	$z = 15 + 8k$

14. Show that the following lines intersect and determine the coordinates of the point of intersection.

   a) L_1: $\dfrac{x+1}{3} = \dfrac{y-2}{-1} = \dfrac{z}{4}$ and L_2: $\dfrac{x+6}{2} = \dfrac{8-y}{5} = \dfrac{z+1}{-3}$

   b) L_1: $\dfrac{x-1}{2} = \dfrac{y+3}{1}, z = -3$ and L_2: $\dfrac{x-2}{3} = \dfrac{y+1}{2} = \dfrac{z}{1}$

15. Determine if the two lines intersect. If they do, find the coordinates of the point of intersection.

a) L_1: $x = 1 + 2t$ and L_2: $x = 1 + 3s$
       $y = -1 - t$ $y = 2 + 2s$
       $z = 3t$ $z = 3 + 4s$

b) L_1: $\frac{x+1}{1} = \frac{y-1}{2} = \frac{3-z}{2}$ and L_2: $\frac{5-x}{2} = \frac{y-3}{1} = \frac{z+3}{1}$

c) L_1: $\frac{x-1}{2} = \frac{y-3}{3} = \frac{z-5}{4}$ and L_2: $\frac{x+1}{2} = \frac{y+4}{-1} = \frac{z+2}{1}$

16. Application The diagram (below left) shows a cube with vertices $(\pm 2, \pm 2, \pm 2)$. Edge AB is shown in colour.

a) Choose another edge that passes through either A or B. Write parametric equations of the lines through each edge. Solve the equations to verify that they both pass through A.

b) Choose an edge that is parallel to AB. Write parametric equations of the lines through each edge. Attempt to solve the equations. Explain why the solution tells you that the lines are parallel and do not intersect.

c) Choose an edge that is not parallel to AB and does not pass through either A or B. Write parametric equations of the lines containing the two edges. Attempt to solve the equations. Explain why the solution tells you that the lines are skew.

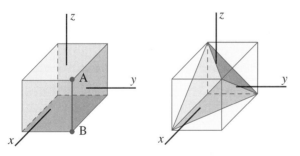

17. The diagram (above right) shows the cube in exercise 16 and the solid formed by joining the vertices $(2, 2, 2)$, $(2, -2, -2)$, $(-2, 2, -2)$, and $(-2, -2, 2)$ in all possible ways. This solid is called a *regular tetrahedron*.

a) Write parametric equations of the 6 lines containing the edges of the tetrahedron.

b) Choose any two edges that meet at a vertex. Calculate the angle of intersection of these edges.

18. On page 138, we replaced the direction vector, $\vec{m} = [2, 4, 1]$, with $\vec{m} = [2, 4, 0]$. This meant that the line passed through A and was parallel to the xy-plane. Consider each situation below. Describe the line. What happens to the parametric and symmetric equations?

a) $\vec{m} = [2, 4, 1]$ is replaced with $\vec{m} = [2, 0, 1]$.

b) $\vec{m} = [2, 4, 1]$ is replaced with $\vec{m} = [0, 4, 1]$.

c) $\vec{m} = [2, 4, 1]$ is replaced with $\vec{m} = [2, 0, 0]$.

19. Communication The points where a line intersects the coordinate planes are significant.

a) Suppose you know the coordinates of a point on a line and its direction vector. Describe how you can determine the coordinates of the points where the line intersects the xy-, xz-, and yz-planes.

b) Illustrate your answer to part a by finding the coordinates of the points where each line intersects the coordinate planes.

   i) $\dfrac{x-5}{1} = \dfrac{y+2}{3} = \dfrac{z-1}{-2}$

   ii) $\dfrac{x+6}{2} = \dfrac{y-2}{3}, z = -2$

20. A line is parallel to one of the coordinate planes, but not to any of the axes. Explain what this tells you about each form of equation. Use examples to illustrate your explanations.

a) parametric equations   **b)** symmetric equations

21. A line is parallel to one of the coordinate axes. Explain what this tells you about each form of equation. Use examples to illustrate your explanations.

a) parametric equations   **b)** symmetric equations

22. Symmetric equations of two lines are given.

$$L_1: \dfrac{x-4}{2} = \dfrac{y-8}{3} = \dfrac{z+1}{-4} \quad \text{and} \quad L_2: \dfrac{x-16}{-6} = \dfrac{y-2}{1} = \dfrac{z+1}{2}$$

a) Show that L_1 and L_2 intersect.

b) Find parametric equations of the line that passes through the point of intersection of L_1 and L_2, and that is perpendicular to both.

23. Thinking/Inquiry/Problem Solving Find parametric equations of a line that intersects both L_1 and L_2 at right angles.

$$L_1: [x, y, z] = [4, 8, -1] + t[2, 3, -4] \quad \text{and} \quad L_2: \dfrac{x-7}{-6} = \dfrac{y-2}{1} = \dfrac{z+1}{2}$$

24. A line has direction angles $60°, 45°, 60°$ and passes through the point $(-2, 1, 3)$. Determine symmetric equations of the line.

25. A line passes through the point $A(0, 0, 4)$. Its first two direction angles are both $60°$.

   a) What possible third direction angles can it have?

   b) Find parametric equations of the line for each set of direction angles.

   c) Draw a diagram illustrating the lines in part b.

C

26. Suppose $\vec{p} = \vec{a} + t\vec{m}$, where $\vec{p}$, $\vec{a}$, and $\vec{m}$ are non-zero vectors.

   a) Prove that $\vec{p} \times \vec{m} = \vec{a} \times \vec{m}$.

   b) Provide a geometric interpretation of the result in part a.

27. On pages 135 and 136, the line was described using *one* vector equation and *three* parametric equations. On page 138 we showed that, in symmetric form, there are *two* equations. With respect to this example, discuss the question:

   a) How many equations are needed to describe a line?

   b) Explain why *two* is the best answer to part a and why there is no inconsistency in having one vector equation and three parametric equations.

28. Refer to the diagram on page 135.

   a) Explain why $(\vec{p} - \vec{a}) \times \vec{m} = \vec{0}$ is the equation of the line passing through the point A and parallel to the vector $\vec{m}$.

   b) Substitute $\vec{p} = [x, y, z]$, $\vec{a} = [-2, 5, 3]$, and $\vec{m} = [2, 4, 1]$ into the expression in part a and determine the cross product. Use the result to determine symmetric equations of the line. Explain.

29. Consider the following parametric equations of a line passing through $A(a_1, a_2, a_3)$ with direction vector $\vec{m} = [m_1, m_2, m_3]$:

   $$x = a_1 + tm_1$$
   $$y = a_2 + tm_2$$
   $$z = a_3 + tm_3$$

   Explain the geometric significance of t if m_1, m_2, and m_3 are the direction cosines of the line.

3.3 | The Equation of a Plane

In this section, we will determine the equations of planes in R^3. A plane is determined by a point and two non-collinear vectors. For example, the diagram below shows the plane passing through the point A(–2, 5, 3) and contains the vectors $\vec{u}$ = [2, 4, 1] and $\vec{v}$ = [1, 4, 2]. The line defined by A and $\vec{u}$ is the same line as the one in the diagram on page 135. The vector $\vec{v}$ determines a plane containing this line. The plane is tilting upwards away from the viewer, as indicated by the triangle formed by the vectors $\vec{u}$ and $\vec{v}$ when their tails are at the origin.

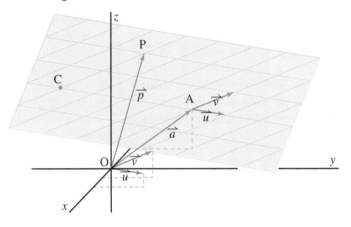

The vector equation

Let P(x, y, z) be any point on this plane. Visualize P moving around the plane in any position. As it moves, points O, A, and P always form a triangle in which the triangle law is satisfied:

$$\overrightarrow{OP} = \overrightarrow{OA} + \overrightarrow{AP}$$

Since P is on the plane, we know that $\overrightarrow{AP}$ is a linear combination of $\vec{u}$ and $\vec{v}$. Hence, $\overrightarrow{AP} = s\vec{u} + t\vec{v}$ where s and t are any scalars. Therefore, we can write the above equation as:

$$\vec{p} = \vec{a} + s\vec{u} + t\vec{v}$$

or $[x, y, z] = [-2, 5, 3] + s[2, 4, 1] + t[1, 4, 2]$ ①

Equation ① is the *vector equation* of the plane. There are two parameters, s and t. These are needed to specify how we get from A to P on the plane by combining scalar multiples of $\vec{u}$ and $\vec{v}$. In the diagram shown, we go in the opposite direction of $\vec{u}$ and 4 times its length to C, then in the direction of $\vec{v}$ and twice its length to P. For the point P shown, s = –4 and t = 2. We can use ① to determine the coordinates of point P. They are (–8, –3, 3).

Vector Equation of a Plane in 3-space

A plane in R^3 is determined by a point $A(a_1, a_2, a_3)$ and two non-collinear vectors $\vec{u} = [u_1, u_2, u_3]$ and $\vec{v} = [v_1, v_2, v_3]$. The vector equation of the plane is:

$$[x, y, z] = [a_1, a_2, a_3] + s[u_1, u_2, u_3] + t[v_1, v_2, v_3]$$

The parameters s and t can represent any real numbers.

Parametric equations

On the right side of equation ① on page 146, we expand the scalar multiples and add the two vectors to obtain:

$$[x, y, z] = [-2 + 2s + t, 5 + 4s + 4t, 3 + s + 2t]$$

Since these vectors are equal, the corresponding components are equal.

$$\left. \begin{array}{l} x = -2 + 2s + t \\ y = 5 + 4s + 4t \\ z = 3 + s + 2t \end{array} \right\} \qquad ②$$

Equations ② are *parametric equations* of the plane. There are two parameters, s and t, because the plane is two-dimensional. Parametric equations of a plane have these properties:

- The constant terms on the right side are the coordinates of a point on the plane.

- The coefficients of s and t are the components of two direction vectors on the plane.

Like parametric equations of a line, parametric equations of a plane are useful because they are formulas for the coordinates of points on the plane. For example, if we substitute $s = 2$ and $t = -1$, we obtain $(1, 9, 3)$. This point is on the plane.

John von Neumann (1903–1957)
Born: Budapest, Hungary

Von Neumann had an incredible memory and, as a child, would memorize pages of the telephone book to entertain guests. Von Neumann earned a degree in chemical engineering and a doctorate in mathematics. By his mid-20s, von Neumann was famous in the mathematical community, becoming a professor at Princeton in 1931. His contributions to mathematics are numerous, including development of the mathematical framework of quantum mechanics. He later turned to applied mathematics, including hydrodynamical turbulence and logical design.

Parametric equations of a plane are not unique. In the above parametric equations, we could replace the constant terms on the right side with the coordinates of any point on the plane. We can also replace the coefficients of s and t with the components of any non-collinear vectors on the plane.

Parametric Equations of a Plane in 3-space

A plane in $\mathbf{R}^3$ is determined by a point $A(a_1, a_2, a_3)$ and two non-collinear vectors $\vec{u} = [u_1, u_2, u_3]$ and $\vec{v} = [v_1, v_2, v_3]$. Parametric equations of the plane are:

$$x = a_1 + su_1 + tv_1$$
$$y = a_2 + su_2 + tv_2$$
$$z = a_3 + su_3 + tv_3$$

The parameters s and t can represent any real numbers.

Example 1

Find parametric equations of the plane that passes through the three points $A(2, -3, 1)$, $B(0, 4, -1)$, and $C(3, 1, -4)$.

Solution

Choose any two non-collinear vectors on the plane.

$\overrightarrow{AB} = [0 - 2, 4 - (-3), -1 - 1]$ and $\overrightarrow{AC} = [3 - 2, 1 - (-3), -4 - 1]$

$\overrightarrow{AB} = [-2, 7, -2]$ $\overrightarrow{AC} = [1, 4, -5]$

Using point A and these two vectors, parametric equations of the plane are:

$$x = 2 - 2s + t$$
$$y = -3 + 7s + 4t$$
$$z = 1 - 2s - 5t$$

Something to Think About

- What are some other parametric equations of the plane in *Example 1*?

Scalar equation

To determine an equation of a plane without parameters, we can eliminate the parameters from its parametric equations (see exercise 23). However, there is a more efficient and more elegant method. We will apply it to the plane described on page 146.

The plane passes through $Q(-2, 5, 3)$ and contains the vectors $\vec{u} = [2, 4, 1]$ and $\vec{v} = [1, 4, 2]$. The vector $\vec{u} \times \vec{v}$ is perpendicular to the plane. We determine this cross product.

4   1   2   4

$\times$ $\times$ $\times$

4   2   1   4

The components of $\overrightarrow{u} \times \overrightarrow{v}$ are:

$(4)(2) - (4)(1) = 4$
$(1)(1) - (2)(2) = -3$
$(2)(4) - (1)(4) = 4$

Therefore, $\overrightarrow{u} \times \overrightarrow{v} = [4, -3, 4]$. Since it is perpendicular to the plane, this vector is called the *normal vector* of the plane.

To determine the equation of the plane, let P(x, y, z) be any point on the plane. Then the vector $\overrightarrow{QP} = [x + 2, y - 5, z - 3]$ lies on the plane and is perpendicular to the normal vector. Hence,

$$\overrightarrow{QP} \bullet [4, -3, 4] = 0$$
$$[x + 2, y - 5, z - 3] \bullet [4, -3, 4] = 0$$
$$4(x + 2) - 3(y - 5) + 4(z - 3) = 0$$
$$4x + 8 - 3y + 15 + 4z - 12 = 0$$
$$4x - 3y + 4z + 11 = 0$$

The equation of the plane is $4x - 3y + 4z + 11 = 0$. This equation is called the *scalar equation* of the plane. Notice that the coefficients of x, y, and z are the components of the normal vector.

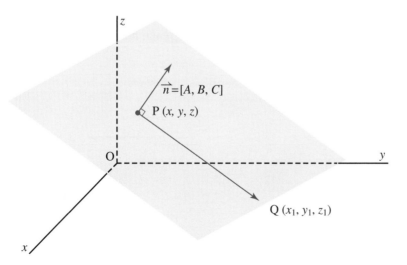

We can use the above method to determine the equation of the plane passing through the point Q(x_1, y_1, z_1) with normal vector $[A, B, C]$. Let P(x, y, z) be any point on the plane. Then the vector $\overrightarrow{QP} = [x - x_1, y - y_1, z - z_1]$ lies on the plane and is perpendicular to the normal vector.

Hence,

$$\overrightarrow{QP} \bullet [A,\ B,\ C] = 0$$
$$[x - x_1,\ y - y_1,\ z - z_1] \bullet [A,\ B,\ C] = 0$$
$$A(x - x_1) + B(y - y_1) + C(z - z_1) = 0$$
$$Ax + By + Cz + (-Ax_1 - By_1 - Cz_1) = 0$$

This equation has the form $Ax + By + Cz + D = 0$, where A, B, and C are the components of the normal vector. This is the general form of the scalar equation of a plane. Instead of memorizing the expression in the brackets, it is easier to remember that D is a constant that needs to be determined in each particular problem.

Take Note

Scalar Equation of a Plane

The scalar equation of a plane has the form $Ax + By + Cz + D = 0$, where A, B, and C are the components of its normal vector, $\overrightarrow{n} = [A, B, C]$.

Example 2

Find the scalar equation of the plane that has normal vector $[4, -3, 2]$ and that passes through the point A(6, 3, -4).

Solution

Since the normal vector is $[4, -3, 2]$, the scalar equation of the plane has the form $4x - 3y + 2z + D = 0$ for some number D.

Since the point A(6, 3, -4) lies on the plane, these coordinates satisfy the equation. Substitute $x = 6$, $y = 3$, and $z = -4$ to obtain:

$$4(6) - 3(3) + 2(-4) + D = 0$$
$$D = -7$$

The scalar equation of the plane is $4x - 3y + 2z - 7 = 0$.

Example 3

A plane passes through the points A(-1, 3, -2), B(-1, 2, -1), and C(4, 1, -2).

a) Find a vector equation of the plane.

b) Find a set of parametric equations of the plane.

c) Determine the scalar equation of the plane.

d) Determine if the point P(3, -1, 1) lies on the plane.

Solution

The key to finding any of the forms of the equation of the plane is to determine a point and two vectors that lie on the plane. Use the point A(−1, 3, −2) and the vectors $\overrightarrow{AB}$ = [0, −1, 1] and $\overrightarrow{AC}$ = [5, −2, 0].

a) A vector equation of the plane is:

$$\overrightarrow{p} = [-1, 3, -2] + s[0, -1, 1] + t[5, -2, 0]$$

b) A set of parametric equations of the plane is:

$$\left.\begin{array}{l} x = -1 + 0s + 5t \\ y = 3 - 1s - 2t \\ z = -2 + 1s + 0t \end{array}\right\} \qquad \text{or} \qquad \left\{\begin{array}{l} x = -1 + 5t \\ y = 3 - s - 2t \\ z = -2 + s \end{array}\right.$$

c) Determine $\overrightarrow{AB} \times \overrightarrow{AC}$:

$$\begin{matrix} -1 & 1 & 0 & -1 \\ -2 & 0 & 5 & -2 \end{matrix}$$

The components of $\overrightarrow{AB} \times \overrightarrow{AC}$ are:

$(-1)(0) - (-2)(1) = 2$

$(1)(5) - 0 = 5$

$(0)(-2) - (5)(-1) = 5$

$\overrightarrow{AB} \times \overrightarrow{AC}$ = [2, 5, 5]

The scalar equation of the plane has the form $2x + 5y + 5z + D = 0$. To determine D, substitute the coordinates of one of the points on the plane, say, A(−1, 3, −2) to obtain:

$2(-1) + 5(3) + 5(-2) + D = 0$

$$D = -3$$

The scalar equation of the plane is $2x + 5y + 5z - 3 = 0$.

d) To determine if the point P(3, −1, 1) lies on the plane, check if these coordinates satisfy the scalar equation.

L.S. $= 2x + 5y + 5z - 3$
$= 2(3) + 5(-1) + 5(1) - 3$
$= 3$

R.S. $= 0$

Since the coordinates of P do not satisfy the equation, P does not lie on the plane.

A

1. A plane has the following vector equation:

   $\vec{p} = [2, 6, -5] + s[-1, 3, 1] + t[4, 2, -1]$

   a) State the coordinates of a point on the plane.

   b) State the coordinates of three other points on the plane.

   c) Write another vector equation of this plane.

2. A plane has the following parametric equations:

   $$x = 3 - 2s + 2t$$
   $$y = 1 + 3s + t$$
   $$z = 5 - s - 2t$$

   a) State the coordinates of a point on the plane.

   b) State the coordinates of three other points on the plane.

   c) Write another set of parametric equations of this plane.

3. A plane has the scalar equation $2x - y + 3z - 6 = 0$.

   a) Determine the coordinates of three points that lie on this plane.

   b) Write a set of parametric equations of the plane.

4. Consider these four points:

   A(1, 1, 2), B(3, −2, 2), C(5, −1, 5), D(4, −2, 5)

   Which of these points lie on the plane with scalar equation
   $x + 2y + z - 5 = 0$?

5. Determine if the point A(5, 2, −1) lies on the plane with vector equation
   $\vec{p} = [2, 1, 0] + s[1, -1, 2] + t[3, 0, 1]$.

6. Determine if the point B(2, 3, −4) lies on the plane with these parametric
   equations:

   $$x = 3 + s - t$$
   $$y = 1 + 5s + 2t$$
   $$z = 2 - 3s - 6t$$

7. Write vector and parametric equations of the plane containing:

   a) the point A(2, 1, 3) and the vectors $\vec{m} = [-1, 3, 4]$ and $\vec{n} = [2, 0, -1]$.

   b) the points B(−2, 5, 1), C(3, 0, −4), and D(7, 5, −2).

   c) the points E(−3, 1, 1) and F(−4, 0, 3), and the vector $\vec{v} = [1, 2, 3]$.

8. Consider the plane with scalar equation $4x - y + 2z + 8 = 0$.

a) Write the normal vector $\vec{n}$.

b) By inspection, determine the coordinates of two different points on this plane. Call these points A and B.

c) Determine $\overrightarrow{AB}$.

d) Show that the vectors $\overrightarrow{AB}$ and $\vec{n}$ are perpendicular.

9. Explain why four points may or may not be coplanar.

B

10. Write a vector equation of the plane passing through the given points.

a) A(1, 2, –3), B(5, 1, 0), C(3, 2, –6)

b) P(8, –4, 2), Q(4, –3, 1), R(–2, 6, 2)

11. Write a set of parametric equations of the plane passing through the given points.

a) A(7, –3, 1), B(0, –4, 3), C(1, –1, 0)

b) P(–2, 6, 1), Q(3, –3, 1), R(2, 5, –5)

12. Find the scalar equation of the plane through the given point R and with the given normal vector $\vec{n}$.

a) R(–3, 1, 2), $\vec{n} = [4, -2, 1]$

b) R(5, 0, –3), $\vec{n} = [1, -1, 4]$

13. Find the equation of the plane that is parallel to the plane $3x - y + 2z - 10 = 0$ and that passes through each point.

a) (0, 0, 0)   **b)** (1, 2, 3)   **c)** (–1, 0, 1)

14. **Knowledge/Understanding** A plane in R^3 has scalar equation $3x + 2y - 12 = 0$.

a) Write the normal vector of this plane.

b) The equation can be written as $3x + 2y + 0z - 12 = 0$. What is the geometric significance of the fact that the coefficient of z is 0 in this equation?

c) Describe how the plane compares with the line in R^2 that has scalar equation $3x + 2y - 12 = 0$.

15. Find the scalar equation of the plane passing through the given points.

a) A(1, 1, 1), B(0, 2, 3), C(–1, 0, 1)

b) D(0, 1, 2), E(1, 2, 1), F(–1, –1, 2)

c) R(3, 5, 2), S(0, 5, –1), T(1, 5, –3)

16. **Thinking/Inquiry/Problem Solving** In each part of exercise 15, the three given points are not collinear. Find out what happens if you try to find the scalar equation of a plane passing through three collinear points. Make up your own example to investigate this situation.

17. The three points A(1, 0, 1), B(3, –2, 0), and C(2, 1, 5) are given.

   a) Write two different vector equations of the plane containing A, B, and C.

   b) Write two different sets of parametric equations of the plane containing A, B, and C.

   c) Determine the scalar equation of the plane containing A, B, and C.

18. **Communication**

   a) Define the angle of intersection of two planes.

   b) Use your definition to calculate the angle of intersection of the planes:
      i) $2x + y - 3z + 7 = 0$ and $4x - y + 7z + 5 = 0$
      ii) $2x - y - 2z + 5 = 0$ and $3x + 4z + 6 = 0$

19. Find the equation of a plane, every point of which is equidistant from the points A(1, 1, 0) and B(5, 3, –2).

20. **Application** The diagram below shows a cube with vertices (±2, ±2, ±2). A plane passing through the midpoints of 6 of its 12 edges forms a regular hexagon inside the cube.

   a) Find the equation of the plane.

   b) The midpoints of 3 of the other 6 edges lie on one side of the plane in the diagram. Find the equation of the plane that passes through these three midpoints.

   c) Find the equation of the plane that passes through the remaining three midpoints.

   d) What geometric property do the planes in part a, b, and c have?

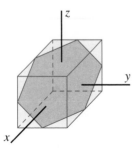

21. Prove that the four points A(1, 6, 3), B(–2, –4, –1), C(3, 9, 4), and D(–3, 0, 1) are coplanar.

22. Determine the equation of the plane that contains the points A(1, 2, 3) and B(2, 3, –1), and that is perpendicular to the plane $3x + y + z + 1 = 0$.

23. Refer to the parametric equations of the plane given on page 147. Determine the scalar equation of this plane by eliminating the parameters from these equations. Compare the result with the scalar equation on page 149.

24. Find the equation of the locus of the point P such that P is equidistant from the points A(1, 2, 3) and B(3, 2, 4).

25. The point A(4, –1, 3) is given.

   a) Find the equation of the locus of the point P such that $\overrightarrow{AP} \cdot \overrightarrow{OA} = 0$.

   b) Describe the locus.

26. Compare the general form of the scalar equation of a plane, $Ax + By + Cz + D = 0$, with the general form of the equation of a line in $\mathbf{R}^2$, $Ax + By + C = 0$.

   a) Explain how the coefficients of the terms containing the variables play a similar role. Use examples to illustrate your explanation.

   b) Why are both equations called linear equations, even though only one of them is the equation of a line?

C

27. Given the vectors $\vec{a} = \overrightarrow{OA}$, $\vec{b} = \overrightarrow{OB}$, and $\vec{c} = \overrightarrow{OC}$, show that the vector equation of the plane containing the points A, B, and C has the form $\vec{p} = r\vec{a} + s\vec{b} + t\vec{c}$, where $r + s + t = 1$.

28. Refer to exercise 20.

   a) Find the equation of another plane passing through the midpoints of 6 edges of the cube.

   b) How many planes are there in all that pass through the midpoints of 6 of the 12 edges of the cube? Write their equations in a systematic way.

3.4 Problems Involving Lines and Planes

In three dimensions, there are three intersection possibilities for a line and a plane.

| The line may intersect the plane in only one point. | The line may lie on the plane. | The line may be parallel to the plane and not intersect it. |

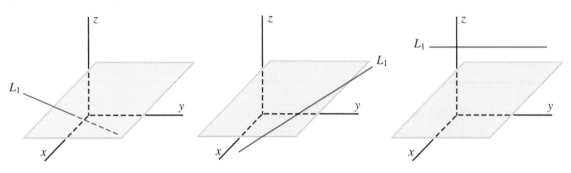

We can use the equations of the line and the plane to distinguish these three possibilities.

Example 1

The plane $4x - 5y - 4z + 2 = 0$ and the parametric equations of lines are given. Determine the points that lie on each line and the plane.

a) $x = 5 + 2t$
$y = -4 - 3t$
$z = 1 + t$

b) $x = 1 + 2t$
$y = 2 - 4t$
$z = -1 + 7t$

c) $x = 5 + 3t$
$y = -2 + 4t$
$z = 9 - 2t$

Solution

Substitute the expressions for x, y, and z from the parametric equations into the equation of the plane.

a) $4x - 5y - 4z + 2 = 0$

Substitute from the parametric equations.
$$4(5 + 2t) - 5(-4 - 3t) - 4(1 + t) + 2 = 0$$
$$20 + 8t + 20 + 15t - 4 - 4t + 2 = 0$$
$$19t + 38 = 0$$
$$t = -2$$

Substitute $t = -2$ into the parametric equations to obtain:

$x = 5 + 2t$
$= 5 + 2(-2)$
$= 1$

$y = -4 - 3t$
$= -4 - 3(-2)$
$= 2$

$z = 1 + t$
$= 1 - 2$
$= -1$

The line intersects the plane at the point $(1, 2, -1)$.

b) $4x - 5y - 4z + 2 = 0$

Substitute from the parametric equations.
$$4(1 + 2t) - 5(2 - 4t) - 4(-1 + 7t) + 2 = 0$$
$$4 + 8t - 10 + 20t + 4 - 28t + 2 = 0$$
$$0t = 0$$

Any real value of t satisfies this equation. Therefore, the expressions for x, y, and z satisfy the scalar equation of the plane for all values of t. This means that every point on the line lies on the plane. That is, the line lies on the plane.

c) $4x - 5y - 4z + 2 = 0$

Substitute from the parametric equations.
$$4(5 + 3t) - 5(-2 + 4t) - 4(9 - 2t) + 2 = 0$$
$$20 + 12t + 10 - 20t - 36 + 8t + 2 = 0$$
$$0t = 4$$

No value of t satisfies this equation. Therefore, the expressions for x, y, and z do not satisfy the scalar equation of the plane for any value of t. This means that there are no points on the line that are also on the plane. That is, the line does not lie on the plane. It must be parallel to the plane.

Something to Think About

- In *Example 1*, visualize the normal vector of the plane and the direction vectors of the lines. How could we use these vectors to determine the following?
  - The line in part a intersects the plane in only one point.
  - The lines in parts b and c either lie on the plane or are parallel to the plane.

In Section 3.2, we defined skew lines to be lines in three dimensions that are not parallel and do not intersect. Two skew lines may lie in parallel planes. The next example shows how to determine the equations of these planes.

Example 2

Two lines L_1 and L_2 have the following symmetric equations.
$$L_1: \frac{x}{3} = \frac{y - 2}{1} = \frac{z - 1}{1} \qquad \text{and} \qquad L_2: \frac{x - 1}{2} = \frac{y + 3}{-1} = \frac{z}{1}$$

a) Show that L_1 and L_2 are skew lines.

b) Determine the equations of two parallel planes that contain L_1 and L_2.

Solution

a) By inspection, the direction vectors, [3, 1, 1] and [2, –1, 1], of the lines are not collinear. Hence, the lines L_1 and L_2 are not parallel.

Now show that the lines do not intersect. Parametric equations of the lines are:

L_1: $x = 3t$ and L_2: $x = 1 + 2s$
     $y = 2 + t$ $y = -3 - s$
     $z = 1 + t$ $z = s$

If the lines intersect, then:
     $3t = 1 + 2s$ ①
     $2 + t = -3 - s$ ②
     $1 + t = s$ ③

Substitute the expression for s from ③ into ①:
     $3t = 1 + 2(1 + t)$
       $t = 3$

Substitute the expression for s from ③ into ②:
      $2 + t = -3 - (1 + t)$
        $t = -3$

Since these values of t are not the same, the equations ①, ②, and ③ are inconsistent. Hence, the lines L_1 and L_2 do not intersect.

Therefore, L_1 and L_2 are skew lines.

b) The diagram below shows the lines L_1 and L_2 seen with L_1 coming directly out of the page towards the viewer and appearing as a point. Since the lines are skew, L_2 appears as a line that does not pass through this point. Any plane containing L_1 will be seen from the edge, and appears as a line on the page. One of these planes, π_1, is parallel to L_2. There is a parallel plane, π_2, that contains L_2 and also appears as a line on the page.

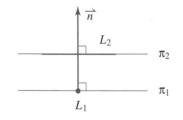

Since the planes π_1 and π_2 are parallel, they have the same normal vector, $\vec{n}$. This vector is perpendicular to both L_1 and L_2. Therefore, $\vec{n}$ is the cross product of their direction vectors, $\vec{m_1} = [3, 1, 1]$ and $\vec{m_2} = [2, -1, 1]$. Determine this cross product.

$$
\begin{matrix} 1 & & 1 & & 3 & & 1 \\ & \times & & \times & & \times & \\ -1 & & 1 & & 2 & & -1 \end{matrix}
$$

The components of $\vec{n}$ are:

$(1)(1) - (-1)(1) = 2$

$(1)(2) - (1)(3) = -1$

$(3)(-1) - (2)(1) = -5$

Therefore, $\vec{n} = [2, -1, -5]$ is the normal vector of both planes π_1 and π_2.

The equation of plane π_1 has the form:

$2x - y - 5z + D = 0$ ④

Since L_1 lies on this plane, any point on L_1 also lies on this plane. From the symmetric equations, the point $(0, 2, 1)$ lies on this line and also on the plane π_1. Substitute these coordinates into equation ④ to obtain:

$2(0) - 2 - 5(1) + D = 0$

$D = 7$

The equation of plane π_1 is $2x - y - 5z + 7 = 0$.

The equation of plane π_2 has the same form. From the symmetric equations of L_2, the point $(1, -3, 0)$ lies on this line and also on the plane π_2. Substitute these coordinates into equation ④ to obtain:

$2(1) - (-3) - 5(0) + D = 0$

$D = -5$

The equation of plane π_2 is $2x - y - 5z - 5 = 0$.

Therefore, the equations of the parallel planes containing the lines L_1 and L_2 are $2x - y - 5z + 7 = 0$ and $2x - y - 5z - 5 = 0$.

Something to Think About

- How could we check the result in *Example 2*?

A

1. Visualize two skew lines containing the edges of the walls of your classroom. Then identify two parallel planes, one containing each line.

2. Explain why two skew lines may lie in parallel planes. Is it possible for skew lines to lie in non-parallel planes? Explain.

B

3. **Knowledge/Understanding** Consider the plane $x - 3y - 2z + 2 = 0$ and three lines with the symmetric equations given below.

L_1: $\dfrac{x - 4}{5} = \dfrac{y}{3} = \dfrac{z + 2}{-2}$

L_2: $\dfrac{x - 5}{1} = \dfrac{y + 1}{-2} = \dfrac{z - 4}{3}$

L_3: $\dfrac{x - 2}{2} = \dfrac{y - 2}{-4} = \dfrac{z + 1}{7}$

   a) Only one of the lines intersects the plane in one point. Which line is this? Explain.

   b) One of the other two lines lies on the plane. Which line is this? Explain.

   c) How is the remaining line related to the plane? Explain.

4. Find the equation of the plane passing through A(2, 1, −1), that is perpendicular to each line.

   a) $\dfrac{x - 5}{1} = \dfrac{y}{3} = \dfrac{z - 1}{-1}$ b) $\dfrac{x - 2}{3} = \dfrac{y + 1}{-1}$, $z = 0$

5. Find the equation of the plane containing the point A(5, −3, 6) that is parallel to the lines $\dfrac{x - 3}{1} = \dfrac{y - 3}{2} = \dfrac{z + 2}{-3}$ and $\dfrac{x - 8}{2} = \dfrac{y - 9}{1}$, $z = 2$.

6. The equations of a line and plane are given. Determine, if possible, the point(s) of intersection of each line and plane. For the lines that intersect the plane in one point, determine the coordinates of the point of intersection.

   a) $\dfrac{x + 1}{-4} = \dfrac{y - 2}{3} = \dfrac{z - 1}{-2}$ and $x + 2y - 3z + 10 = 0$

   b) $\dfrac{x + 3}{4} = \dfrac{y - 1}{1} = \dfrac{z - 5}{-2}$ and $x + 2y + 3z - 5 = 0$

   c) $\dfrac{x - 4}{2} = \dfrac{y}{1} = \dfrac{z + 1}{-1}$ and $3x - 2y + 4z - 8 = 0$

   d) $\dfrac{x - 3}{4} = \dfrac{y - 2}{3} = \dfrac{z + 1}{-1}$ and $4x - z + 5 = 0$

   e) $\dfrac{x}{1} = \dfrac{y - 3}{7} = \dfrac{z - 1}{4}$ and $x - 3y + 5z + 4 = 0$

   f) $x = 2$, $\dfrac{y}{1} = \dfrac{z - 5}{2}$ and $3x - 4y + 2z + 16 = 0$

   g) $\dfrac{x - 4}{1} = \dfrac{y - 1}{2} = \dfrac{z - 5}{3}$ and $5x + 3y + 4z - 20 = 0$

7. Show that the two lines whose symmetric equations are given below form a plane.

$L_1: \dfrac{x+5}{3} = \dfrac{y-2}{2} = \dfrac{z+7}{6}$ and $L_2: \dfrac{x}{1} = \dfrac{y+6}{-5} = \dfrac{z+3}{-1}$

8. Find the point of intersection of the line and the plane.

$L: x = 4 + k$ and $\pi: x = -1 - s + 2t$
$ y = 2 - 2k$ $ y = 1 - s + 4t$
$ z = 6 + 3k$ $ z = 2 + 3s + t$

9. **Thinking/Inquiry/Problem Solving** The plane with scalar equation $2x - y + 3z - 12 = 0$ is given. Determine parametric equations of three different lines that lie on this plane in each case.

a) The lines must all pass through the same point.

b) The lines must all be parallel.

10. **Communication** Suppose a line intersects a plane at one point. Define what is meant by the "angle of intersection of the line and the plane". Describe a method you can use to determine the angle of intersection of a line and a plane. Then use your method to calculate the angle of intersection of the given line and plane.

a) $\dfrac{x}{2} = \dfrac{y-1}{1} = \dfrac{z+1}{-1}$ and $x + 2y + 3z - 4 = 0$

b) $\dfrac{x-2}{-1} = \dfrac{y+1}{3} = \dfrac{z-5}{2}$ and $x - 3y - 2z - 23 = 0$

11. **Application** The projection of a point P on a plane is the point P′ on the plane such that PP′ is perpendicular to the plane. Describe a method you can use to determine the projection of a point on a plane. Then use your method to determine the projections of the given point on the plane.

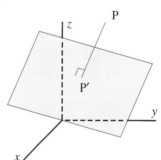

a) P(–3, 1, 1)   and $2x - y + z - 5 = 0$

b) P(2, 0, 3)   and $x + 3y - z + 7 = 0$

12. Prove that the line that passes through the points A(1, 5, 1) and B(0, 4, 2) lies on the plane $2x + y + 3z - 10 = 0$.

13. a) Describe the possible ways a line and a plane can intersect. Illustrate your descriptions with sketches.

b) Suppose you are given parametric equations of a line and the scalar equation of a plane in R^3. Outline a method you could use to determine how the line intersects the plane.

14. Find the coordinates of the point where the line that passes through $P(1, 2, 3)$ and $Q(-1, 3, -2)$ intersects the plane $2x + 3y + 2z - 3 = 0$.

15. Two lines L_1 and L_2 have the following symmetric equations.

$$L_1: \frac{x}{3} = \frac{y-2}{1} = \frac{z-1}{1} \qquad \text{and} \qquad L_2: \frac{x-1}{2} = \frac{y+3}{-1} = \frac{z}{1}$$

a) Show that L_1 and L_2 are skew lines.

b) Determine the equations of two parallel planes that contain L_1 and L_2.

16. The equations of two parallel planes are given.

$\pi_1: 3x - 2y + z - 8 = 0$
$\pi_2: 3x - 2y + z + 4 = 0$

Determine the equations of two skew lines, one on each plane.

17. A line has the following symmetric equations:

$$\frac{x-1}{2} = \frac{y+2}{-3} = \frac{z+1}{1}$$

a) Write symmetric equations of a line that is skew to this line.

b) Verify that the two lines are skew.

c) Determine the equations of two parallel planes that contain these two lines.

18. Show that the lines $L_1: \frac{x-2}{3} = \frac{y-3}{5} = \frac{z-1}{1}$ and $L_2: \frac{x-4}{1} = \frac{y-1}{7} = \frac{z}{2}$ are coplanar.

C

19. Refer to *Example 2*. The distance between the skew lines L_1 and L_2 is defined to be the length of the shortest segment AB, where A is a point on L_1 and B is a point on L_2. Calculate the distance between these two skew lines.

20. Determine the distance from the given point to the given plane.

a) $A(2, 3, -1)$ and $2x + y - 2z + 9 = 0$

b) $B(0, -2, 1)$ and $3x - y + z - 2 = 0$

c) $P(x_1, y_1, z_1)$ and $Ax + By + Cz + D = 0$

3.5 Problems Involving Two Planes

Two distinct planes may be either parallel or intersecting. It is easy to distinguish these two cases because parallel planes have collinear normal vectors. For example, the following planes are parallel because their normal vectors, $[3, -1, 4]$ and $[6, -2, 8]$ respectively, are collinear.

$$3x - y + 4z - 7 = 0$$
$$6x - 2y + 8z - 9 = 0$$

The following planes are not parallel, and intersect in a line.

$$3x - y + 4z - 7 = 0$$
$$x + y - 2z + 5 = 0$$

These two equations, taken together, can be regarded as equations of the line. However, they are not very useful in this form because they do not contain specific information about the line such as a direction vector or the coordinates of a point on the line.

The following example shows how to determine parametric and scalar equations of the line of intersection of two planes.

Example 1

Find parametric and symmetric equations of the line of intersection of the planes $3x - y + 4z - 7 = 0$ and $x + y - 2z + 5 = 0$.

Solution

Consider the system of equations:

$$3x - y + 4z - 7 = 0 \qquad ①$$
$$x + y - 2z + 5 = 0 \qquad ②$$

To find the parametric equations of the line of intersection, first eliminate y and express z in terms of x. Then eliminate z and express y in terms of x.

Eliminate y from ① and ② by adding them:

$$4x + 2z - 2 = 0$$
$$2x + z - 1 = 0$$

Solve for z: $\qquad z = 1 - 2x \qquad ③$

Eliminate z from ① and ② by multiplying ② by 2 and adding ①:

$$5x + y + 3 = 0$$

Solve for y: $\qquad y = -3 - 5x \qquad ④$

Introduce the parameter, t, by letting $x = t$. Substitute t for x into ③ and ④ to obtain the parametric equations of the line of intersection of the two planes.

$$x = t$$
$$y = -3 - 5t$$
$$z = 1 - 2t$$

Solve each equation for t to obtain:

$$\frac{x}{1} = \frac{y + 3}{-5} = \frac{z - 1}{-2}$$

These are symmetric equations of the line of intersection of the two planes.

Something to Think About

- What other ways are there to solve *Example 1* ?

In many problems involving the line of intersection of two planes, it is not necessary to determine the equation of the line. Sometimes only a direction vector of the line is needed. The following diagrams show that the direction vector of the line is perpendicular to the normal vector of each plane. The diagram below right shows the planes seen from the edge, with the line of intersection coming directly out of the page towards the viewer and appearing as a point. On this diagram, the direction vector $\vec{m}$ comes out of the page at right angles to the normal vectors of the two planes, $\vec{n_1}$ and $\vec{n_2}$.

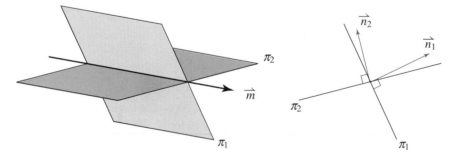

The cross product of the normal vectors of the two planes is a direction vector of their line of intersection.

Example 2

Find the equation of the plane that passes through the point A(3, –1, 2) and is perpendicular to the line of intersection of the planes $x + y + 3z - 12 = 0$ and $7x - y + 3z - 2 = 0$.

Solution

The normal vectors of the two planes are $\overrightarrow{n_1} = [1, 1, 3]$ and $\overrightarrow{n_2} = [7, -1, 3]$. Determine their cross product:

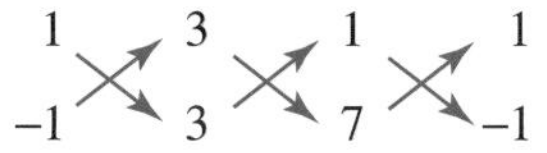

$$
\begin{matrix}
1 & & 3 & & 1 & & 1 \\
 & \times & & \times & & \times & \\
-1 & & 3 & & 7 & & -1
\end{matrix}
$$

The components of $\overrightarrow{n_1} \times \overrightarrow{n_2}$ are:

$(1)(3) - (-1)(3) = 6$
$(3)(7) - (3)(1) = 18$
$(1)(-1) - (7)(1) = -8$

The direction vector of the line of intersection of the planes is [6, 18, –8]. Since any scalar multiple of this vector is also a direction vector of the line, use [3, 9, –4]. This vector is also a normal vector of the required plane.

Let the equation of the plane be $3x + 9y - 4z + D = 0$. Since the point A(3, –1, 2) lies on the plane, its coordinates satisfy the equation. Hence,

$$3(3) + 9(-1) - 4(2) + D = 0$$
$$D = 8$$

The equation of the plane is $3x + 9y - 4z + 8 = 0$.

Something to Think About

- Suppose we had used the vector [6, 18, –8] instead of [3, 9, –4]. What value of D would we have obtained?

Linear combinations of equations of planes

Infinitely many planes pass through a given line in space. In problems involving a plane passing through the line of intersection of two planes, the following approach is very effective.

Consider the planes π_1 and π_2 with these equations.

π_1: $3x - y + z - 2 = 0$ ①

π_2: $x + 2y - 4z + 1 = 0$ ②

We can tell by inspection that the normal vectors of π_1 and π_2 are not collinear. Hence, these two planes have a line of intersection. Suppose we combine their equations as follows.

Multiply ① by s: $s(3x - y + z - 2) = 0$

Multiply ② by t: $t(x + 2y - 4z + 1) = 0$

Add to obtain:

π_3: $s(3x - y + z - 2) + t(x + 2y - 4z + 1) = 0$ ③

Equation ③ is a linear combination of equations ① and ②. Assuming that $s \neq 0$, we can divide both sides of ③ by s to obtain:

π_3: $3x - y + z - 2 + \dfrac{t}{s}(x + 2y - 4z + 1) = 0$

Since t and s are both real numbers, their quotient is also a real number. Hence, we can replace $\dfrac{t}{s}$ with a single symbol, k. Then the equation becomes:

π_3: $3x - y + z - 2 + k(x + 2y - 4z + 1) = 0$ ④

Equation ④ is just another way of writing equation ③. This equation is significant because any point on the line of intersection of planes π_1 and π_2 also lies on π_3. We can tell this because any point on both π_1 and π_2 has coordinates that satisfy ① and ②, and so these coordinates also satisfy both ③ and ④. We can also tell that equation ④ represents a plane because it can be written as:

$(3 + k)x + (-1 + 2k)y + (1 - 4k)z + (-2 + k) = 0$,

which has the form $Ax + By + Cz + D = 0$.

Take Note

Linear Combinations of Equations of Planes

Suppose $A_1x + B_1y + C_1z + D_1 = 0$ and $A_2x + B_2y + C_2z + D_2 = 0$ represent any two planes that intersect in a line. Then the following equation represents another plane that contains this line, where k is any real number.

$$A_1x + B_1y + C_1z + D_1 + k(A_2x + B_2y + C_2z + D_2) = 0$$

We can use linear combinations to solve problems involving planes that intersect in a line without having to find specific information about the line itself.

Example 3

Find the equation of the plane passing through the line of intersection of the planes $3x - y + z - 2 = 0$ and $x + 2y - 4z + 1 = 0$, and that satisfies the given condition.

a) The plane passes through the point A(3, 1, 3).

b) The plane is also parallel to the plane $5x + 3y - 7z - 6 = 0$.

Solution

a) Let the equation of the required plane be as follows, where the number k is to be determined.
$$3x - y + z - 2 + k(x + 2y - 4z + 1) = 0 \qquad ①$$

Since this plane passes through the point A(3, 1, 3), its coordinates satisfy the equation. Substitute $x = 3$, $y = 1$, and $z = 3$ in ①.
$$3(3) - 1 + 3 - 2 + k(3 + 2 - 12 + 1) = 0$$
$$9 - 6k = 0$$
$$k = \frac{3}{2}$$

Substitute $k = \frac{3}{2}$ in ① to obtain:
$$3x - y + z - 2 + \frac{3}{2}(x + 2y - 4z + 1) = 0$$

Multiply both sides by 2:
$$2(3x - y + z - 2) + 3(x + 2y - 4z + 1) = 0$$
$$9x + 4y - 10z - 1 = 0$$

The equation of the plane is $9x + 4y - 10z - 1 = 0$.

b) Write equation ① in the form $Ax + By + Cx + D = 0$.
$$(3 + k)x + (-1 + 2k)y + (1 - 4k)z + (-2 + k) = 0 \qquad ②$$

Since this plane is parallel to the plane $5x + 3y - 7z - 6 = 0$, their normal vectors must be multiples of one another. These normal vectors are $[3 + k, -1 + 2k, 1 - 4k]$ and $[5, 3, -7]$ respectively.

Hence, $\dfrac{3 + k}{5} = \dfrac{-1 + 2k}{3} = \dfrac{1 - 4k}{-7}$

From the first equation:
$$\frac{3 + k}{5} = \frac{-1 + 2k}{3}$$
$$3(3 + k) = 5(-1 + 2k)$$
$$-7k = -14$$
$$k = 2$$

From the second equation:
$$\frac{-1 + 2k}{3} = \frac{1 - 4k}{-7}$$
$$-7(-1 + 2k) = 3(1 - 4k)$$
$$-2k = -4$$
$$k = 2$$

Substitute this value of k in equation ② to obtain:
$$5x + 3y - 7z = 0$$

The equation of the plane is $5x + 3y - 7z = 0$.

Something to Think About

- How could we check the results in *Example 3*?

We could have solved *Example 3* by letting the equation of the required plane be $k(3x - y + z - 2) + x + 2y - 4z + 1 = 0$ (see exercise 13).

3.5 Exercises

A

1. Describe the three different ways in which a line and a plane may be situated with respect to each other.

2. Refer to *Example 1*.

  a) Repeat the solution, but form parametric equations in a different way.

  b) Compare the result of part a with the result in *Example 1*. Explain the similarities and the differences in the two symmetric equations.

3. Refer to *Example 1*. Here is another way to solve this example.

  a) Verify that the cross product of the normal vectors of the two planes is a direction vector of their line of intersection.

  b) The direction vector in part a occurs in the symmetric equations of the line. To determine these equations we require the coordinates of a point on the line. How could we determine these coordinates?

4. Communication If two planes intersect in a line, explain why the cross product of the normal vectors of the planes is collinear with the direction vector of the line.

B

5. Knowledge/Understanding Find parametric and symmetric equations of the line of intersection of the two planes.

  a) $x - 2y + 3z - 6 = 0$ and $2x + y + z - 7 = 0$

  b) $2x + y + z - 5 = 0$ and $3x + 2y + 2z - 8 = 0$

  c) $22x + y + 8z - 20 = 0$ and $11x + 2y + 5z - 18 = 0$

6. Find symmetric equations of the line that passes through the point A(7, –2, 4) and that is parallel to the line of intersection of the planes $4x - 3y - z - 1 = 0$ and $2x + 4y + z - 5 = 0$.

7. Find the equation of the plane that passes through the point A(3, –1, 2) and that is perpendicular to the line of intersection of the planes $3x - y + 5 = 0$ and $4x + 3z - 7 = 0$.

8. Determine a vector equation of the line of intersection of the planes $\pi_1\colon 3x - y + 4z - 2 = 0$ and $\pi_2\colon x + 6y + 10z + 8 = 0$.

9. **Application** Write the equations of three different planes that contain the line of intersection of $\pi_1\colon 2x + 3y - z + 4 = 0$ and $\pi_2\colon x + 3z - 5 = 0$.

10. Find the equation of the plane that passes through the line of intersection of the planes $2x - 3y - z + 1 = 0$ and $3x + 5y - 4z + 2 = 0$, and that also passes through the point (3, –1, 2).

11. Find the equation of the plane that passes through the line of intersection of the planes $3x - 2y + 4z - 3 = 0$ and $2x + 3z - 5 = 0$, and that is parallel to the plane $3x + 2y + 5z - 4 = 0$.

12. Find the equation of the plane that passes through the line of intersection of the planes $4x - 2y + z - 3 = 0$ and $2x - y + 3z + 1 = 0$, and that is perpendicular to the plane $3x + y - z + 7 = 0$.

13. Refer to *Example 3*.

    a) Solve part a of this example by letting the equation of the plane be
    $$k(3x - y + z - 2) + x + 2y - 4z + 1 = 0.$$

    b) Compare the two values of k obtained in the two solutions. Describe how they are related. Explain.

14. Find the equation of the plane(s) that passes through the line of intersection of the planes $x - y + 2z + 5 = 0$ and $2x + 3y - z - 1 = 0$, and that satisfy each condition.

    a) It passes through the origin.

    b) It passes through C(1, –1, 4).

    c) It is parallel to the z-axis.

    d) It is perpendicular to the plane $x + 2y - 2z = 0$.

    e) It is parallel to the line segment with endpoints A(1, 1, –1) and B(3, 5, –3).

    f) It has equal y- and z-intercepts.

15. a) Explain why the planes $x + 2y - 3z + 4 = 0$ and $2x + 4y - 6z + 5 = 0$ are parallel.

    b) What does the following equation represent? Explain.
    $$x + 2y - 3z + 4 + k(2x + 4y - 6z + 5) = 0$$

16. **Thinking/Inquiry/Problem Solving** Two planes, π_1 and π_2, intersect in the line with symmetric equations $\frac{x-1}{2} = \frac{y-2}{3} = \frac{z+4}{1}$. Plane π_1 contains the point A(2, 1, 1) and plane π_2 contains the point B(1, 2, –1). Find the scalar equations of planes π_1 and π_2.

17. Two planes, π_1 and π_2, intersect in the line with vector equation $[x, y, z] = [3, 5, 4] + s[2, 3, 1]$. Point A(0, 0, 0) lies on plane π_1 and point B(1, 1, 1) lies on plane π_2. Determine the scalar equations of planes π_1 and π_2.

C

18. The diagram below shows a cube with vertices (±2, ±2, ±2) containing an inscribed tetrahedron. Suppose the cube is cut along the plane determined by vertices A, B, and C. Determine parametric equations of the lines where this plane intersects the faces of the cube.

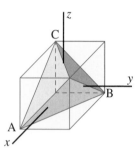

19. There is only one plane that passes through the line of intersection of the planes $A_1x + B_1y + C_1z + D_1 = 0$ and $A_2x + B_2y + C_2z + D_2 = 0$ that is not represented by the equation:
$A_1x + B_1y + C_1z + D_1 + k(A_2x + B_2y + C_2z + D_2) = 0$
Which plane is this? Explain.

3.6 Problems Involving Three Planes

There are several intersection possibilities for three planes. We will assume the planes are distinct, unless stated otherwise. The key to identifying the way three planes intersect is to examine their normal vectors.

In the following examples, we will represent planes by $\pi_1, \pi_2, \pi_3, \dots$, their normal vectors by $\overrightarrow{n_1}, \overrightarrow{n_2}, \overrightarrow{n_3}, \dots$, and their equations by ①, ②, ③, …, respectively.

Case 1: Three parallel planes

The three planes are all parallel to one another. The diagram below right shows a side view of the planes, which appear as parallel lines on the page. The planes come out of the page towards the viewer. The normal vectors are perpendicular to the planes, and lie flat on the page. Notice that the normal vectors are collinear, and also coplanar.

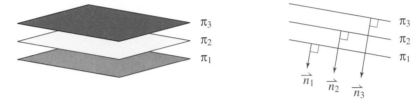

The equations below represent this situation. We can tell this because all three normal vectors $[2, -1, 3]$, $[4, -2, 6]$, and $[6, -3, 9]$ are collinear. That is, $\overrightarrow{n_2} = 2\overrightarrow{n_1}$ and $\overrightarrow{n_3} = 3\overrightarrow{n_1}$. The planes are distinct because their equations do not satisfy these relationships. That is, equation ② is not equal to 2 times equation ①, and equation ③ is not equal to 3 times equation ①.

$\pi_1: 2x - y + 3z - 2 = 0$ ①
$\pi_2: 4x - 2y + 6z - 3 = 0$ ②
$\pi_3: 6x - 3y + 9z - 4 = 0$ ③

Something to Think About

- What constant terms in equations ② and ③ would make these equations represent the same plane as equation ①?

We will now modify the diagram and the equations to represent other intersection possibilities for three planes.

Case 2: Two parallel planes

Suppose we replace plane π_3 with another plane, π_4, that is not parallel to the other two planes. Then π_4 intersects π_1 and π_2 forming two parallel lines. The side view shows the planes π_1 and π_2 as two parallel lines with a third line, π_4, intersecting them. The normal vectors lie flat on the page and are coplanar.

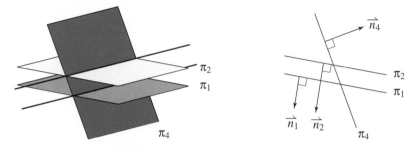

The equations below represent this situation. We can tell this because the normal vectors [2, –1, 3] and [4, –2, 6] are collinear but are not collinear with the third normal vector [1, –3, 2]. That is, $\overrightarrow{n_2} = 2\overrightarrow{n_1}$ is the only relationship involving the normal vectors or the equations.

π_1: $2x - y + 3z - 2 = 0$ ①
π_2: $4x - 2y + 6z - 3 = 0$ ②
π_4: $x - 3y + 2z + 10 = 0$ ④

The above system of equations is inconsistent.

Case 3: Planes intersecting in pairs

Suppose we replace plane π_2 with another plane, π_5, that is not parallel to either of the other two planes. The planes π_1, π_5, and π_4 intersect in pairs, forming three parallel lines. The side view shows the planes as lines forming a triangle. Again, the normal vectors lie flat on the page and are coplanar.

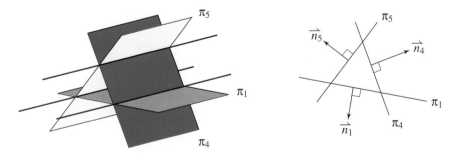

The equations at the top of the following page represent this situation. We can tell this by showing that one of the normal vectors is a linear combination of the other two normal vectors, but the equations are not linear combinations of each other.

π_1: $2x - y + 3z - 2 = 0$ ①
π_4: $x - 3y + 2z + 10 = 0$ ④
π_5: $5x - 5y + 8z + 3 = 0$ ⑤

The normal vector of π_5, [5, –5, 8], is a linear combination of the other two normal vectors: $\overrightarrow{n_5} = 2\overrightarrow{n_1} + \overrightarrow{n_4}$. The planes do not intersect in a single line because the equations do not satisfy the same relationship. That is, equation ⑤ is not equal to 2 times equation ① plus ④. The system of equations is inconsistent.

In Cases 1, 2, and 3, each system of equations has no solution because there is no point on all three planes. It is impossible for the coordinates of a point to satisfy all three equations. We say that each system of equations is *inconsistent*.

Case 4: Planes intersecting in a line

Suppose we replace plane π_5 with another plane, π_6, that contains the line of intersection of π_1 and π_4. Then, there is a line of intersection for all three planes. The side view shows the planes as lines intersecting at a point (which is the line of intersection coming out of the page towards the viewer). Again, the normal vectors lie flat on the page and are coplanar.

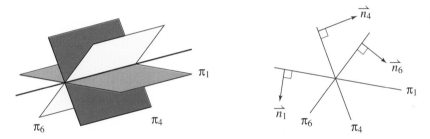

The equations below represent this situation. We can tell this by showing that one of the normal vectors is a linear combination of the other two normal vectors, and the corresponding equation is the same linear combination of the other two equations.

π_1: $2x - y + 3z - 2 = 0$ ①
π_4: $x - 3y + 2z + 10 = 0$ ④
π_6: $5x - 5y + 8z + 6 = 0$ ⑥

The normal vector of π_6, [5, –5, 8], is a linear combination of the other two normal vectors: $\overrightarrow{n_6} = 2\overrightarrow{n_1} + \overrightarrow{n_4}$. The planes intersect in a single line because the equations satisfy the same relationship. That is, equation ⑥ is 2 times equation ① plus equation ④.

The above system of equations has infinitely many solutions because the points on the line of intersection are on all three planes. The coordinates of any point on this line satisfy all three equations. We can determine the equation of the line of solutions using the methods in Section 3.5.

As long as the planes are distinct, there is only one other intersection possibility for three planes. This is the only one in which the normal vectors are not coplanar.

Case 5: Planes intersecting at a point

Suppose we replace plane π_6 with another plane, π_7, so that the planes intersect in a single point. Since a side view showing all three planes as lines cannot be drawn, the normal vectors are not coplanar.

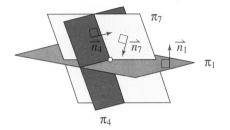

The equations below represent this situation. We can tell this by showing that it is not possible to express one of the normal vectors as a linear combination of the other two.

π_1: $2x - y + 3z - 2 = 0$ ①
π_4: $x - 3y + 2z + 10 = 0$ ④
π_7: $3x + y - z - 4 = 0$ ⑦

The normal vectors are $\vec{n_1} = [2, -1, 3]$, $\vec{n_4} = [1, -3, 2]$, and $\vec{n_7} = [3, 1, -1]$. To show that these vectors are not coplanar, we use the test for coplanar vectors from Section 2.5.

Calculate the cross product of any two of the vectors, say $\vec{n_4} \times \vec{n_7}$.

$$\begin{matrix} -3 & & 2 & & 1 & & -3 \\ & \times & & \times & & \times & \\ 1 & & -1 & & 3 & & 1 \end{matrix}$$

The components of $\vec{n_4} \times \vec{n_7}$ are:

$(-3)(-1) - (1)(2) = 1$
$(2)(3) - (-1)(1) = 7$
$(1)(1) - (3)(-3) = 10$

Therefore, $\vec{n_4} \times \vec{n_7} = [1, 7, 10]$.

Now calculate $\vec{n_1} \bullet \vec{n_4} \times \vec{n_7}$.

$\vec{n_1} \bullet \vec{n_4} \times \vec{n_7} = [2, -1, 3] \bullet [1, 7, 10]$
$\phantom{\vec{n_1} \bullet \vec{n_4} \times \vec{n_7}} = 2 - 7 + 30$
$\phantom{\vec{n_1} \bullet \vec{n_4} \times \vec{n_7}} = 25$

Since the result is not 0, the three normal vectors are not coplanar.

Since the normal vectors are not coplanar, the planes intersect in a single point. Therefore the system of equations has only one solution because there is only one point on all three planes. This is the only point whose coordinates satisfy all three equations. You will determine the solution in exercise 7.

Something to Think About

- Notice that we can tell that there is a unique solution without solving the system.

In Cases 4 and 5, each system of equations has solution(s) because there are point(s) on all three planes. The coordinates of these point(s) satisfy all three equations. We say that each system of equations is *consistent*.

Intersections of Three Planes

Suppose three distinct planes have normal vectors $\vec{n_1}$, $\vec{n_2}$, and $\vec{n_3}$. To determine if there is a unique point of intersection, calculate $\vec{n_1} \bullet \vec{n_2} \times \vec{n_3}$.

- If $\vec{n_1} \bullet \vec{n_2} \times \vec{n_3} \neq 0$, the normal vectors are not coplanar. There is a single point of intersection.
- If $\vec{n_1} \bullet \vec{n_2} \times \vec{n_3} = 0$, the normal vectors are coplanar. There may or may not be points of intersection. If there are any points of intersection, then they lie on a line.

Instead of $\vec{n_1} \bullet \vec{n_2} \times \vec{n_3}$, we can use $\vec{n_2} \bullet \vec{n_1} \times \vec{n_3}$ or $\vec{n_3} \bullet \vec{n_1} \times \vec{n_2}$.

Example 1

The equations of three planes are given.

$$\pi_1: 3x - 3y - 2z - 14 = 0$$
$$\pi_2: 5x + y - 6z - 10 = 0$$
$$\pi_3: x - 2y + 4z - 9 = 0$$

a) Show that the three planes intersect at a single point.

b) Find the coordinates of the point of intersection.

Solution

a) Choose any two planes and find the cross product of their normal vectors.
Choose π_1 and π_2. Determine $\vec{n_1} \times \vec{n_2}$, where $\vec{n_1} = [3, -3, -2]$ and $\vec{n_2} = [5, 1, -6]$.

3.6 PROBLEMS INVOLVING THREE PLANES **175**

$$\begin{array}{ccccccc} -3 & & -2 & & 3 & & -3 \\ & \times & & \times & & \times & \\ 1 & & -6 & & 5 & & 1 \end{array}$$

The components of $\vec{n_1} \times \vec{n_2}$ are:

$(-3)(-6) - (1)(-2) = 20$
$(-2)(5) - (-6)(3) = 8$
$(3)(1) - (5)(-3) = 18$

The vector $\vec{n_1} \times \vec{n_2} = [20, 8, 18]$ is perpendicular to π_1 and π_2.

Determine $\vec{n_3} \bullet \vec{n_1} \times \vec{n_2}$.

$\begin{aligned} \vec{n_3} \bullet \vec{n_1} \times \vec{n_2} &= [1, -2, 4] \bullet [20, 8, 18] \\ &= 76 \end{aligned}$

Since $\vec{n_3} \bullet \vec{n_1} \times \vec{n_2} \neq 0$, the normal vectors of the planes are not coplanar. Therefore, the three planes intersect at a single point.

b) Solve the system:

$3x - 3y - 2z - 14 = 0$ ①
$5x + y - 6z - 10 = 0$ ②
$x - 2y + 4z - 9 = 0$ ③

Recall from Section 3.5 that when two planes intersect in a line, any linear combination of their equations contains this line. Hence, forming linear combinations of the given equations does not change the solution of the system. Form linear combinations in two different ways to eliminate the same variable, say, y.

Copy ①	$3x - 3y - 2z - 14 = 0$	② × 2	$10x + 2y - 12z - 20 = 0$
② × 3	$15x + 3y - 18z - 30 = 0$	Copy ③	$x - 2y + 4z - 9 = 0$
Add.	$18x \quad\quad - 20z - 44 = 0$	Add.	$11x \quad\quad - 8z - 29 = 0$
or	$9x \quad\quad - 10z - 22 = 0$		

The given system has been reduced to this system in two variables.

$\quad 9x - 10z - 22 = 0$ ④

$\quad 11x - 8z - 29 = 0$ ⑤

④ × 4 $36x - 40z - 88 = 0$
⑤ × 5 $55x - 40z - 145 = 0$
Subtract. $-19x \quad\quad + 57 = 0$
$\quad\quad\quad\quad\quad\quad\quad\quad x = 3$

Substitute $x = 3$ in equation ④.
$\quad 27 - 10z - 22 = 0$
$\quad\quad\quad\quad z = \dfrac{1}{2}$

Substitute $x = 3$ and $z = \frac{1}{2}$ in equation ②.

$$15 + y - 3 - 10 = 0$$
$$y = -2$$

The solution of this linear system is $(3, -2, \frac{1}{2})$. These are the coordinates of the point of intersection of the three planes.

Example 2

The equations of three planes are given.

π_1: $x + 2y + 3z + 4 = 0$
π_2: $x - y - 3z - 8 = 0$
π_3: $x + 5y + 9z + 16 = 0$

a) Show that the three planes do not intersect at a single point.

b) Show that the three planes intersect along a line.

Solution

a) Choose any two planes and find the cross product of their normal vectors.

Choose π_1 and π_3. Determine $\vec{n_1} \times \vec{n_3}$, where $\vec{n_1} = [1, 2, 3]$ and $\vec{n_3} = [1, 5, 9]$.

$$\begin{matrix} 2 & 3 & 1 & 2 \\ 5 & 9 & 1 & 5 \end{matrix}$$

The components of $\vec{n_1} \times \vec{n_3}$ are:

$(2)(9) - (5)(3) = 3$
$(3)(1) - (9)(1) = -6$
$(1)(5) - (1)(2) = 3$

The vector $\vec{n_1} \times \vec{n_3} = [3, -6, 3]$ is perpendicular to π_1 and π_3.

Determine $\vec{n_2} \bullet \vec{n_1} \times \vec{n_3}$.

$\vec{n_2} \bullet \vec{n_1} \times \vec{n_3} = [1, -1, -3] \bullet [3, -6, 3]$
$\qquad\qquad\quad = 0$

Since $\vec{n_2} \bullet \vec{n_1} \times \vec{n_3} = 0$, the normal vectors of the planes are coplanar. Hence, the planes do not intersect at a single point.

b) Attempt to solve the system:

$x + 2y + 3z + 4 = 0$ ①
$x - y - 3z - 8 = 0$ ②
$x + 5y + 9z + 16 = 0$ ③

Eliminate x by subtracting ② from ① and also by subtracting ③ from ①. The result will be two equations in y and z.

| ① − ② $3y + 6z + 12 = 0$ | ① − ③ $-3y - 6z - 12 = 0$ |
| or $y + 2z + 4 = 0$ | or $y + 2z + 4 = 0$ |

The given system has been reduced to this system in two variables, consisting of two identical equations.

$$y + 2z + 4 = 0 \qquad ④$$
$$y + 2z + 4 = 0 \qquad ⑤$$

The solution of this system consists of all the values of y and z that satisfy the equation $y + 2z + 4 = 0$. To determine these values, let $z = t$ and solve for y to obtain $y = -4 - 2t$. To determine values of x, substitute these expressions into any of the given equations, say ①.

$$x + 2y + 3z + 4 = 0$$
$$x + 2(-4 - 2t) + 3t + 4 = 0$$
$$x = 4 + t$$

Hence, the solution of the system, where t is any real number, is:

$$x = 4 + t$$
$$y = -4 - 2t$$
$$z = t$$

Since these equations are parametric equations of a line, the planes intersect along this line.

Something to Think About

- How could we check the solution of *Example 2*?

3.6) Exercises

Ⓐ

1. Refer to Case 3 on page 172.

  a) Verify that $\vec{n_5} = 2\vec{n_1} + \vec{n_4}$.

  b) Verify that ⑤ $\neq 2 \times ① + ④$.

2. Refer to Case 4 on page 173.

  a) Verify that $\vec{n_6} = 2\vec{n_1} + \vec{n_4}$.

  b) Verify that ⑥ $= 2 \times ① + ④$.

3. Refer to *Example 1*.

 a) In the solution of part b, after the first addition, we divided each side of the equation $18x - 20z - 44 = 0$ by 2 to obtain $9x - 10z - 22 = 0$. Is this necessary? Explain.

 b) Describe a different way to solve part b.

4. Refer to *Example 2*. Describe a different way to solve part b.

5. The equations of two intersecting planes are given.

$$x + y + z + 5 = 0$$
$$x + 2y + 3z + 4 = 0$$

 Write a third equation such that the three equations represent:

 a) three planes intersecting in a line.

 b) three planes intersecting in pairs.

 c) two parallel planes intersected by a third plane.

 d) three planes intersecting at a point.

6. Give an example of a system of equations that has no solution. Explain, both algebraically and geometrically.

B

7. Solve the system of equations in Case 5 on page 174.

8. Solve each linear system.

 a) $2x + y - z = 1$
   $x + 3y + z = 10$
   $x + 2y - 2z = -1$

 b) $x + 4y + 3z - 5 = 0$
   $x + 3y + 2z - 4 = 0$
   $x + y - z + 1 = 0$

 c) $3x + 2y - z = 6$
   $x + y + z = 5$
   $2x - 3y + 2z = -10$

 d) $5x + 2y - z = 13$
   $x - y - z = 0$
   $2x + y + 3z = -1$

 e) $3x + y + 2z = 5$
   $2x - y + z = -1$
   $4x + 2y - z = -3$

 f) $x + y + 2z = -8$
   $3x - y - z = 0$
   $2x + 2y - z = -2$

9. In *Example 1*, we found the coordinates of the point of intersection of the three planes by forming linear combinations of their equations.

 a) Solve this system using the following method. Choose any two of the planes and determine parametric equations of their line of intersection. Then determine the coordinates of the point where this line intersects the third plane.

 b) Compare your solution from part a with the one on pages 176 and 177. Describe the similarities and the differences in the two solutions.

10. In Case 4 on page 173, we showed that the three planes intersect along a line. Find parametric equations of this line.

11. Point P lies on three distinct planes with normal vectors $\vec{n_1}$, $\vec{n_2}$ and $\vec{n_3}$.

   a) If $\vec{n_1} \cdot \vec{n_2} \times \vec{n_3} \neq 0$, explain why the planes intersect at P.

   b) If $\vec{n_1} \cdot \vec{n_2} \times \vec{n_3} = 0$, explain why the planes intersect in a line passing through P.

12. **Communication** Suppose you are given three equations forming a linear system. Explain how you could determine whether the system is consistent or inconsistent. Illustrate your explanation with some examples.

13. In each linear system, show that one of the equations is a linear combination of the other two equations. Then express the solution of the system in parametric form.

   a) $x + 2y + 3z - 2 = 0$
   $x + y + z + 5 = 0$
   $2x + 3y + 4z + 3 = 0$

   b) $2x - y + z + 4 = 0$
   $5x + y - z - 10 = 0$
   $9x - y + z - 2 = 0$

14. Express the solution of each linear system in parametric form.

   a) $x + 3y + 2z = 1$
   $2x + y - z = 4$

   b) $4x - y + 5z + 2 = 0$
   $2x + y + 7z + 3 = 0$

15. **Knowledge/Understanding** Describe how the planes in each linear system are related. If there is a unique point of intersection, find its coordinates. If there is a line of intersection, express the solution in parametric form.

   a) $3x + 2y - z - 4 = 0$
   $x + 3y + z = 5$
   $4x + 5y = 8$

   b) $x + 2y - 3z = 11$
   $2x + y = 7$
   $3x + 6y - 8z = 22$

   c) $x + 2y - z + 3 = 0$
   $2x + y + 3z - 8 = 0$
   $2x + 4y - 2z - 5 = 0$

   d) $5x + 2y - 5z = 4$
   $2x + 3y - 4z = 2$
   $x + y + z = 3$

   e) $x + 3y + 3z - 8 = 0$
   $x - y + 3z - 4 = 0$

16. In *Example 2*, we found parametric equations of the line of intersection of the three planes by forming linear combinations of their equations.

   a) Solve this system using the following method. Choose any two of the planes and determine parametric equations of their line of intersection. Then show that the third plane contains this line.

   b) Compare your solution from part a with the one on pages 177 and 178. Describe the similarities and the differences in the two solutions.

17. Thinking/Inquiry/Problem Solving If the three planes with the equations below have a line in common, show that $ab + bc + ac = 2abc + 1$.

$\pi_1: x + by + cz = 0$
$\pi_2: ax + y + cz = 0$
$\pi_3: ax + by + z = 0$

18. Application A parabola has an equation of the form $y = ax^2 + bx + c$. Determine its equation if it passes through the points A(1, 0), B(4, 3), and C(6, –5).

19. Given $\pi_1: 3x - 4y + z - 35 = 0$ and $\pi_2: ax + by - 5z + 23 = 0$, find the relationship between a and b that will make π_1 and π_2 intersect in the line $\frac{x-1}{3} = \frac{y+5}{4} = \frac{z-12}{7}$.

C

20. Consider the linear system:

$x + y + z = 6$
$2x - y + 2z = 6$
$3x + 2y + z = 10$

The coefficients of the variables, and the constant terms, form sets of three numbers. These numbers can be considered to be components of vectors. That is, we can define $\vec{a} = [1, 2, 3]$, $\vec{b} = [1, -1, 2]$, $\vec{c} = [1, 2, 1]$ and $\vec{d} = [6, 6, 10]$.

a) Explain why we can represent the system by the vector equation
$$\vec{a}x + \vec{b}y + \vec{c}z = \vec{d}.$$

b) By taking appropriate cross products and dot products of both sides of the equation, show that the solution of the system is:

$$x = \frac{\vec{d} \cdot \vec{b} \times \vec{c}}{\vec{a} \cdot \vec{b} \times \vec{c}}, \quad y = \frac{\vec{a} \cdot \vec{d} \times \vec{c}}{\vec{a} \cdot \vec{b} \times \vec{c}}, \quad z = \frac{\vec{a} \cdot \vec{b} \times \vec{d}}{\vec{a} \cdot \vec{b} \times \vec{c}}$$

21. Given the linear system below, express x, y and z as linear combinations of a, b, and c.

$x + 2y - z = a$
$x - y + 2z = b$
$3x + 3y + z = c$

We often encounter systems of equations in which the context is not lines and planes. Economists often have to work with systems of dozens of equations involving dozens of unknowns. Relying on a geometric interpretation would not be very useful.

To help organize such vast amounts of data, mathematicians have created a powerful tool called a *matrix*. A matrix is simply numerical data arranged in a rectangular array. We usually enclose the array in square brackets.

The method of solving a linear system developed in Section 3.6 amounts to combining linear combinations of the equations in certain ways. Since several similar steps are involved, this method is ideally suited for technology. Solving a linear system using technology requires a systematic approach because a calculator or computer uses the same method every time.

Beginning in this section, we will write all equations of planes with the constant terms on the right side.

For example, consider the linear system below. The data are repeated at the right without the variables, and without the + and = signs.

$2x +$	$4y +$	z	$=$	2	2	4	1	2
$5x +$	$5y +$	$3z$	$=$	17	5	5	3	17
$4x -$	$y +$	$3z$	$=$	26	4	-1	3	26

$$
\begin{array}{rrrcr}
2x + & 4y + & z & = & 2 \\
5x + & 5y + & 3z & = & 17 \\
4x - & y + & 3z & = & 26
\end{array}
\qquad
\begin{array}{rrrr}
2 & 4 & 1 & 2 \\
5 & 5 & 3 & 17 \\
4 & -1 & 3 & 26
\end{array}
$$

We will solve the system by forming linear combinations of the equations in a systematic way.

Step 1: Eliminate x from the second and third equations.

Copy the first equation.
Multiply the first equation by 5 and the second equation by 2, and subtract. Replace the second equation with the result.
Multiply the first equation by 2 and subtract the third equation. Replace the third equation with the result.

$$
\begin{array}{rrrcr}
2x + & 4y + & z & = & 2 \\
0x + & 10y - & z & = & -24 \\
0x + & 9y - & z & = & -22
\end{array}
\qquad
\begin{array}{rrrr}
2 & 4 & 1 & 2 \\
0 & 10 & -1 & -24 \\
0 & 9 & -1 & -22
\end{array}
$$

Step 2: *Eliminate y from the third equation.*

Copy the first two equations.
Multiply the second equation by 9 and the third equation by 10, and subtract. Replace the third equation with the result.

$$
\begin{aligned}
2x + 4y + z &= 2 \\
0x + 10y - z &= -24 \\
0x + 0y + z &= 4
\end{aligned}
\qquad
\begin{array}{rrrr}
2 & 4 & 1 & 2 \\
0 & 10 & -1 & -24 \\
0 & 0 & 1 & 4
\end{array}
$$

Step 3: *Eliminate z from the first and second equations.*

Copy the third equation, keeping it in the same position. Add the second and third equations. Replace the second equation with the result. Subtract the third equation from the first equation. Replace the first equation with the result.

$$
\begin{aligned}
2x + 4y + 0z &= -2 \\
0x + 10y + 0z &= -20 \\
0x + 0y + 1z &= 4
\end{aligned}
\qquad
\begin{array}{rrrr}
2 & 4 & 0 & -2 \\
0 & 10 & 0 & -20 \\
0 & 0 & 1 & 4
\end{array}
$$

Step 4: *Eliminate y from the first equation.*

Copy the second and third equations, keeping them in the same positions. Multiply the first equation by 5 and the second equation by 2, and subtract. Write the result in the first position.

$$
\begin{aligned}
10x + 0y + 0z &= 30 \\
0x + 10y + 0z &= -20 \\
0x + 0y + 1z &= 4
\end{aligned}
\qquad
\begin{array}{rrrr}
10 & 0 & 0 & 30 \\
0 & 10 & 0 & -20 \\
0 & 0 & 1 & 4
\end{array}
$$

Step 5: *Divide to obtain the solution.*

Divide the first equation by the coefficient of x.
Divide the second equation by the coefficient of y.

$$
\begin{aligned}
1x + 0y + 0z &= 3 \\
0x + 1y + 0z &= -2 \\
0x + 0y + 1z &= 4
\end{aligned}
\qquad
\begin{array}{rrrr}
1 & 0 & 0 & 3 \\
0 & 1 & 0 & -2 \\
0 & 0 & 1 & 4
\end{array}
$$

The solution of the system is $x = 3$, $y = -2$, and $z = 4$.

Study the patterns in this solution. In each step, each highlighted equation is the same as in the previous step. The other equations are obtained by forming linear combinations of each remaining equation with the nearest highlighted equation. The objective is to form two small triangles of zeros as shown in Step 4. A final step produces three coefficients of 1 along a diagonal line. Then the solution appears in the final column.

A solution like the one shown on pages 182 and 183 is usually written using only the arrays of numbers, enclosed in square brackets as shown below. These arrays are *matrices*. They contain data about the system of equations and its solution. Each row corresponds to an equation. The columns correspond to the coefficients of *x*, *y*, and *z*, and the constant terms. You have to remember what the various positions represent. The vertical line inside each matrix serves as a reminder that the equations have the form $Ax + By + Cz = D$, with the constant term on the right side. It is not essential to use the vertical line.

$$\begin{bmatrix} 2 & 4 & 1 & | & 2 \\ 5 & 5 & 3 & | & 17 \\ 4 & -1 & 3 & | & 26 \end{bmatrix}$$

$$\begin{bmatrix} 2 & 4 & 1 & | & 2 \\ 0 & 10 & -1 & | & -24 \\ 0 & 9 & -1 & | & -22 \end{bmatrix}$$

$$\begin{bmatrix} 2 & 4 & 1 & | & 2 \\ 0 & 10 & -1 & | & -24 \\ 0 & 0 & 1 & | & 4 \end{bmatrix}$$

$$\begin{bmatrix} 2 & 4 & 0 & | & -2 \\ 0 & 10 & 0 & | & -20 \\ 0 & 0 & 1 & | & 4 \end{bmatrix}$$

$$\begin{bmatrix} 10 & 0 & 0 & | & 30 \\ 0 & 10 & 0 & | & -20 \\ 0 & 0 & 1 & | & 4 \end{bmatrix}$$

$$\begin{bmatrix} 1 & 0 & 0 & | & 3 \\ 0 & 1 & 0 & | & -2 \\ 0 & 0 & 1 & | & 4 \end{bmatrix}$$

Katherine Okikiolu (1965–)
Born: England

Okikiolu, daughter of high school math teacher and mathematician George Okikiolu, received her BA in math from Cambridge University. She attended graduate school in the United States.
Since receiving her PhD in 1991, Okikiolu has taught at Princeton, MIT, and is currently a professor at the University of California, San Diego. In 1997, she was awarded two prestigious prizes that honour outstanding young mathematicians. Okikiolu also creates videos that feature inner-city children learning math concepts in interesting ways. She believes in creating lessons that emphasize real-world perspectives.

The first matrix contains the data from the given linear system, and the last one contains the solution. Each matrix represents a linear system that is equivalent to the original one. This means that it has the same solution. The matrices were created by performing certain elementary operations on the rows. These operations correspond to the operations we use when we solve a system of equations.

Elementary Row Operations

A system of linear equations can be represented by a matrix. To obtain an equivalent system, perform any of these operations.

- Multiply the numbers in any row by any constant.
- Replace any row by adding the numbers in any other row to the numbers in that row.
- Replace any row with a linear combination of that row and another row.

A system of three linear equations in x, y, and z represents three planes in R^3. It can be represented by a matrix having the form $\begin{bmatrix} * & * & * & | & * \\ * & * & * & | & * \\ * & * & * & | & * \end{bmatrix}$, where each $*$ represents a real number. When we solve the system using matrices, we attempt to use the elementary row operations to obtain a matrix having the form

$\begin{bmatrix} 1 & 0 & 0 & | & * \\ 0 & 1 & 0 & | & * \\ 0 & 0 & 1 & | & * \end{bmatrix}$. The method of doing this is called *row reduction*. The matrix

that results is called the *reduced matrix* and is in *row reduced echelon form*.

A system of two linear equations in x and y represents two lines in R^2. It can be represented by a matrix having the form $\begin{bmatrix} * & * & | & * \\ * & * & | & * \end{bmatrix}$. To solve the system, we attempt to use row reduction to obtain a matrix having the form $\begin{bmatrix} 1 & 0 & | & * \\ 0 & 1 & | & * \end{bmatrix}$.

Example 1

Solve the linear system using row reduction.

$$4x - 3y = -10$$
$$3x + 5y = 7$$

Solution

Write the system as a matrix.
$\begin{bmatrix} 4 & -3 & | & -10 \\ 3 & 5 & | & 7 \end{bmatrix}$ ①
   ②

Copy ①.
Replace ② with $3 \times ① - 4 \times ②$.
$\begin{bmatrix} 4 & -3 & | & -10 \\ 0 & -29 & | & -58 \end{bmatrix}$ ①
   ②

Divide ② by −29.

$$\begin{bmatrix} 4 & -3 & | & -10 \\ 0 & 1 & | & 2 \end{bmatrix} \quad \begin{matrix} ① \\ ② \end{matrix}$$

Copy ②, leaving it where it was.
Replace ① with ① + 3 × ②.

$$\begin{bmatrix} 4 & 0 & | & -4 \\ 0 & 1 & | & 2 \end{bmatrix} \quad \begin{matrix} ① \\ ② \end{matrix}$$

Divide ① by 4 to obtain the reduced matrix.

$$\begin{bmatrix} 1 & 0 & | & -1 \\ 0 & 1 & | & 2 \end{bmatrix}$$

The solution of the system is $x = -1$ and $y = 2$.

Example 2

Solve the linear system using row reduction.

$$\begin{aligned} 3x - y - 3z &= 4 \\ 2x - 2y &= -3 \\ 5x - 2y + 3z &= -6 \end{aligned}$$

Solution

Write the system as a matrix.

$$\begin{bmatrix} 3 & -1 & -3 & | & 4 \\ 2 & -2 & 0 & | & -3 \\ 5 & -2 & 3 & | & -6 \end{bmatrix} \quad \begin{matrix} ① \\ ② \\ ③ \end{matrix}$$

Copy ①.
Replace ② with 2 × ① − 3 × ②.
Replace ③ with 5 × ① − 3 × ③.

$$\begin{bmatrix} 3 & -1 & -3 & | & 4 \\ 0 & 4 & -6 & | & 17 \\ 0 & 1 & -24 & | & 38 \end{bmatrix} \quad \begin{matrix} ① \\ ② \\ ③ \end{matrix}$$

Copy ①.
Copy ②.
Replace ③ with ② − 4 × ③.

$$\begin{bmatrix} 3 & -1 & -3 & | & 4 \\ 0 & 4 & -6 & | & 17 \\ 0 & 0 & 90 & | & -135 \end{bmatrix} \quad \begin{matrix} ① \\ ② \\ ③ \end{matrix}$$

Divide ③ by 45.

$$\begin{bmatrix} 3 & -1 & -3 & | & 4 \\ 0 & 4 & -6 & | & 17 \\ 0 & 0 & 2 & | & -3 \end{bmatrix} \quad \begin{matrix} ① \\ ② \\ ③ \end{matrix}$$

Copy ③, leaving it where it was.
Replace ② with ② + 3 × ③.
Replace ① with 2 × ① + 3 × ③.

$$\begin{bmatrix} 6 & -2 & 0 & | & -1 \\ 0 & 4 & 0 & | & 8 \\ 0 & 0 & 2 & | & -3 \end{bmatrix} \quad \begin{matrix} ① \\ ② \\ ③ \end{matrix}$$

Copy ③, leaving it where it was.
Copy ②, leaving it where it was.
Replace ① with 2 × ① + ②.

$$\begin{bmatrix} 12 & 0 & 0 & | & 6 \\ 0 & 4 & 0 & | & 8 \\ 0 & 0 & 2 & | & -3 \end{bmatrix} \quad \begin{matrix} ① \\ ② \\ ③ \end{matrix}$$

Divide ① by 12.
Divide ② by 4.
Divide ③ by 2.

$$\begin{bmatrix} 1 & 0 & 0 & | & \frac{1}{2} \\ 0 & 1 & 0 & | & 2 \\ 0 & 0 & 1 & | & -\frac{3}{2} \end{bmatrix}$$

The result is the reduced matrix.

The solution of the system is $x = \frac{1}{2}$, $y = 2$, $z = -\frac{3}{2}$.

It is not always possible to reduce a matrix of the form $\begin{bmatrix} * & * & * & | & * \\ * & * & * & | & * \\ * & * & * & | & * \end{bmatrix}$ to one

of the form $\begin{bmatrix} 1 & 0 & 0 & | & * \\ 0 & 1 & 0 & | & * \\ 0 & 0 & 1 & | & * \end{bmatrix}$ using row reduction. If one of the equations is a

linear combination of the other two, a row of zeros will occur at some point. It

may be possible to reduce the matrix to a form such as $\begin{bmatrix} 1 & 0 & * & | & * \\ 0 & 1 & * & | & * \\ 0 & 0 & 0 & | & 0 \end{bmatrix}$. Then

the system is consistent, and the corresponding planes intersect in a line.
Parametric equations of this line constitute the solution of the system.

Example 3

Solve the system using row reduction, and interpret the solution geometrically.

$$2x + 7y + 2z = 3$$
$$6x + y - 4z = -1$$
$$2x + 9y + 3z = 4$$

Solution

Write the system as a matrix.

$$\begin{bmatrix} 2 & 7 & 2 & | & 3 \\ 6 & 1 & -4 & | & -1 \\ 2 & 9 & 3 & | & 4 \end{bmatrix} \quad \begin{matrix} ① \\ ② \\ ③ \end{matrix}$$

Copy ①.
Replace ② with $3 \times ① - ②$.
Replace ③ with $① - ③$.

$$\begin{bmatrix} 2 & 7 & 2 & | & 3 \\ 0 & 20 & 10 & | & 10 \\ 0 & -2 & -1 & | & -1 \end{bmatrix} \quad \begin{matrix} ① \\ ② \\ ③ \end{matrix}$$

Copy ①.
Divide ② by 10.
Replace ③ with $② + 10 \times ③$.

$$\begin{bmatrix} 2 & 7 & 2 & | & 3 \\ 0 & 2 & 1 & | & 1 \\ 0 & 0 & 0 & | & 0 \end{bmatrix} \quad \begin{matrix} ① \\ ② \\ ③ \end{matrix}$$

Copy ③, leaving it where it was.
Copy ②, leaving it where it was.
Replace ① with $2 \times ① - 7 \times ②$.

$$\begin{bmatrix} 4 & 0 & -3 & | & -1 \\ 0 & 2 & 1 & | & 1 \\ 0 & 0 & 0 & | & 0 \end{bmatrix} \quad \begin{matrix} ① \\ ② \\ ③ \end{matrix}$$

Divide ① by 4.

Divide ② by 2.

Copy ③.

The result is the reduced matrix.

$$\left[\begin{array}{ccc|c} 1 & 0 & -\dfrac{3}{4} & -\dfrac{1}{4} \\ 0 & 1 & \dfrac{1}{2} & \dfrac{1}{2} \\ 0 & 0 & 0 & 0 \end{array}\right] \begin{array}{l} ① \\ ② \\ ③ \end{array}$$

The equation corresponding to row ③ is $0x + 0y + 0z = 0$. This equation is satisfied for all values of the variables. In particular, it is satisfied when $z = t$.

The equation corresponding to row ② is $y + \dfrac{1}{2}z = \dfrac{1}{2}$.

Substitute $z = t$ to obtain:

$$y + \dfrac{1}{2}t = \dfrac{1}{2}$$
$$y = \dfrac{1}{2} - \dfrac{1}{2}t$$

The equation corresponding to row ① is $x - \dfrac{3}{4}z = -\dfrac{1}{4}$.

Substitute $z = t$ to obtain:

$$x - \dfrac{3}{4}t = -\dfrac{1}{4}$$
$$x = -\dfrac{1}{4} + \dfrac{3}{4}t$$

The solution of the system is given by these equations, where t is any real number. These are parametric equations of the line of intersection of the three planes.

$$x = -\dfrac{1}{4} + \dfrac{3}{4}t$$
$$y = \dfrac{1}{2} - \dfrac{1}{2}t$$
$$z = t$$

3.7 Exercises

1. Solve each linear system using row reduction.

a) $3x + y = 5$
$x + y = 3$

b) $2x - y = 2$
$x + 3y = 8$

c) $5x + 2y = 0$
$3x + y = 5$

d) $x + 3y = 5$
$4x - y = -6$

2. Solve each linear system using row reduction.

a) $5x - 2y = 7$
$3x + 4y = -2$

b) $9x + 4y = -5$
$4x - 3y = 8$

c) $2x + y = -7$
$3x + 4y = 2$

d) $6x - 5y = 9$
$2x - 3y = 2$

3. When two 2 by 2 systems of equations were solved using row reduction, the reduced matrices shown below were obtained.

a) Why did zeros appear in the first two positions of the second row of each matrix?

b) What do these matrices tell you about the solution of the original system? Explain, both algebraically and geometrically.

Two reduced matrices

Matrix 1

$$\begin{bmatrix} 2 & -3 & | & 6 \\ 0 & 0 & | & 0 \end{bmatrix}$$

Matrix 2

$$\begin{bmatrix} 2 & -3 & | & 6 \\ 0 & 0 & | & 8 \end{bmatrix}$$

4. Communication Three linear systems are shown below. Results from solving the systems using row reduction are also shown, but not necessarily in the same order. For each linear system, identify the corresponding reduced matrix. Explain.

Three linear systems

a) $x + 2y = 3$
$2x + 4y = 6$

b) $x + 2y = 3$
$2x + 4y = 5$

c) $x + 2y = 3$
$2x + y = 0$

Three reduced matrices

Matrix 1

$$\begin{bmatrix} 1 & 0 & | & -1 \\ 0 & 1 & | & 2 \end{bmatrix}$$

Matrix 2

$$\begin{bmatrix} 1 & 2 & | & 0 \\ 0 & 0 & | & 1 \end{bmatrix}$$

Matrix 3

$$\begin{bmatrix} 1 & 2 & | & 3 \\ 0 & 0 & | & 0 \end{bmatrix}$$

5. Solve each linear system using row reduction.

a) $x + 3y + 4z = 19$
$x + 2y + z = 12$
$x + y + z = 8$

b) $x + y + z = -4$
$x - y + 2z = -13$
$2x + y - 3z = 15$

c) $4x + 2y - 3z = 7$
$x + 3y + z = 2$
$x + 4y - 2z = -9$

d) $x + y + z = 0$
$16x + 4y + z = 3$
$x + y - z = 0$

6. **Knowledge/Understanding** Solve each linear system using row reduction, if possible. If it is not possible, explain why.

a) $x - y + 2z = 7$
$2x + y - z = 3$
$x + y + z = 9$

b) $-x + y + 3z = 2$
$x - 3y + 5z = 6$
$x - 2y + z = 2$

c) $4x - 6y + 2z = 10$
$2x - 3y + z = 0$
$x - 9y - 4z = 5$

d) $x + y - z = 3$
$2x - y + z = 5$
$x - 2y + 2z = 6$

7. Solve each linear system using row reduction.

a) $x + 4y - z = -3$
$x + 5y - 3z = 2$

b) $2x + y - 4z = 3$
$x + y + 3z = 2$

c) $x + 2y - z = 3$
$3x + y + 2z = 1$

d) $5x + 3y + z = -1$
$2x + y - 2z = 2$

8. **Thinking/Inquiry/Problem Solving** When two 3 by 3 systems of equations were solved using row reduction, the results shown below were obtained.

a) Why did zeros appear in the first three positions of the third row of each matrix?

b) What do these matrices tell you about the solution of the original system? Explain, both algebraically and geometrically.

Two reduced matrices

Matrix 1

$$\begin{bmatrix} 2 & 1 & 2 & -3 \\ 0 & -5 & 4 & -5 \\ 0 & 0 & 0 & 0 \end{bmatrix}$$

Matrix 2

$$\begin{bmatrix} 2 & 1 & 2 & -3 \\ 0 & -5 & 4 & -5 \\ 0 & 0 & 0 & 10 \end{bmatrix}$$

9. **Application** Three linear systems are shown below. Results from solving the systems using row reduction are also shown, but not necessarily in the same order. For each linear system, identify the corresponding reduced matrix. Explain, both algebraically and geometrically.

Three linear systems

a) $2x - 3y + z = -6$
$x + y + z = 7$
$3x - y + 2z = 4$

b) $2x - 3y + z = -6$
$x + y + z = 7$
$3x - 2y + 2z = 1$

c) $2x - 3y + z = -1$
$4x - 6y + 2z = -2$
$6x - 9y + 3z = -3$

Three reduced matrices

Matrix 1

$$\begin{bmatrix} 1 & 0 & 0 & -1 \\ 0 & 1 & 0 & 3 \\ 0 & 0 & 1 & 5 \end{bmatrix}$$

Matrix 2

$$\begin{bmatrix} 1 & 0 & \frac{4}{5} & 3 \\ 0 & 1 & \frac{1}{5} & 4 \\ 0 & 0 & 0 & 0 \end{bmatrix}$$

Matrix 3

$$\begin{bmatrix} 2 & -3 & 1 & -1 \\ 0 & 0 & 0 & 0 \\ 0 & 0 & 0 & 0 \end{bmatrix}$$

3.8 Solving Linear Systems Using a Graphing Calculator

You can use a TI-83 or TI-83 Plus calculator to solve a linear system. There are two methods, but the TI-83 Plus calculator is required for the second method.

Using matrix operations

Consider once again the system that was solved in Section 3.7.

$$2x + 4y + \ z = \ 2$$
$$5x + 5y + 3z = 17$$
$$4x - \ y + 3z = 26$$

To solve the system using matrix operations, follow these steps.

- Press $\boxed{\text{2nd}}$ $\boxed{\text{MATRX}}$ $\boxed{\blacktriangleright}$ $\boxed{\blacktriangleright}$ to display the matrix edit menu.
- Press **1** to select **1: [A]**.
- Press 3 $\boxed{\text{ENTER}}$ 4 $\boxed{\text{ENTER}}$ to define a matrix with 3 rows and 4 columns.
- Press 2 $\boxed{\text{ENTER}}$ 4 $\boxed{\text{ENTER}}$ 1 $\boxed{\text{ENTER}}$ 2 $\boxed{\text{ENTER}}$ to complete the first row for $2x + 4y + z = 2$.
- Press 5 $\boxed{\text{ENTER}}$ 5 $\boxed{\text{ENTER}}$ 3 $\boxed{\text{ENTER}}$ 17 $\boxed{\text{ENTER}}$ to complete the second row for $5x + 5y + 3z = 17$.
- Press 4 $\boxed{\text{ENTER}}$ -1 $\boxed{\text{ENTER}}$ 3 $\boxed{\text{ENTER}}$ 26 $\boxed{\text{ENTER}}$ to complete the third row for $4x - y + 3z = 26$.
- Press $\boxed{\text{2nd}}$ $\boxed{\text{QUIT}}$ to return to the home screen.
- Press $\boxed{\text{2nd}}$ $\boxed{\text{MATRX}}$ $\boxed{\blacktriangleright}$ to display the matrix math menu.
- Press $\boxed{\blacktriangledown}$ several times to scroll down to the line **B:rref(**.
- Press $\boxed{\text{ENTER}}$ to copy rref(to the home screen.
- Press $\boxed{\text{2nd}}$ $\boxed{\text{MATRX}}$ **1** to select **1: [A]** from the matrix names menu.
- Press $\boxed{\ )\ }$ $\boxed{\text{ENTER}}$ to display the solution.

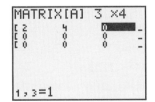 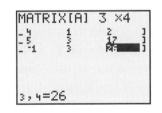

```
rref([A])
     [[1 0 0 3 ]
      [0 1 0 -2]
      [0 0 1 4 ]]
```

The program displays the matrix of results. The solution is $x = 3$, $y = -2$, and $z = 4$.

The number of equations does not have to be the same as the number of unknowns. In the following example, we solve a system of 2 equations in 3 unknowns.

Example 1

Solve the system using matrix operations, and interpret the solution geometrically.

$$3x - y + 4z = 7$$
$$x + y - 2z = -5$$

Solution

Use the steps shown on the previous page. Set up a 2 by 4 matrix and enter the data to obtain the following results.

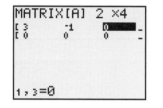
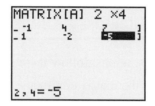
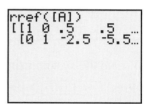

On the third screen, the dots at the right indicate that the matrix is too large to fit on the screen. You can use the arrow key to scroll to the right. In this case, all that is missing are the square brackets to complete the matrix.

The third screen gives the solution in the following form:

$$x + 0.5z = 0.5$$
$$y - 2.5z = -5.5$$

Let $z = t$ and solve for x and y to obtain the solution in parametric form.

$$x = 0.5 - 0.5t$$
$$y = -5.5 + 2.5t$$
$$z = t$$

These are parametric equations of the line of intersection of the planes with the given equations.

Using the PolySmlt application

The solution of linear systems is so important that many routines have been created to do this. The Applications menu of your TI-83 Plus calculator may contain a program for solving linear systems. To determine if it does, press APPS. You should see "PolySmlt" in the list of applications. If it is not there, it is available for you to download to a computer at no cost from Texas Instruments' website on the Internet. You can then transfer it to your calculator using TI's Graph Link software and cable. You can also download documentation containing detailed instructions for using the application.

Consider once again the system that was solved in Section 3.7.

$$2x + 4y + z = 2$$
$$5x + 5y + 3z = 17$$
$$4x - y + 3z = 26$$

To solve the system using PolySmlt, follow these steps.

- Press [APPS] and select PolySmlt.
- Press any key to display the main menu.
- Select SimultEqnSolver.
- Enter the number of equations and the number of unknowns. Press [ENTER] after each entry.
- Enter the data from the system in the matrix that appears.
- Press [GRAPH] to select SOLVE.

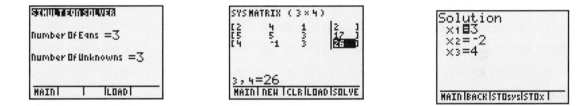

Notice that the program displays the results, using x_1, x_2, and x_3 for the variables.

The number of equations does not have to be the same as the number of unknowns. In the following example, we solve a system of 2 equations in 3 unknowns.

Example 2

Solve the system using PolySmlt, and interpret the solution geometrically.

$$3x - y + 4z = 7$$
$$x + y - 2z = -5$$

Solution

Use the steps above. Enter the data to obtain the following results.

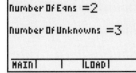
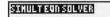

On the third screen, the values of x_1 and x_2 are given in terms of x_3. These are parametric equations of the solution. The variable x_3 can take any value, then the values of x_1 and x_2 can be calculated using the expressions displayed. Therefore, the solution of the given system is:

$$x = 0.5 - 0.5t$$
$$y = -5.5 + 2.5t$$
$$z = t$$

These are parametric equations of the line of intersection of the planes with the given equations.

When you use PolySmlt to solve certain systems, the entire solution may not fit on the screen. For example, you may obtain a screen like the one at the right. The dots at the right on the line for x_2 indicate that there is more information. To view this information, use the arrow key.

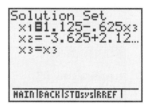

3.8 Exercises

A

1. Use the results shown on either page 191 or page 193. Verify that the solution satisfies all three given equations.

2. Use the results of either *Example 1* or *Example 2*.

a) Verify that the parametric equations given in the solution satisfy both given equations.

b) Interpret the result of part a geometrically.

B

3. Solve each linear system.

a) $3x - y + 2z = 2$
$4x + 3z = 1$
$3x + 2y + 5z = 2$

b) $7x - 2y + 3z = 1$
$3x - 4y + 2z = -2$
$x - y + 2z = 5$

4. Solve each linear system.

a) $x + 2y - 2z = 3$
$2x + 5y - z = 2$

b) $3x - y + z = -2$
$4x + 2y + 5z = 1$

5. Find out what happens when you try to solve a linear system that has no solution.

6. Communication

a) Find a way to use PolySmlt to determine parametric equations of a plane.

b) Describe your method, and illustrate it with an example.

7. Knowledge/Understanding Find parametric equations of the line of intersection of the given planes. Explain your method.

a) π_1: $2x + 3y - z = 7$ and π_2: $x + 2y - 2z = 4$

b) π_1: $4x - 2y + 3z = 1$ and π_2: $3x + y + 3z = -8$

8. Kathy works at *The Clothing Store*. She orders clothing from the manufacturer. In August, she ordered 54 shirts, 33 sweaters, and 25 coats at a total cost of $3245.60. In September, she ordered 92 shirts, 56 sweaters, and 37 coats at a total cost of $5255.35. In October, she ordered 77 shirts, 45 sweaters, and 28 coats at a total cost of $4196.70. What is the cost of one shirt, one sweater, and one coat?

9. Application A farmer needs 500 kg of fertilizer that is 50% nitrogen, 15% phosphorus, and 35% potassium. Three different brands are available. Their compositions are shown below. How many kilograms of each brand should he use?

	Brand X (%)	Brand Y (%)	Brand Z (%)
Nitrogen	40	50	60
Phosphorus	20	20	0
Potassium	40	30	40

10. Three business students are playing an investment game. They each pretend to invest $100 000 in three stocks. The amounts invested in each stock and the total gain or loss after one year are listed in the following table. Determine the annual rate of return for each of the three stocks.

	Stock #1 ($)	Stock #2 ($)	Stock #3 ($)	Gain/loss ($)
Student A	50 000	30 000	20 000	12 570
Student B	30 000	30 000	40 000	6 030
Student C	50 000	0	50 000	-8 650

11. **Thinking/Inquiry/Problem Solving** An oven is set to 200°C. While it is warming up, its temperature, T degrees Celsius, can be modelled by a quadratic function in terms of the number of seconds, t, after the oven has been turned on.

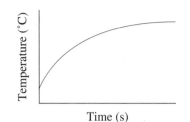

$$T = at^2 + bt + c$$

The temperature was 20°C at $t = 0$ s. It reached 70°C at $t = 49$ s, and 100°C at $t = 84$ s.

a) Determine the temperature after each time.

   i) 60 s   **ii)** 120 s

b) How long does it take the temperature to reach 200°C?

12. A company produces three combinations of mixed vegetables that sell in 1-kg packages. Italian style combines 0.3 kg of zucchini, 0.3 kg of broccoli, and 0.4 kg of carrots. Oriental style combines 0.2 kg of zucchini, 0.5 kg of broccoli, and 0.3 kg of carrots. French style combines 0.6 kg of broccoli, and 0.4 kg of carrots. The company has 16 200 kg of zucchini, 41 400 kg of broccoli, and 29 400 kg of carrots in stock. How many packages of each style should they produce to use up their supplies?

3.9 Solving Linear Systems Using a Spreadsheet

Spreadsheets can be used effectively to solve linear systems. The instructions in this section are for Microsoft Excel. If you use a different spreadsheet program, consult its user manual.

Consider once again the system that was solved in Section 3.7.

$$2x + 4y + \ \ z = \ \ 2$$
$$5x + 5y + 3z = 17$$
$$4x - \ \ y + 3z = 26$$

One of the steps in solving this system was to multiply the first equation by 2 and subtract the third equation. When a calculator or computer solves a system like this one, it is simpler to set it up so that it always multiplies each equation by an appropriate coefficient from another equation. Otherwise, additional steps would be needed to check for common factors. For the above system, the computer will multiply the first equation by 4 and the third equation by 2 before subtracting.

This spreadsheet shows the steps in the solution of the above system that correspond to the steps in the solution on pages 182 and 183 (see exercise 1).

To set up a spreadsheet like this one, start a new spreadsheet document.

	A	B	C	D	E
1	System	2	4	1	2
2		5	5	3	17
3		4	-1	3	26
4					
5	Step 1	2	4	1	2
6		0	10	-1	-24
7		0	18	-2	-44
8					
9	Step 2	2	4	1	2
10		0	10	-1	-24
11		0	0	2	8
12					
13	Step 3	-4	-8	0	4
14		0	-20	0	40
15		0	0	2	8
16					
17	Step 4	-80	0	0	-240
18		0	-20	0	40
19		0	0	2	8
20					
21	Step 5	1	0	0	3
22		0	1	0	-2
23		0	0	1	4

- Enter the text in the appropriate cells in column A.
- Enter the numbers shown in the first three rows.
- Enter the following formulas in column B.

  B5:   = B1

  B6:   = B1*$B2 – B2*$B1

  B7:   = B1*$B3 – B3*$B1

  B9:   = B5

  B10: = B6

  B11: = B6*$C7 – B7*$C6

  B13: = B11*$D9 – B9*$D11

  B14: = B11*$D10 – B10*$D11

  B15: = B11

  B17: = B14*$C13 – B13*$C14

  B18: = B14

  B19: = B15

  B21: = B17/$B17

  B22: = B18/$C18

  B23: = B19/$D19

- Copy the formulas in column B into columns C through E.

Compare the numbers in your spreadsheet with those on page 197. They should be the same. If they are, you can use your spreadsheet in the exercises. If not, you will need to make corrections to your formulas.

3.9 Exercises

A

1. Compare the numbers in the spreadsheet on page 197 with the numbers shown in the solution of the same system on page 184.

2. Test your spreadsheet. Use it to solve some systems of equations in the examples or exercises of Section 3.6 or 3.7. Do the results agree with the previous results?

B

3. Solve each linear system using your spreadsheet.

a) $4x - y + 3z = 26$
   $x + 3y + 6z = -2$
   $3x - 2y + z = 5$

b) $4x + 2y - 7z = 3$
   $5x - 6y + 3z = -4$
   $3x - y + 4z = 7$

4. A similar spreadsheet was created to solve a linear system of two equations in two variables. The results for two different systems are shown below.

a) One of these systems has a line of solutions.

    i) Which system is this?

    ii) How can you tell this from the results?

    iii) Determine parametric equations of the line.

b) How can you tell that the other system has no solution?

c) Explain why the division by 0 errors occurred for both systems.

System A

	A	B	C	D
1	System	3	-1	-5
2		6	-2	-10
3				
4	Step 1	3	-1	-5
5		0	0	0
6				
7	Step 2	0	0	0
8		0	0	0
9				
10	Step 3	#DIV/0!	#DIV/0!	#DIV/0!
11		#DIV/0!	#DIV/0!	#DIV/0!

System B

	A	B	C	D
1	System	3	-1	-5
2		6	-2	5
3				
4	Step 1	3	-1	-5
5		0	0	-45
6				
7	Step 2	0	0	45
8		0	0	-45
9				
10	Step 3	#DIV/0!	#DIV/0!	#DIV/0!
11		#DIV/0!	#DIV/0!	#DIV/0!

5. Communication To solve a 2 by 2 system using technology, you could create a spreadsheet like the one on page 197 that displays results like those in exercise 4. However, this is not necessary because you can use the one you have already created for a 3 by 3 system.

a) Explain how you could use your spreadsheet to solve a 2 by 2 system, without changing any of the formulas.

b) Use your spreadsheet to solve each system. Check the results mentally.

    i) $4x + 7y = 10$ **ii)** $3x + 2y = 19$

       $3x - 2y = -8$ $4x - 3y = 14$

6. Knowledge/Understanding A spreadsheet was used to solve two linear systems, with the results shown at the top of the following page.

a) One of these systems has a line of solutions.

    i) Which system is this?

    ii) How can you tell this from the results?

    iii) Determine parametric equations of the line.

b) How can you tell that the other system has no solution?

c) Explain why the division by 0 errors occurred for both systems.

System A

	A	B	C	D	E
1	System	2	-3	1	-4
2		1	2	5	3
3		3	-1	6	-1
4					
5	Step 1	2	-3	1	-4
6		0	-7	-9	-10
7		0	-7	-9	-10
8					
9	Step 2	2	-3	1	-4
10		0	-7	-9	-10
11		0	0	0	0
12					
13	Step 3	0	0	0	0
14		0	0	0	0
15		0	0	0	0
16					
17	Step 4	0	0	0	0
18		0	0	0	0
19		0	0	0	0
20					
21	Step 5	#DIV/0!	#DIV/0!	#DIV/0!	#DIV/0!
22		#DIV/0!	#DIV/0!	#DIV/0!	#DIV/0!
23		#DIV/0!	#DIV/0!	#DIV/0!	#DIV/0!

System B

	A	B	C	D	E
1	System	2	-3	1	-4
2		1	2	5	3
3		3	-1	6	2
4					
5	Step 1	2	-3	1	-4
6		0	-7	-9	-10
7		0	-7	-9	-16
8					
9	Step 2	2	-3	1	-4
10		0	-7	-9	-10
11		0	0	0	-42
12					
13	Step 3	0	0	0	-42
14		0	0	0	378
15		0	0	0	-42
16					
17	Step 4	0	0	0	0
18		0	0	0	378
19		0	0	0	-42
20					
21	Step 5	#DIV/0!	#DIV/0!	#DIV/0!	#DIV/0!
22		#DIV/0!	#DIV/0!	#DIV/0!	#DIV/0!
23		#DIV/0!	#DIV/0!	#DIV/0!	#DIV/0!

7. **Application** Use your spreadsheet to help you find parametric equations of the line of intersection of the given planes. Explain your method.

a) π_1: $3x + 2y - z = 5$ and π_2: $4x + 3y - 2z = 5$

b) π_1: $x + 3y + z = 10$ and π_2: $2x - 6y - z = -1$

8. Tamika has a part-time job at the ballpark. On Friday, she sold 12 posters, 18 pennants, and 7 caps for a total of $368.72. On Saturday, she sold 37 posters, 29 pennants, and 18 caps for a total of $860.75. On Sunday, she sold 22 posters, 19 pennants, and 9 caps for a total of $505.85. How much do one poster, one pennant, and one cap cost?

9. **Thinking/Inquiry/Problem Solving** The total number of oranges, N, in a square pyramid of oranges is a cubic function in terms of the number of layers, x.

$$N = ax^3 + bx^2 + cx$$

a) How many oranges are there in a square pyramid with each number of layers?
   i) one layer   ii) two layers   iii) three layers

b) Determine the values of a, b, and c.

10. In a certain study, the number of accidents in one month, n, was approximated by a quadratic function in terms of the age of the driver, x years.

$$n = ax^2 + bx + c$$

Eighteen-year-old drivers had 2478 accidents. Thirty-five-year-old drivers had 1875 accidents. Sixty-year-old drivers had 2765 accidents. Determine the values of a, b, and c.

11. A bridge is designed with expansion joints to allow for thermal expansion. The exact length of a steel girder, L millimetres, is a linear function in terms of the temperature, T degrees Celsius.

$$L = mT + b$$

a) At 5°C, a certain girder is 9982 mm long. At 34°C, it is 10 016 mm long. Determine the values of m and b for this girder.

b) What do m and b represent?

12. On a certain road surface, the stopping distance of a car, d metres, is a quadratic function in terms of its speed, v kilometres per hour.

$$d = mv^2 + bv$$

A car travelling at 50 km/h takes 48 m to stop. A car travelling at 100 km/h takes 170 m to stop. Determine the values of m and b.

C

13. In exercise 20 on page 181, you showed that the solution of a linear system of three equations in three variables is given by the following formulas.

$$x = \frac{\vec{d} \cdot \vec{b} \times \vec{c}}{\vec{a} \cdot \vec{b} \times \vec{c}}, \quad y = \frac{\vec{a} \cdot \vec{d} \times \vec{c}}{\vec{a} \cdot \vec{b} \times \vec{c}}, \quad z = \frac{\vec{a} \cdot \vec{b} \times \vec{d}}{\vec{a} \cdot \vec{b} \times \vec{c}}$$

In these formulas, $\vec{a}$, $\vec{b}$, and $\vec{c}$ are vectors formed by the coefficients of x, y, and z, respectively. The vector $\vec{d}$ is formed by the constant terms. Use these formulas to create a spreadsheet for solving linear systems.

Mathematics Toolkit

Equations of a Line

2-space

(a_1, a_2) is a point on the line.

$[m_1, m_2]$ is a direction vector.

Vector equation

$[x, y] = [a_1, a_2] + t[m_1, m_2]$

Parametric equations

$$x = a_1 + tm_1$$
$$y = a_2 + tm_2$$

Symmetric equation

$$\frac{x - a_1}{m_1} = \frac{y - a_2}{m_2}$$

where $m_1 \neq 0$, and $m_2 \neq 0$

3-space

(a_1, a_2, a_3) is a point on the line.

$[m_1, m_2, m_3]$ is a direction vector.

Vector equation

$[x, y, z] = [a_1, a_2, a_3] + t[m_1, m_2, m_3]$

Parametric equations

$$x = a_1 + tm_1$$
$$y = a_2 + tm_2$$
$$z = a_3 + tm_3$$

Symmetric equations

$$\frac{x - a_1}{m_1} = \frac{y - a_2}{m_2} = \frac{z - a_3}{m_3}$$

where $m_1 \neq 0$, $m_2 \neq 0$, and $m_3 \neq 0$

Equations of a Plane

(a_1, a_2, a_3) is a point on the plane.

$[u_1, u_2, u_3]$ and $[v_1, v_2, v_3]$ are two non-collinear vectors on the plane.

Vector equation

$[x, y, z] = [a_1, a_2, a_3] + s[u_1, u_2, u_3] + t[v_1, v_2, v_3]$

Parametric equations

$$x = a_1 + su_1 + tv_1$$
$$y = a_2 + su_2 + tv_2$$
$$z = a_3 + su_3 + tv_3$$

Scalar equation

$Ax + By + Cz + D = 0$, where A, B, and C are the components of its normal vector, $\vec{n} = [A, B, C]$. The normal vector is perpendicular to the plane.

Two Lines

Two distinct lines may intersect, be parallel, or be skew.

Lines and Planes

Suppose a line and a plane are given. The line may:

- intersect the plane at a unique point.
- lie on the plane.
- be parallel to the plane and not intersect it.

Two Planes

Two distinct planes may be either parallel or intersect in a line. When two planes intersect in a line, the direction vector of the line is the cross product of the normal vectors of the planes.

Linear Combinations of Equations of Planes

Suppose two planes with scalar equations $A_1x + B_1y + C_1z + D_1 = 0$ and $A_2x + B_2y + C_2z + D_2 = 0$ intersect in a line. Any linear combination of these equations represents a plane that contains this line. In particular, this is true of the following equation.

$$A_1x + B_1y + C_1z + D_1 + k(A_2x + B_2y + C_2z + D_2) = 0$$

Three Planes

Three distinct planes can be situated with respect to each other in five different ways. The three orientations shown below correspond to inconsistent systems of equations.

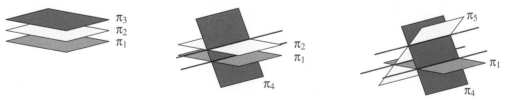

The two orientations shown below correspond to consistent systems of equations. There is either a line of solutions or a unique solution.

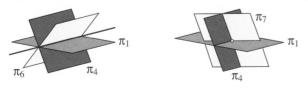

Test for a Unique Solution

Three distinct planes have normal vectors $\overrightarrow{n_1}$, $\overrightarrow{n_2}$, and $\overrightarrow{n_3}$. To test for a unique solution, calculate $\overrightarrow{n_1} \bullet \overrightarrow{n_2} \times \overrightarrow{n_3}$.

- If $\overrightarrow{n_1} \bullet \overrightarrow{n_2} \times \overrightarrow{n_3} \neq 0$, the normal vectors are not coplanar. There is a single point of intersection.

- If $\overrightarrow{n_1} \bullet \overrightarrow{n_2} \times \overrightarrow{n_3} = 0$, the normal vectors are coplanar. There may or may not be points of intersection. If there are any points of intersection, then it is a line.

Solving a Linear System Using Matrices

Use row reduction to reduce a matrix of the form $\begin{bmatrix} * & * & * & | & * \\ * & * & * & | & * \\ * & * & * & | & * \end{bmatrix}$ to one

of the form $\begin{bmatrix} 1 & 0 & 0 & | & * \\ 0 & 1 & 0 & | & * \\ 0 & 0 & 1 & | & * \end{bmatrix}$.

If this is possible, there is a unique solution.

If it is not possible, there is a line of solutions if the matrix can be reduced

to one of the form $\begin{bmatrix} 1 & 0 & * & | & * \\ 0 & 1 & * & | & * \\ 0 & 0 & 0 & | & 0 \end{bmatrix}$.

If neither of these is possible, there is no solution.

1. Consider the equation $y = 3$. What does this equation represent in R^2? What does this equation represent in R^3? Explain. Support your explanation with sketches.

2. Consider the equation $x = 3$. What does this equation represent in R^2? What does this equation represent in R^3? Explain. Support your explanation with sketches.

3. Find the coordinates of the point of intersection of the following lines.

L_1: $\dfrac{x+3}{-1} = \dfrac{y-7}{4} = \dfrac{z-2}{1}$

L_2: line through the points A(0, 2, 1) and B(−4, 4, 1)

4. Find the coordinates of the point of intersection of the following lines.

L_1: $\dfrac{x+2}{3} = \dfrac{y-1}{-1} = \dfrac{z-1}{1}$

L_2: $\dfrac{x-7}{-1} = \dfrac{y+4}{1}$, $z = 3$

5. The point A(1, 4, 2) and the direction vector $\vec{d} = [2, -1, 0]$ are given.

   a) Find a vector equation of the line l_1 passing through point A with direction vector $\vec{d}$.

   b) Find three other points on l_1.

   c) Find the parametric equations of l_1.

   d) Find the symmetric equations of l_1.

6. Which two of the following lines are the same? Explain.

   a) $[x, y, z] = [1, 2, 3] + s[3, -1, 2]$

   b) $[x, y, z] = [-2, 3, 1] + t[-3, 1, -2]$

   c) $[x, y, z] = [7, 0, 6] + p[3, -1, 2]$

7. The points A(1, 2, 3), B(−1, 3, 2), and C(3, −2, −1) are given.

   a) Determine a vector equation of the line that passes through A and that is parallel to the segment BC.

   b) Determine the parametric equations of the line that passes through B and that is parallel to the segment AC.

   c) Determine the symmetric equations of the line that passes through C and that is parallel to the segment AB.

8. Find the scalar equation of each plane.

   a) the plane with normal vector $\vec{n} = [4, -1, 9]$ passing through the point R(2, −1, −1)

   b) the plane passing through S(4, 0, −1) and containing the direction vectors $\vec{m_1} = [2, 1, 5]$ and $\vec{m_2} = [-3, 0, 1]$

   c) the plane passing through the points A(4, −5, 1), B(2, 3, 3), and C(0, 2, −4)

9. The vector, parametric, and scalar equations of three planes are given below. Two of the planes are the same. Which planes are they?

   π_1: $\vec{p} = [2, 3, 5] + s[1, 2, 4] + t[1, 0, 2]$

   π_2: $x = 2 + s$, $y = 3 + 2t$, $z = 3 + 2s + 2t$

   π_3: $2x + y - z = 2$

10. Find the scalar equation of the plane containing the point A(−3, 1, 2) and that is parallel to the lines $\frac{x+3}{1} = \frac{y}{2} = \frac{z-5}{3}$ and $x = 2$, $\frac{y+1}{-2} = \frac{z+3}{1}$.

11. Find the scalar equation of the plane through the points P(2, 2, 2) and Q(3, 2, 1), and that is perpendicular to the plane $4x - y + 2z - 7 = 0$.

12. Given π_1: $3x - 4y + z - 35 = 0$ and π_2: $ax + by - 5z + 23 = 0$, find the relationship between a and b that will make π_1 perpendicular to π_2.

13. A plane has normal vector $\vec{n} = [3, -1, 4]$ and passes through the point A(1, 2, 5).

    a) Determine the scalar equation of the plane.

    b) Determine parametric equations of the plane.

14. Determine, if possible, the point(s) of intersection of each line and each plane. If there is a point of intersection, find the angle between the line and the plane.

    a) $\dfrac{x+4}{2} = \dfrac{y+2}{3} = \dfrac{z-3}{2}$ and $3x - y + 2z - 3 = 0$

    b) $\dfrac{x-2}{3} = \dfrac{y+1}{-2} = \dfrac{z+5}{-1}$ and $3x + y + 7z + 30 = 0$

15. Show that the given line lies on the given plane.

    a) l: $[x, y, z] = [0, 4, -4] + t[1, -2, 1]$ and π: $x + 5y + 9z + 16 = 0$

    b) l: $[x, y, z] = [1, 1, 1] + t[0, 2, 1]$ and π: $3x - 2y + 4z - 5 = 0$

16. Determine the projection of the point $(1, -1, 4)$ on the plane $2x + y - 2z - 6 = 0$.

17. Two lines with the following symmetric equations are given.

    L_1: $\dfrac{x-4}{-1} = \dfrac{y-2}{-2} = \dfrac{z+3}{2}$ and L_2: $\dfrac{x+6}{-2} = \dfrac{y+2}{2} = \dfrac{z-3}{1}$

    a) Prove that L_1 and L_2 are skew lines.

    b) Find the equations of two parallel planes containing L_1 and L_2.

18. Find vector and symmetric equations for the line of intersection of each pair of planes.

    a) π_1: $3x + 2y - z = 0$ and π_2: $2x + 2y - 3z = 0$

    b) π_1: $2x - y + 2z = 6$ and π_2: $x - 3y + 4z = 1$

19. Find a set of parametric equations for the line of intersection of the planes $5x + y + z - 9 = 0$ and $x + y - z - 1 = 0$.

20. The planes π_1: $2x + 3y + z = 2$ and π_2: $5x - 2y + 2z = -4$ are given. Find the scalar equation of the plane that contains the line of intersection of π_1 and π_2, and that passes through the origin.

21. Given the planes $3x - 2y + 7z - 8 = 0$ and $2x + y - 5z + 1 = 0$:

    a) Explain how you can tell that the planes intersect in a line.

    b) Write the equation of any other plane that contains this line.

    c) Write the scalar equation of any plane that is parallel to the line.

22. Find the equation of the plane that passes through the line of intersection of the planes $3x + 4y - z + 5 = 0$ and $2x + y + z + 10 = 0$, and that satisfies each condition.

    a) It passes through the point $(-2, 5, 1)$.

    b) It is perpendicular to the plane $6x + y + 2z - 5 = 0$.

23. The equations of three planes are given.

    π_1: $x + 2y + 3z = -4$

    π_2: $x - y - 3z = 8$

    π_3: $2x + y + 6z = -14$

    a) Show that the three planes intersect at a single point.

    b) Find the coordinates of the point of intersection.

24. Show that the following planes form a triangular prism.

    π_1: $3x + 2y + z = 0$

    π_2: $x + 2y + 3z = 4$

    π_3: $x + y + z = 16$

25. Solve each linear system using row reduction.

    a) $2x + 3y = -4$
                        b) $2x - y = -4$

       $3x + y = 1$
                          $3x + 2y = 1$

    c) $3x + 2y - z = 6$
                    d) $3x + y - 2z = -14$

       $x - 4y + z = 7$
                      $2x - 3y + 4z = -23$

       $2x - 6y - 5z = -1$
                   $5x + 4y - 10z = -13$

26. Use the method of row reduction to solve each system of equations completely. Give a geometric interpretation of the solution.

    a) $x + 2y + 3z = 5$
                    b) $4x - 3y + 2z = 5$

       $2x - y - 4z = -10$
                   $x - 2y + z = 3$

       $5x + 7y + 6z = 7$
                   $3x + 4y - z = -5$

1. Show that the following lines intersect and determine the angle of intersection.

L_1: $\dfrac{x-2}{1} = \dfrac{y-6}{5}$ and L_2: $\dfrac{x-4}{2} = \dfrac{1-y}{1}$

2. Show that the following lines are parallel.

L_1: $\dfrac{x-2}{1} = \dfrac{y-1}{-2} = \dfrac{z+1}{3}$ and L_2: $\dfrac{x-4}{1} = \dfrac{y+3}{-2} = \dfrac{z-1}{3}$

3. Show that the following lines are skew.

L_1: the line through the points A(1, 1, 1) and B(1, −1, −1)

L_2: the line through the points C(−1, −1, 1) and D(−1, 1, −1)

4. Find the scalar equation of the plane that is perpendicular to the plane with normal vector $\vec{n}$ = [3, 1, −2] and that passes through the points A(2, −6, −1) and B(1, 2, −4).

5. **Thinking/Inquiry/Problem Solving** Determine the scalar equation of the plane that contains the point A(3, −1, 1) and the line with symmetric equations $\dfrac{x+1}{2} = \dfrac{y-1}{-3} = \dfrac{z-2}{-3}$.

6. Determine the coordinates of all points of intersection for each line and plane.

a) L: $\dfrac{x-4}{2} = \dfrac{y}{-1} = \dfrac{z-11}{1}$ and π: $x + 3y - z + 1 = 0$

b) L: $\dfrac{x-1}{2} = \dfrac{y+1}{4} = \dfrac{z-2}{1}$ and π: $4x - 3y + 4z - 15 = 0$

7. **Knowledge/Understanding** Find parametric equations of the line of intersection of the following planes.

π_1: $5x + 4y + 3z = 2$ and π_2: $3x + 2y + z = 0$

8. **Communication** Suppose you have the equations of three planes. Describe a test you could use to determine, without solving the system, whether or not the planes intersect at a single point. Make up an example to illustrate your test.

9. Solve each linear system using row reduction.

a) $3x + 2y = -3$
   $5x + 4y = 2$

b) $x + 6y - 2z = 2$
   $2x - 5y + 4z = 3$
   $7x + 3y - z = 1$

10. **Application** The sum of the digits of a 3-digit number is 21. If the units and tens digits are interchanged, the sum is increased by 18. If the hundreds and tens digits are interchanged, the number is increased by 180. What is the number?

Performance Problems for Vectors

The problems in this section offer you the opportunity to solve some complex problems related to the topics you have studied. Some of these problems are challenging. You may find it helpful to work with others, to share ideas and strategies. You may be unable to complete a solution to some of the problems at the first attempt. Be prepared to research, to return to a problem again and again.

Curriculum Expectations

By the end of this section you will:

- Solve complex problems and present the solutions with clarity and justification.

- Solve problems of significance, working independently, as individuals and in small groups.

- Solve problems requiring effort over extended periods of time.

- Demonstrate significant learning and the effective use of skills in tasks such as solving challenging problems, researching problems, applying mathematics, creating proofs, using technology effectively, and presenting course topics or extensions of course topics.

Focus on ... The Dot Product

Suppose we draw a triangle in R^2, and calculate the dot products of the side vectors having tails at each vertex. This gives three dot products. Suppose we add these values. Is the result related to the triangle in any way?

Problem 1

a) For each triangle in the diagram:

   i) Calculate the dot products of the two vectors with tails at each vertex.

   ii) Determine the sum of the dot products.

b) Choose any of the triangles in part a. Suppose this triangle were moved to a different position, without changing its size or shape. Explain why the sum of the dot products you calculated in part a would not change.

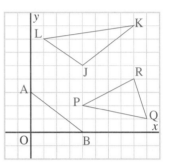

Problem 2

This problem is a generalization of problem 1. Let A, B, and C be the vertices of any triangle with side lengths a, b, and c.

a) Show that $bc \cos A + ca \cos B + ab \cos C = \dfrac{a^2 + b^2 + c^2}{2}$.

b) Describe the special case that occurs for a right triangle.

Focus on ... Plotting Points and Lines in R^3 on Paper

When we plot points in R^3 on a two-dimensional piece of paper, it is possible for different points to coincide on the diagram. In the next three problems, assume that the diagrams are created like the one at the right. The positive x-axis makes an angle of 135° with the positive y-axis, and the scales are the same along all three axes.

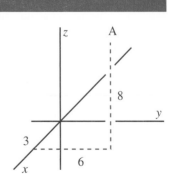

Problem 3

a) The diagram shows the point A(3, 6, 8) in R^3. Copy the diagram on grid paper, and determine the coordinates of three other points in R^3 that would be plotted in the same position on the diagram.

b) Describe how the coordinates of the points in part a are related.

Problem 4

In the diagram for problem 3, point A has coordinates (3, 6, 8). This is actually a two-dimensional diagram that was created on a computer. Point A was plotted using the approximate coordinates (3.9, 5.9) relative to the origin and the y- and z-axes.

a) Explain how the coordinates (3.9, 5.9) can be determined from the coordinates (3, 6, 8).

b) Let (x_3, y_3, z_3) represent the coordinates of a point, A, in R^3. Write formulas for the coordinates (y_2, z_2) of the point A′ in R^2 that should be plotted to represent point A on paper.

c) Check your formulas in part b. Use the 3 points determined in problem 3.

Problem 5

When we plot a line in R^3 on a two-dimensional piece of paper, it is possible for all the points on the line to coincide on the diagram. Such a line will appear as a point. Given the parametric equations of the line in R^3, how can we tell if this will happen?

Focus on ... Area of a Parallelogram in R^2

In Section 2.4, we calculated the area of a parallelogram in R^3 by calculating the cross product of two side vectors and determining its magnitude. Although cross products are not defined for vectors in R^2, we can still use cross products to determine areas of parallelograms in R^2.

Problem 6

The diagram below left shows the parallelogram in R^2 determined by the vectors $\overrightarrow{OU} = [4, 2]$ and $\overrightarrow{OV} = [1, 6]$. You can calculate its area by visualizing the same parallelogram drawn on the xy-plane in R^3 (below right). Calculate the area of the parallelogram determined by the vectors $\overrightarrow{OU} = [4, 2, 0]$ and $\overrightarrow{OV} = [1, 6, 0]$. This is the area of the parallelogram in R^2.

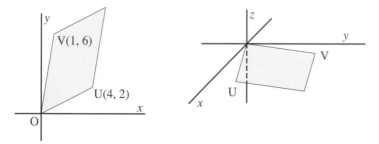

Problem 7

To calculate the area of a parallelogram in R^2, we do not need to go into three dimensions and use cross products. We should be able to determine the area using only two-dimensional concepts.

a) Find a way to determine the area of the parallelogram in the first diagram for problem 6 without using cross products.

b) Derive a formula for the area of a parallelogram in R^2 determined by the vectors $\vec{a} = [a_1, a_2]$ and $\vec{b} = [b_1, b_2]$.

Focus on ... Scalar Triple Products

In Section 2.5, we used the scalar triple product, $\vec{u} \cdot \vec{v} \times \vec{w}$, to test for coplanar vectors in three dimensions. For vectors that are not coplanar, $\vec{u} \cdot \vec{v} \times \vec{w}$ has a non-zero value. In the next problem, you will determine how the value of $\vec{u} \cdot \vec{v} \times \vec{w}$ is related geometrically to the vectors $\vec{u}$, $\vec{v}$, and $\vec{w}$.

Suppose $\vec{u} \cdot \vec{v} \times \vec{w} \neq 0$, so the vectors $\vec{u}$, $\vec{v}$, and $\vec{w}$ are not coplanar. When drawn tail-to-tail, they form an object, called a *parallelepiped*, whose faces are parallelograms.

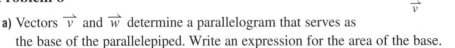

Problem 8

a) Vectors $\vec{v}$ and $\vec{w}$ determine a parallelogram that serves as the base of the parallelepiped. Write an expression for the area of the base.

b) The vector $\vec{v} \times \vec{w}$ is perpendicular to the base. Find the magnitude of the projection of $\vec{u}$ on $\vec{v} \times \vec{w}$. This represents the height of the parallelepiped.

c) The volume of the parallelepiped is the product of the base area and the height. Show that the volume of the parallelepiped is $|\vec{u} \cdot \vec{v} \times \vec{w}|$.

d) Under what condition is it not necessary to use the absolute value signs in part c?

Problem 9

Explain why $\vec{u} \cdot \vec{v} \times \vec{w} = \vec{v} \cdot \vec{w} \times \vec{u} = \vec{w} \cdot \vec{u} \times \vec{v}$.

The pattern in the letters in the above equations is an example of *cyclic symmetry*. Cyclic symmetry also occurred in problem 2.

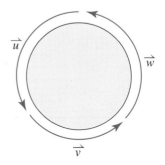

Problem 10

Calculate the volume of each parallelepiped.

a) the parallelepiped formed by the vectors $\vec{u} = [2, 1, 3]$, $\vec{v} = [1, -4, 2]$, and $\vec{w} = [0, 3, 5]$

b) the parallelepiped determined by the points A(1, 2, 2), B(3, 2, 0), C(2, 4, 3), and D(−1, 4, 3)

Problem 11

Show that the dot and the cross in $\vec{u} \cdot \vec{v} \times \vec{w}$ can be interchanged without changing its value. That is, explain why:

$$\vec{u} \cdot \vec{v} \times \vec{w} = \vec{u} \times \vec{v} \cdot \vec{w}$$

Focus on ... Perpendicular Distance

In exercise 20 on page 162, you calculated the perpendicular distance from given points to given planes. In part a, you may have calculated the perpendicular distance from A(2, 3, −1) to the plane $2x + y - 2z + 9 = 0$ using the following method.

Since the normal vector of the plane is $\vec{n} = [2, 1, -2]$, the line through A and perpendicular to the plane has parametric equations $x = 2 + 2t$, $y = 3 + t$, $z = -1 - 2t$. Solve these with the equation of the plane to determine the point of intersection, B(−2, 1, 3). The length of segment AB is 6, which is the perpendicular distance from A to the plane.

A simpler method uses projections, and applies to other problems involving perpendicular distance. You will use this method in problem 12, then apply it to other situations involving perpendicular distance in problems 13 and 14.

Problem 12

a) Calculate the perpendicular distance from A(2, 3, −1) to the plane $2x + y - 2z + 9 = 0$ using the following method.
   By inspection, determine the coordinates of any point C on the plane. Calculate the projection $\overrightarrow{AC} \downarrow \vec{n}$, where $\vec{n}$ is the normal vector to the plane. Calculate the magnitude of $\overrightarrow{AC} \downarrow \vec{n}$.

b) Use a diagram to explain why the magnitude of $\overrightarrow{AC} \downarrow \vec{n}$ is the perpendicular distance from A to the plane.

Problem 13

Calculate the perpendicular distance from the point P(6, 3, −10) to the line
$\frac{x-6}{4} = \frac{y+2}{3} = \frac{z+5}{-5}$.

Problem 14

In problems 12 and 13, you calculated the perpendicular distance from a point to a plane and to a line. There are situations involving two lines or two planes where it is also meaningful to calculate perpendicular distances. Make up an example and calculate the perpendicular distance between:

a) two parallel lines.

b) two skew lines.

c) two parallel planes.

Focus on ... Planes from Symmetric Equations

Suppose we cross-multiply the symmetric equations of a line in R^2. For example:

$$\frac{x-3}{-2} = \frac{y+4}{3}$$
$$3(x-3) = -2(y+4)$$
$$3x + 2y - 1 = 0$$

The result is the equation of the line in a different form. This is the general equation of the line.

Problem 15

The situation is different in R^3. Consider typical symmetric equations of a line, such as:

$$\frac{x-2}{6} = \frac{y-5}{10} = \frac{z-4}{7}$$

a) Choose any two of these equations, cross-multiply, and simplify the result. Repeat for other pairs of equations.

b) Since the equations you obtained have the form $Ax + By + Cz + D = 0$, they represent planes in R^3. Describe how these planes are related to the line.

c) Draw a diagram to show how the planes and the line are related.

Problem 16

Each plane in problem 15 contains the given line and is parallel to one of the coordinate axes. Make up examples and draw diagrams to illustrate the special cases that occur when the given line is:

a) parallel to one of the coordinate planes.

b) parallel to one of the coordinate axes.

Other Problems

Problem 17

Points A and B are any two points on a circle with centre O. The heads of vectors $\overrightarrow{OA}$ and $\overrightarrow{OB}$ lie on the circle. Vector $\overrightarrow{OC}$ is the sum of $\overrightarrow{OA}$ and $\overrightarrow{OB}$. In the diagram, the head of $\overrightarrow{OC}$ lies outside the circle. Explain your answer to each question.

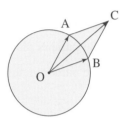

a) Is it possible for the head of $\overrightarrow{OC}$ to lie on the circle?

b) Is it possible for the head of $\overrightarrow{OC}$ to lie inside the circle?

c) Where are all the possible positions for C?

Problem 18

Illustrate the results of problem 17 using *The Geometer's Sketchpad*.

Problem 19

Let A be the point (1, 1). Describe the locus of the point P which moves according to each condition. Draw a graph to illustrate each result.

a) $\overrightarrow{OP} \cdot \overrightarrow{OA} = 0$ **b)** $\overrightarrow{OP} \cdot \overrightarrow{OA} = 0.5$ **c)** $\overrightarrow{OP} \cdot \overrightarrow{OA} = 1$

Problem 20

The vectors $\vec{a}$ and $\vec{b}$ have an angle θ between them. Determine $\vec{a} \downarrow \vec{b}$ for each given value of θ.

a) $0°$ **b)** $90°$ **c)** $180°$

Problem 21

Determine two vectors that are perpendicular to each other and also perpendicular to $\vec{u} = [4, -3, 1]$.

Problem 22

Let $\vec{a} = [1, 2, 3]$, $\vec{b} = [-1, 2, -1]$ and $\vec{c} = [0, 1, -2]$. Do these vectors, taken in this order, satisfy the right-hand rule? Explain.

Problem 23

Given $\vec{a} = \overrightarrow{OA}$, $\vec{b} = \overrightarrow{OB}$ and $\vec{c} = \overrightarrow{OC}$ where points A, B, and C are non-collinear, explain why the vector $\vec{v} = \vec{a} \times \vec{b} + \vec{b} \times \vec{c} + \vec{c} \times \vec{a}$ is perpendicular to the plane containing A, B, and C.

Problem 24

Determine the perpendicular distance between:

a) the parallel planes $x + 2y + 3z + 6 = 0$ and $x + 2y + 3z - 6 = 0$.

b) the parallel lines $\frac{x-1}{1} = \frac{y}{2} = \frac{z+2}{-1}$ and $\frac{x}{1} = \frac{y-1}{2} = \frac{z-3}{-1}$.

c) the skew lines $\frac{x+2}{3} = \frac{y-1}{-1} = \frac{z-3}{-7}$ and $\frac{x-2}{2} = \frac{y-2}{-1} = \frac{z-2}{-2}$.

Problem 25

Write the symmetric equations of any line that is skew to the line $\frac{x-3}{1} = \frac{y+2}{2} = \frac{z-1}{3}$. Explain how you can be certain that the two lines are skew lines.

Problem 26

Given the point P(1, 2, 3), find the two points, A and B on the line $\vec{p} = [9, 5, 1] + t[4, 3, 1]$ such that $\left|\overrightarrow{AP}\right| = \left|\overrightarrow{BP}\right| = 5$.

Problem 27

Let P be any point on the line
l_1: $[x, y, z] = [4, 8, -1] + t[2, 0, -4]$, and let Q be any point on the line l_2: $\frac{x-7}{-6} = \frac{y-2}{2} = \frac{z+1}{2}$.

a) Prove that the locus of the midpoint of segment PQ is a plane.

b) Determine the scalar equation of the plane in part a.

**Mary Somerville
(1780–1872)**
Born: Jedburgh, Scotland

Somerville did not receive a formal education but began to teach herself mathematics by reading algebra texts.
Although the social and cultural traditions of the time did not encourage intellectual pursuits by women, Somerville continued her studies. Her most famous mathematical work, *The Mechanism of the Heavens*, was published in 1831. In 1835, she was elected to the Royal Astronomical Society. Somerville was a strong supporter of women's education, and Somerville College in Oxford is named in her honour.

Problem 28

Find the scalar equation of the plane which passes through the line of intersection of the planes $x + y + z - 4 = 0$ and $y + z - 2 = 0$, and satisfies each condition.

a) It is 2 units from the origin.

b) It is 3 units from the point A(5, –3, 7).

Challenge Problem 29

a) Refer to the diagram on page 135, which shows the line in R^3 with parametric equations $x = -2 + 2t$, $y = 5 + 4t$, $z = 3 + t$. This is actually a line on a two-dimensional diagram with y- and z-axes. Determine the slope and the z-intercept of this line.

b) Given the parametric equations of a line in R^3, how can we determine the slope and the z-intercept of the line on a two-dimensional diagram that represents it?

Challenge Problem 30

This problem appears deceptively simple, but the challenge is to obtain three independent equations in x, y, and z that can be solved to determine the areas of the regions.

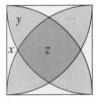

A square has sides 6 cm long. Four quarter circles are inscribed in the square. Determine the areas of the three different kinds of regions that are formed.

6 cm

Challenge Problem 31

Let $\vec{a} = \overrightarrow{OA}$ and $\vec{b} = \overrightarrow{OB}$ be two vectors drawn tail-to-tail, forming a parallelogram OACB. Let M be the midpoint of the diagonals of the parallelogram. Squares with sides MC and MB are constructed, as shown.

a) Prove that:

$$\vec{a} \cdot \vec{b} = \text{(area of square on MC)} - \text{(area of square on MB)}$$

b) Describe what happens in each situation.

   i) The vectors $\vec{a}$ and $\vec{b}$ are collinear.

   ii) The vectors $\vec{a}$ and $\vec{b}$ are perpendicular.

   iii) ∠BOA is obtuse.

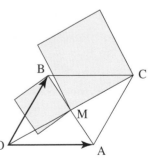

c) Suppose the dot product $\vec{a} \cdot \vec{b}$ is *defined* to be:

$$\vec{a} \cdot \vec{b} = \text{(area of square on MC)} - \text{(area of square on MB)}$$

Prove that $\vec{a} \cdot \vec{b} = |\vec{a}||\vec{b}| \cos \theta$, where $\theta = $ ∠BOA.

PROOF AND PROBLEM SOLVING

Babylonian tablets, dated approximately between 1800 B.C.E. and 1600 B.C.E., contain the earliest tangible record of the Pythagorean Theorem.

Curriculum Expectations

By the end of this chapter, you will:

- Prove some properties of plane figures algebraically, using analytic geometry.

- Prove some properties of plane figures, using vector methods.

- Prove some properties of plane figures, using indirect methods.

- Demonstrate an understanding of the relationship between formal proof and the illustration of properties that is carried out by using dynamic geometry software.

- Generate multiple solutions to the same problem.

- Use technology effectively in making and testing conjectures.

- Demonstrate significant learning and the effective use of skills in tasks such as solving challenging problems, researching problems, applying mathematics, creating proofs, using technology effectively, and presenting course topics or extensions of course topics.

In earlier grades, we discovered many geometric properties through investigation. For example, we determined that the sum of the angles in a triangle is 180° by tearing the corners off a paper triangle and reassembling the pieces to form a straight line. When we repeated this with other triangles, we obtained the same result. We conjectured that the sum of the angles in *any* triangle is 180°.

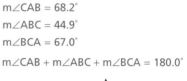

We demonstrated the same result using *The Geometer's Sketchpad*. We constructed a triangle, and changed its size and shape by dragging the vertices to new positions. We observed that although the measures of the angles changed, the sum of the angles was always 180°. We conjectured that the sum of the angles in *any* triangle is 180°. We cannot be certain that the sum of the angles in every triangle is 180° because we cannot draw all possible triangles even with a computer.

m∠CAB = 68.2°
m∠ABC = 44.9°
m∠BCA = 67.0°
m∠CAB + m∠ABC + m∠BCA = 180.0°

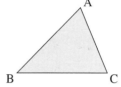

When we make a conjecture by observing and generalizing a pattern, we are using *inductive reasoning*. With inductive reasoning, we reach a conclusion on the basis of a series of examples. However, we can rarely look at all possible examples. Thus, we can never be certain that a conclusion based on inductive reasoning is always true.

For example, suppose we want to determine if there is a relationship between the number of points on a circle and the number of regions formed by connecting the points.

We look at specific cases and try to find a pattern.

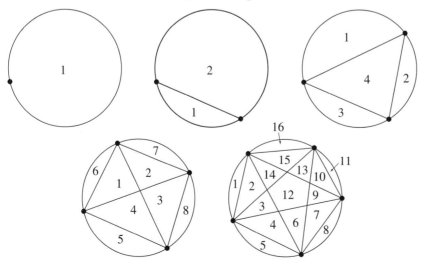

Number of points	Number of regions
1	1
2	2
3	4
4	8
5	16

It appears that for each additional point on the circle, the number of regions doubles. Inductive reasoning suggests that for 6 points on the circle, 32 regions will be formed; for 7 points, 64 regions will be formed; and so on.

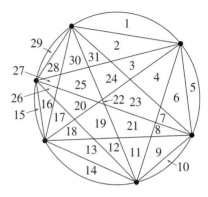

However, when we join 6 points, we find that only 31 regions are formed. Our conjecture was incorrect.

It has been proved that the number of regions formed by joining n points on a circle is given by the expression:

$$\frac{n^4 - 6n^3 + 23n^2 - 18n + 24}{24}$$

Substituting values of n from 1 to 7 gives:

  1, 2, 4, 8, 16, 31, 57

Thus, for 7 points, 57 regions are formed, not 64 as we predicted. Inductive reasoning led to an incorrect conclusion.

This example illustrates that we cannot be certain that a conclusion is true in general just because it is true in particular instances. Thus, when we discover a pattern, we can accept its validity only when we can prove that it is true for all possible cases. In this chapter and the next, we will prove many of the geometric properties you discovered in earlier grades.

When testing a conclusion obtained by inductive reasoning, it only takes one example that does not work to prove the conclusion false. An example that shows that a possible conclusion is false is called a *counterexample*.

On page 220, we discussed the angle sum property of a triangle. We will now give two proofs of this result.

Angle Sum Theorem

In any triangle, the sum of the angles is 180°.

  $\angle A + \angle B + \angle C = 180°$

Proof using rotations

Construct a large △ABC on a piece of paper. Using a pencil and a ruler, follow these steps:

Place the edge of the ruler along side BC. With the pencil at B, rotate the ruler counterclockwise about B until the edge lies along AB.

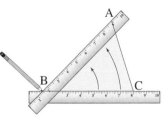

With the pencil at A, rotate the ruler counterclockwise again until the edge lies along AC.

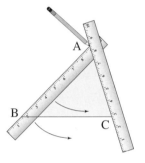

With the pencil at C, rotate the ruler counterclockwise again until the edge lies along BC.

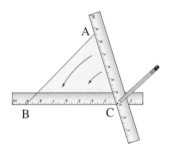

After each step, the ruler rotates through one angle in the triangle. When the ruler returns to side BC, it is upside down compared with its original position. Thus, the ruler has rotated through an angle of 180°. Therefore, the sum of the angles in the triangle is 180°.

Something to Think About

- Does this prove the angle sum theorem for all triangles and not just the one in the diagram? Explain.
- Does it matter that the three rotations have different centres? Explain.

Proof using parallel lines

In the diagram, $\triangle ABC$ represents any triangle. Construct a line through A, parallel to BC, and call it DE.

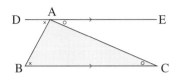

Constructing the line through one vertex and parallel to the opposite side is not obvious, but it is the key to solving this problem. We do not know who first did this, but we do know that he or she lived more than 2000 years ago.

DE is parallel to BC. Alternate angles between parallel lines are equal. So,

$$\angle DAB = \angle ABC \qquad ①$$
$$\angle EAC = \angle ACB \qquad ②$$

Since $\angle DAE$ is a straight angle:
$$\angle DAB + \angle BAC + \angle EAC = 180° \qquad ③$$

Substitute ① and ② into ③.
$$\angle ABC + \angle BAC + \angle ACB = 180°$$

Therefore, the sum of the angles in every triangle is 180°.

Student Reference

Parallel lines

Something to Think About

- Refer to the geometric properties in the student reference. Which one(s) did we use in the above proof?
- How do we know for certain that the sum of the angles forming a straight angle is 180°?

Strategy

Notice how a line was constructed and used to advantage in the above proof.

The above proof involved geometric properties. We can also prove properties in arithmetic and algebra.

Consider these products of two odd numbers:
$$3 \times 5 = 15$$
$$7 \times 9 = 63$$
$$11 \times 9 = 99$$
$$17 \times 15 = 255$$

It appears that the product is always odd. We could make the following conjecture:

The product of any two odd integers is an odd integer
To prove this statement, we use logical reasoning to explain why the product of every possible pair of odd integers is odd. We will use the fact that an even integer is divisible by 2, so it can be represented by the expression $2n$, where n is any integer. An odd integer leaves a remainder of 1 when it is divided by 2, so it can be represented by $2n + 1$.

Proof:

Let $2n + 1$ and $2m + 1$ represent any two odd integers.

$$(2n + 1)(2m + 1) = 4nm + 2n + 2m + 1$$
$$= 2(2nm + n + m) + 1$$

This expression is an odd integer because it has the form $2k + 1$ where k is an integer. Therefore, the product of any two odd integers is an odd integer.

Something to Think About

- How does the above proof explain why the product of every possible pair of odd integers is an odd integer?

4.1 Exercises

A

1. Many natural numbers can be written as the sum of consecutive numbers. Here are some examples:

$10 = 1 + 2 + 3 + 4$ $\qquad$ $18 = 5 + 6 + 7$

$33 = 16 + 17$ $\qquad$ $75 = 13 + 14 + 15 + 16 + 17$

We might use inductive reasoning to conclude that every natural number can be written as the sum of consecutive numbers. Find a counterexample to show that this is not true.

2. Many natural numbers can be written as the sum of three or fewer perfect squares. For example:

$8 = 2^2 + 2^2$ $\qquad$ $26 = 4^2 + 3^2 + 1^2$

$36 = 6^2$ $\qquad$ $70 = 6^2 + 5^2 + 3^2$

We might suspect that all natural numbers can be written as the sum of three or fewer perfect squares. Find a counterexample to show that this is not true.

All natural numbers can be expressed as the sum of four or fewer perfect squares. However, this cannot be proved using inductive reasoning because we cannot be certain that there is no number that requires more than four perfect squares.

3. Show that the following statements are false by finding a counterexample.

a) A number that is not positive is negative.

b) The square of a number is always greater than the number.

c) The altitude of a triangle always lies inside the triangle.

d) Any number divided by itself equals 1.

e) All prime numbers are odd.

4. By using a calculator, $\sin 30° = 0.5$. Is this a proof that $\sin 30° = 0.5$? Explain.

B

5. Communication Create a general statement that is true in some cases but not in all cases. Explain how your statement fits these criteria.

6. Find a counterexample to show that the expression $n^2 - n + 41$ does not represent a prime number for all positive integers, n.

7. Any polygon can be divided into triangles by joining vertices.

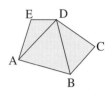

   a) Determine the sum of the angles in polygons with 4, 5, 6, and n sides.

   b) A *regular polygon* is one that has all sides the same length and all angles equal. Determine the measures of the angles in regular polygons with 4, 5, 6, and n sides.

8. The diagram at the right was made using *The Geometer's Sketchpad*. On the screen, you can drag P around the circle. Although the positions of AP and BP change, the measure of ∠APB never changes.

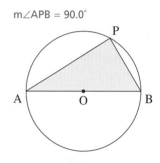

m∠APB = 90.0°

   a) Does this prove that the angle formed by joining the endpoints of the diameter of the circle, with any point on the circle, is a right angle? Explain.

   b) Prove that ∠APB = 90°. Start the proof by constructing line segment PO to form two isosceles triangles.

9. Prove the **Opposite Angle Theorem**
When two lines intersect, the opposite angles are equal.

10. Prove the **Exterior Angle Theorem**
Suppose one side of a triangle is extended. Then the exterior angle formed is equal to the sum of the two interior and opposite angles.

11. Determine the sum of the shaded angles in each figure.

   a)   **b)**   **c)**

State a probable conclusion based on these results. Then prove your conclusion.

12. Application The yin yang symbol consists of a circle bisected by a curve formed by two semicircles, passing through the centre.

  a) Show how to draw a curve that bisects both regions, then prove that it does.

  b) Prove that the curve also bisects the perimeters of the regions.

  c) Repeat part a, replacing "curve" with "straight line".

13. Knowledge/Understanding Make a conjecture about the sum of two even integers. Prove that your conjecture is true.

14. Find a pattern that exists when the square of an odd number is divided by 4. Make a conjecture and then prove it.

15. Thinking/Inquiry/Problem Solving In △ABC, ∠A is the largest angle and ∠B is the smallest. The sides of the triangle are consecutive natural numbers greater than 1. Using consecutive numbers 2, 3, and 4, determine the ratio $\frac{\sin A}{\sin C}$. Try another case using the numbers 3, 4, and 5. Make a conjecture about the ratio. Prove your conjecture.

16. Discuss the validity of the statement: *If a natural number is a factor of a second natural number, then the square of that number is also a factor of the square of the second number.*
If the statement is true, prove it. If the statement is false, find a counterexample.

C

17. a) In the diagram below, prove that:
  i) ∠XAB = 2∠O
  ii) ∠YBC = 3∠O
  iii) ∠XCD = 4∠O
  iv) ∠YDE = 5∠O
  v) ∠XEF = 6∠O

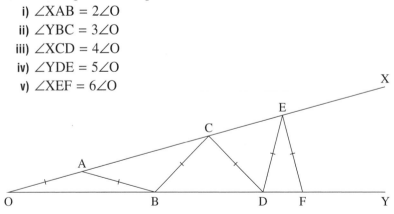

  b) Can this sequence of angles related to ∠O be continued indefinitely? Give two reasons for your answer.

4.2 Proving the Pythagorean Theorem

You have been using the Pythagorean Theorem in your mathematics courses for many years. The Pythagorean Theorem is so significant that it has probably been proved in more ways than any other theorem in mathematics. A book entitled *The Pythagorean Proposition* contains hundreds of proofs of the Pythagorean Theorem. In this section, we will examine some of these proofs.

Pythagorean Theorem

In a right triangle, the area of the square on the hypotenuse is equal to the sum of the areas of the squares on the other two sides.

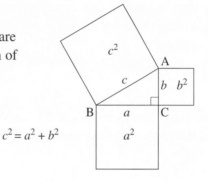

$$c^2 = a^2 + b^2$$

The Pythagorean Theorem is stated in terms of the areas of squares on the sides of a right triangle. Hence, many proofs of the Pythagorean Theorem illustrate how the area of the largest square can be divided to form the areas of the two smaller squares, or vice versa. In the following demonstration, the largest square is split into two rectangles whose areas are respectively equal to the areas of the two smaller squares.

Demonstration using parallelograms

Draw a right triangle and construct squares on each side. Extend the outer sides of the two smaller squares to form a rectangle. Draw lines through the vertices of the triangle, perpendicular to the hypotenuse. The largest square has been divided into two rectangles. Now show that the areas of the two smaller squares are equal respectively to the areas of the rectangles.

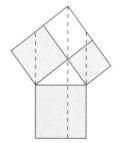

When looking at the following sequence of diagrams, keep in mind that parallelograms with equal bases and equal heights have equal areas.

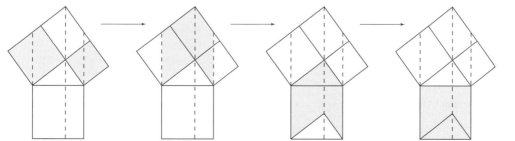

At each step, the areas of the coloured regions remain constant. Therefore, the area of the square on the longer leg is equal to the area of the larger rectangle inside the square on the hypotenuse. Similarly, the area of the square on the shorter leg is equal to the area of the smaller rectangle inside the square on the hypotenuse. Hence, the sum of the areas of the squares on the legs is equal to the area of the square on the hypotenuse.

Something to Think About

- How do we know that the vertical line through the right-angled corner of the right triangle passes through the top vertex of the rectangle between the two squares?
- Explain each step in the demonstration.

The previous demonstration of the Pythagorean Theorem was geometric. Now we will look at a proof that uses algebra to prove the Pythagorean Theorem. It, too, involves area.

Demonstration using a square

Start with a right triangle with sides a, b, and c.

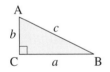

Make four copies of this triangle and arrange them to form a square with sides $a + b$.

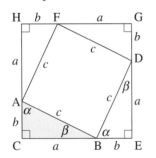

The triangles enclose an inner figure with side c. To prove that this figure is a square, show that one of its angles is 90°.

For example, consider $\angle ABD$. Because CE is a straight line:

Emmy Noether (1882–1935)
Born: Erlangen, Germany

Because women could not officially register at university, Noether had to obtain permission from each professor to audit classes. In 1907, she received her PhD but was denied a faculty position. Noether taught courses advertised under the name of a male colleague until 1919 when she was finally granted a professorship.

Noether contributed to formulations for several concepts of Einstein's general theory of relativity, and to the development of modern algebra. In 1933, circumstances dictated that Noether move to the United States where she taught at Bryn Mawr College and Princeton.

$$\angle CBA + \angle ABD + \angle DBE = 180°$$
$$\beta + \angle ABD + \alpha = 180° \qquad ①$$

Since α and β are the acute angles of a right triangle:
$$\alpha + \beta = 90° \qquad ②$$

Substitute ② into ①.
$$90° + \angle ABD = 180°$$

Therefore, $\angle ABD = 90°$ and ABDF is a square.

Now find the area of square CEGH in two ways.
Area of CEGH $= (a + b)^2$

Area of CEGH = Area of ABDF + 4(Area of $\triangle$ABC)
$$= c^2 + 4\left(\frac{1}{2}ab\right)$$
$$= c^2 + 2ab$$

The two expressions represent the area of the same figure. Therefore, they must be equal.
$$(a + b)^2 = c^2 + 2ab$$
$$a^2 + 2ab + b^2 = c^2 + 2ab$$
$$a^2 + b^2 = c^2$$

Something to Think About

Strategy

Write two expressions for the same thing, then equate them.

- How do we know that this proves the Pythagorean Theorem for all right triangles and not just the one in the diagram?
- Notice that we found two different expressions for the area of the large square, then equated them.

Here is a third area proof of the Pythagorean Theorem. This time we make use of the area property of similar triangles. Recall that for similar triangles, the ratio of the areas is equal to the square of the ratios of the corresponding sides.

Proof using areas of similar right triangles

Construct any right $\triangle$ABC with $\angle C = 90°$. Construct a perpendicular from C to AB and call it CD. There are now 3 right triangles: $\triangle$ABC, $\triangle$ACD, and $\triangle$CBD. The angles in these triangles are correspondingly equal, so the triangles are similar.

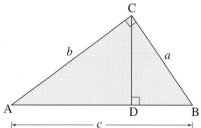

According to the area property of similar triangles, the areas of these triangles are proportional to the squares of the corresponding sides.

Student Reference

Similar triangles

So, $\dfrac{\text{Area} \triangle ABC}{\text{Area} \triangle ACD} = \dfrac{c^2}{b^2}$ and $\dfrac{\text{Area} \triangle ACD}{\text{Area} \triangle CBD} = \dfrac{b^2}{a^2}$

That is, $\dfrac{\text{Area} \triangle ABC}{c^2} = \dfrac{\text{Area} \triangle ACD}{b^2} = \dfrac{\text{Area} \triangle CBD}{a^2}$

This means that there is a constant k such that:

Area of $\triangle ABC = kc^2$
Area of $\triangle CBD = ka^2$
Area of $\triangle ACD = kb^2$

From the diagram,
Area of $\triangle ABC$ = Area of $\triangle CBD$ + Area of $\triangle ACD$
$$kc^2 = ka^2 + kb^2$$
Divide each side by k.
$$c^2 = a^2 + b^2$$

Something to Think About

- Prove that $\triangle ABC$, $\triangle ACD$, and $\triangle CBD$ are similar triangles.

In the exercises, you will use similar triangles to prove the Pythagorean Theorem. This proof does not use area; rather it uses the property that corresponding sides of similar triangles are proportional.

4.2 Exercises

A

1. In the diagram at the right, the squares on the legs of right $\triangle ABC$ have each been divided into 4 triangles.

   a) Copy the diagram on a sheet of paper. Cut out the triangles and arrange them to exactly cover the square on the hypotenuse.

   b) Does this demonstrate the Pythagorean Theorem for all right triangles? Explain.

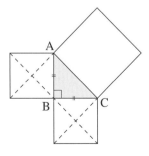

2. Explain how the following sequence of diagrams demonstrates the Pythagorean Theorem.

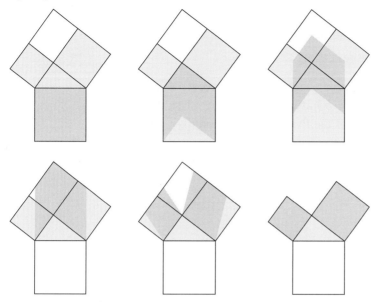

3. Communication Gemma was asked by her teacher, "What is the Pythagorean Theorem?" She replied, "It is $a^2 = b^2 + c^2$." Explain whether her response is correct, giving reasons to support your answer.

B

4. Knowledge/Understanding Prove the Pythagorean Theorem using similar triangles by carrying out the following steps:

Draw right $\triangle ABC$ with $\angle C = 90°$. From C, draw CD perpendicular to AB. Segment CD divides AB into two parts. Let $AD = x$. Then $DB = c - x$.

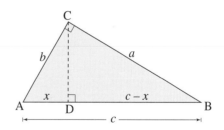

a) Explain why $\triangle ABC$ and $\triangle CBD$ are similar.

b) Write the equal ratios of corresponding sides for the similar triangles in part a. Use the result to write an equation involving a, c, and x.

c) Explain why $\triangle ABC$ and $\triangle ACD$ are similar.

d) Write the equal ratios of corresponding sides for the similar triangles in part b. Use the result to write an equation involving b, c, and x.

e) From the equations you obtained in parts b and d, prove that $a^2 + b^2 = c^2$.

5. In the diagram at the right, four congruent right triangles are arranged to form a square with side c. The triangles also enclose a central square with side $b - a$.

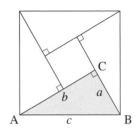

a) How do you know that the central figure is a square?

b) Prove the Pythagorean Theorem using this figure.

6. In the diagrams below, four congruent right triangles have been arranged in a square with side $a + b$ in two different ways. Use these two figures to complete a proof of the Pythagorean Theorem.

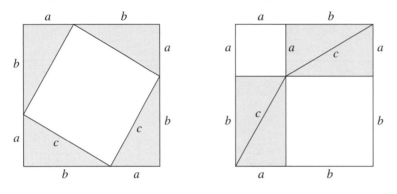

7. Application Three cylindrical logs each with radius 10 cm are piled on a conveyor belt. The logs are strapped together as shown. Determine the length of strapping required if 8 cm is needed for overlapping.

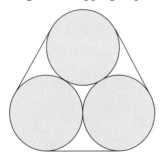

8. Thinking/Inquiry/Problem Solving In 1876, a future president of the United States, James A. Garfield, published a proof of the Pythagorean Theorem. Two congruent right triangles are arranged as shown in the diagram at the right, and a trapezoid is completed. The trapezoid also encloses right $\triangle ABE$.

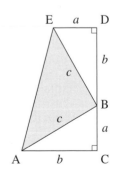

a) How do you know that ACDE is a trapezoid?

b) How do you know that $\triangle ABE$ is a right triangle?

c) By finding the area of the trapezoid in two different ways, prove the Pythagorean Theorem.

9. This exercise is a geometric interpretation of exercise 4. In the diagram at the right, squares have been constructed on the sides of right △ABC. A line is drawn from the vertex of the right angle perpendicular to the hypotenuse. This line divides the hypotenuse into two parts with lengths x and $c - x$. The line also divides the large square into two rectangles.

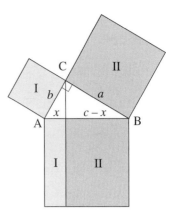

a) Explain why the area of rectangle I is b^2.

b) Explain why the area of rectangle II is a^2.

c) Use the results of parts a and b to prove the Pythagorean Theorem.

10. Dissection demonstration of the Pythagorean Theorem

Open a new *Sketchpad* file and perform the following steps:

a) Construct a right triangle in the middle of the screen. Label the hypotenuse AB and the longer leg BC.

b) Construct a square on each side of the triangle.

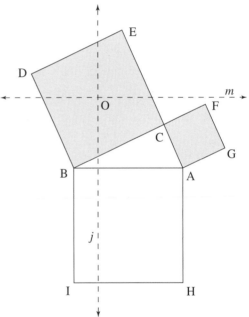

c) Locate the centre of square BCED by finding the intersection of diagonals BE and CD. Label the point of intersection O. Hide BE and CD.

d) Through point O, construct:
   i) line j perpendicular to the hypotenuse
   ii) line m parallel to the hypotenuse

e) Lines j and m divide the square into four parts. Construct the points where j and m intersect the sides of BCED. Hide j and m.

f) For each of the four parts of square BCED, select the vertices in order and construct the polygon interior. Then construct the polygon interior of ACFG.

g) Select the five polygon interiors. Cut and paste them. This frees the interiors so that they can be moved around on the screen. Click on a blank area of the screen to deselect everything.

h) Arrange the five pieces to exactly cover the square ABIH on the hypotenuse. Explain how this demonstrates the Pythagorean Theorem.

11. ABCD is a square with sides 6 cm long. If AM and AN divide the square into three regions with equal areas, find the lengths of AM and AN.

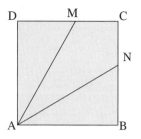

C

12. Square ceramic tiles are made with the pattern shown below. The tiles have a symmetrically located square in the middle. Express y as a function of x if:

   a) all five figures have the same area

   b) all interior segments have the same length

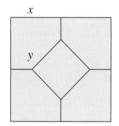

One of the most useful problem-solving strategies in geometry is credited to two great French mathematicians of the seventeenth century, René Descartes (1596–1650) and Pierre de Fermat (1601–1665). Their idea was to place a coordinate system on a geometric figure and then use algebra to prove geometric results.

We will use their method to prove the following property of a triangle.

Side-Splitting Theorem

The line segment joining the midpoints of two sides of a triangle is parallel to the third side and one-half as long as the third side.

DE ∥ BC and

DE = $\frac{1}{2}$BC

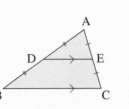

Proof using coordinates

Draw any △ABC. Mark the midpoints, D and E, of AB and AC, respectively. We must prove that DE ∥ BC and DE = $\frac{1}{2}$BC.

Draw coordinate axes on the figure, as follows.
Let B be the origin. Draw the x-axis along side BC.
Draw the y-axis through B perpendicular to BC.

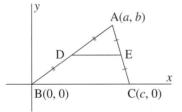

Let the coordinates of the vertices of △ABC be A(a, b), B(0, 0), C(c, 0).

Since D is the midpoint of AB, D has coordinates $\left(\frac{a+0}{2}, \frac{b+0}{2}\right)$ or D$\left(\frac{a}{2}, \frac{b}{2}\right)$.

Since E is the midpoint of AC, E has coordinates $\left(\frac{a+c}{2}, \frac{b+0}{2}\right)$ or E$\left(\frac{a+c}{2}, \frac{b}{2}\right)$.

To prove that DE ∥ BC, show that their slopes are equal.

$$\text{Slope DE} = \frac{\frac{b}{2} - \frac{b}{2}}{\frac{a+c}{2} - \frac{a}{2}}$$

$$= 0$$

Since BC lies on the x-axis, the slope of BC is 0. Therefore, DE ∥ BC.

To prove that DE = $\frac{1}{2}$BC, calculate their lengths using the distance formula.

$$\text{DE} = \sqrt{\left(\frac{a+c}{2} - \frac{a}{2}\right)^2 + \left(\frac{b}{2} - \frac{b}{2}\right)^2}$$

$$= \frac{c}{2}$$

$$\text{BC} = \sqrt{(c-0)^2 + (0-0)^2}$$

$$= c$$

Hence, DE = $\frac{1}{2}$BC.

Since DE ∥ BC and DE = $\frac{1}{2}$BC, the line segment joining the midpoints of two sides of a triangle is parallel to the third side and one-half as long as the third side.

Euclid
(c. 325–265 BC)
Born: Greece

Euclid is considered the father of geometry. His famous work, *Elements*, is a compilation of the mathematics and geometry known at the time. It was used as a textbook of geometry right up to the early 20th century. Although the definitions and postulates are not Euclid's original work, *Elements* was highly regarded for the clarity with which the theorems are stated and proved.
It is believed that Euclid founded the school of mathematics at the university in Alexandria, Egypt, and may have been a mentor to Archimedes.

Something to Think About

- Why does the proof of the side-splitting theorem apply to all triangles, not just those with one vertex at the origin and one side along the x-axis?

- In the proof of the side-splitting theorem, the axes were placed to coincide as much as possible with parts of the triangle. Why? What other positions might be good choices for the origin and the axes?

- Let the vertices of △ABC be A(2a, 2b), B(0, 0), and C(2c, 0), and follow the same steps as in the proof above. What is the advantage of using the 2 in the coordinates of A and C? How would you know in advance that using a 2 in the coordinates of A and C might simplify the proof?

An important part of a coordinate proof is to make a good choice of axes and coordinates. When placing a system of coordinates on a figure, we are free to choose:

- any convenient point to be the origin

- any line through the origin to be the x-axis (or y-axis)

Diagram	Good choice of axes and coordinates
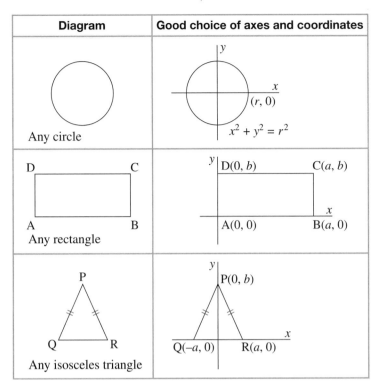Any circle	
D C A B Any rectangle	
P Q R Any isosceles triangle	

Some theorems of plane geometry can be easily proved using coordinates. To construct these proofs, we use results of coordinate geometry learned in earlier years such as those related to distance, midpoint, and slope. For example, to prove the following theorem, we use the property that the product of the slopes of perpendicular line segments is -1.

Semicircle Theorem

If P is any point on a semicircle with diameter AB, then $\angle APB = 90°$.

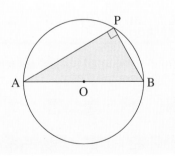

Proof using coordinates

Draw a circle with diameter AB. Let P be any point on the circle. Prove that $\angle APB = 90°$.

Draw coordinate axes on the figure. Let the centre of the circle be the origin. Let the x-axis coincide with diameter AB. Draw the y-axis through the centre perpendicular to AB.

Let the radius of the circle be r. Then the coordinates of the endpoints of the diameter AB are A($-r$, 0) and B(r, 0). The equation of the circle is $x^2 + y^2 = r^2$.

Let the coordinates of P be (a, b).

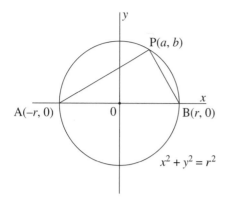

To prove that $\angle APB = 90°$, show that $AP \perp BP$, that is,
(slope AP) × (slope BP) = -1.

$$\text{(slope AP)} \times \text{(slope BP)} = \frac{b}{a+r} \times \frac{b}{a-r}$$

$$= \frac{b^2}{a^2 - r^2}$$

Since P lies on the circle, its coordinates must satisfy the equation $x^2 + y^2 = r^2$.
Thus, $a^2 + b^2 = r^2$, or $a^2 - r^2 = -b^2$.
Substitute $a^2 - r^2 = -b^2$ in the expression above.

So, (slope AP) × (slope BP) = $\dfrac{b^2}{-b^2}$

$$= -1$$

Hence, $\angle APB = 90°$

Something to Think About

- Why does this proof apply to all circles, not just circles with centre (0, 0)?

4.3) Exercises

A

1. Which of the two choices of axes is better? Explain.

a) i)   ii)   b) i)   ii)

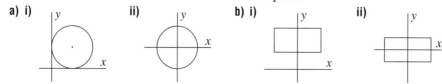

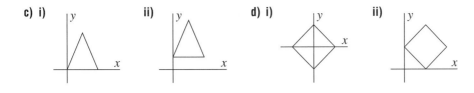

c) i) **ii)** **d) i)** **ii)**

B

2. Supply the missing variables for each figure without introducing any new coordinates.

a) ABCD is a rectangle. **b)** ABCD is a parallelogram.

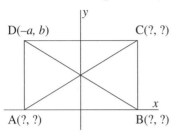

D($-a$, b) C(?, ?)

A(?, ?) B(?, ?)

D(c, b) C(?, ?)

A(0, 0) B(a, 0)

c) ABCD is a rhombus. **d)** $\triangle$ABC is equilateral.

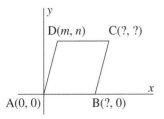

D(m, n) C(?, ?)

A(0, 0) B(?, 0)

C(?, ?)

A($-a$, 0) B(a, 0)

3. Communication A student gave this "proof" of the Pythagorean Theorem. Let $\triangle$ABC have vertices A(a, 0), B(0, b), and C(0, 0). Then, according to the distance formula, AB $= \sqrt{(0-a)^2 + (b-0)^2} = \sqrt{a^2 + b^2}$. Square both sides to obtain AB$^2 = a^2 + b^2$. Therefore, $c^2 = a^2 + b^2$. Explain why this "proof" is not correct.

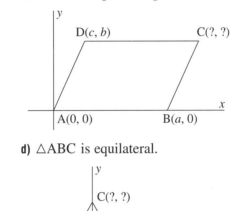

B(0, b)

C(0, 0) A(a, 0)

4. Knowledge/Understanding Use the diagram below left. Prove that the diagonals of a square are perpendicular.

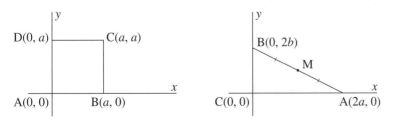

D(0, a) C(a, a)

A(0, 0) B(a, 0)

B(0, $2b$)

M

C(0, 0) A($2a$, 0)

5. Use the diagram at the lower right of the previous page. Prove that the midpoint of the hypotenuse of a right triangle is equidistant from the three vertices.

6. In the diagram at the right, OB = BC and AD = DB. Prove that the area of △DOB is one-quarter the area of △AOC by completing the following steps.

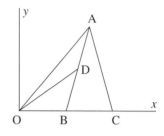

a) Label point C as (2*a*, 0) and point A as (2*b*, 2*c*).

b) Find the coordinates of B and D.

c) Find the areas of △DOB and △AOC and compare results.

7. Point P is any point on the perpendicular bisector of a line segment AB. Prove that PA = PB.

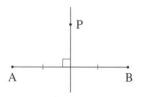

8. In quadrilateral ABCD, AB = DC and AB ∥ DC. Prove that AD = BC and AD ∥ BC.

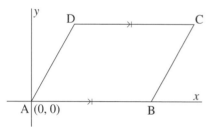

9. Prove that the perpendicular bisector of a chord of a circle passes through the centre of the circle by completing the following steps.

a) Draw a circle with centre at the origin. Draw a horizontal chord AB in the circle, above the *x*-axis.

b) Write expressions for the coordinates of the endpoints of the chord AB.

c) Let M be the midpoint of AB. Write the coordinates of M.

d) Identify the perpendicular bisector of AB.

e) Explain why the perpendicular bisector of AB passes through the centre of the circle.

f) Explain why the proof applies to all chords in all circles.

10. Prove that the diagonals of a parallelogram bisect each other.

11. M and N are the midpoints of the equal sides of an isosceles triangle. Prove that the medians to M and N are equal in length.

12. **Application** Prove that if the diagonals of a parallelogram are equal, then the parallelogram is a rectangle.

13. Prove that any point P(a, b) on the parabola $y^2 = 4px$ is equidistant from the point F(p, 0) and the line $x + p = 0$.

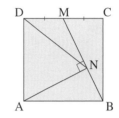

14. The diagonals of a quadrilateral bisect each other at right angles. What kind of quadrilateral is it? Use coordinates to prove your answer.

15. **Thinking/Inquiry/Problem Solving** In the diagram, ABCD is a square. M is the midpoint of DC, and AN ⊥ MB. Prove that DN = DA.

16. In △ABC, ∠B = 90°. A square is drawn on the hypotenuse AC and P is the centre of the square. Prove that ∠PBC = 45°.

C

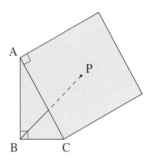

17. In exercise 15, visualize how the diagram changes if side BC moves to the left or the right, forming a rectangle ABCD.

   a) Prove that DN = DA.

   b) Calculate the ratio of the length to the width of the rectangle such that △DAN is equilateral.

4.4 Vector Proofs Using the Addition Law

Vectors provide another powerful method for proving certain geometric properties. Since vectors have both magnitude and direction, a statement that two vectors are equal or are scalar multiples of each other gives *two* facts about the corresponding line segments. Thus vectors are efficient for solving problems in geometry involving parallel line segments.

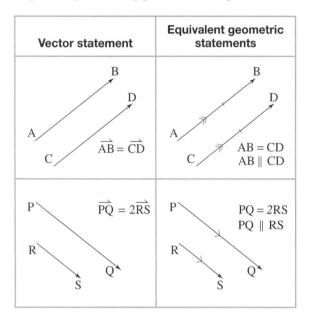

Vector statement	Equivalent geometric statements
$\overrightarrow{AB} = \overrightarrow{CD}$	AB = CD AB ∥ CD
$\overrightarrow{PQ} = 2\overrightarrow{RS}$	PQ = 2RS PQ ∥ RS

Recall that in Section 4.3, page 235, we proved the Side-Splitting Theorem using coordinates. Now we give two different vector proofs of this theorem.

Side-Splitting Theorem

The line segment joining the midpoints of two sides of a triangle is parallel to the third side and one-half as long as the third side.

DE ∥ BC and
DE = $\frac{1}{2}$BC

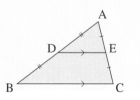

The two statements to be proved are equivalent to the single vector statement $\overrightarrow{DE} = \frac{1}{2}\overrightarrow{BC}$.

Proof using vectors

Consider vector $\overrightarrow{DE}$. To get from D to E, go from D to A to E.

$$\overrightarrow{DE} = \overrightarrow{DA} + \overrightarrow{AE} \qquad \textcircled{1}$$

Alternatively, to get from D to E, go from D to B to C to E.

$$\overrightarrow{DE} = \overrightarrow{DB} + \overrightarrow{BC} + \overrightarrow{CE} \qquad \textcircled{2}$$

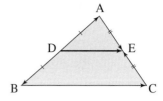

Add ① and ②.

$$2\overrightarrow{DE} = \overrightarrow{DA} + \overrightarrow{AE} + \overrightarrow{DB} + \overrightarrow{BC} + \overrightarrow{CE}$$

$$= (\overrightarrow{DA} + \overrightarrow{DB}) + (\overrightarrow{AE} + \overrightarrow{CE}) + \overrightarrow{BC}$$

$$= \overrightarrow{0} + \overrightarrow{0} + \overrightarrow{BC}$$

$$= \overrightarrow{BC}$$

Hence,

$$\overrightarrow{DE} = \tfrac{1}{2}\overrightarrow{BC}$$

Therefore, $DE = \tfrac{1}{2}BC$ and $DE \parallel BC$.

Something to Think About

- Why do $\overrightarrow{DA} + \overrightarrow{DB}$ and $\overrightarrow{AE} + \overrightarrow{CE}$ equal $\overrightarrow{0}$?
- Notice that we used the law of addition twice—by going from D to A to E in △DAE, and by going from D to B to C to E in quadrilateral DBCE.

Strategy

Look for two different figures where the addition law of vectors can be used twice.

In the above proof, the two figures used were △DAE and quadrilateral DBCE. We can give a different proof using the overlapping triangles, △DAE and △BAC.

Alternate proof

$$\overrightarrow{DE} = \overrightarrow{DA} + \overrightarrow{AE}$$

$$= \tfrac{1}{2}\overrightarrow{BA} + \tfrac{1}{2}\overrightarrow{AC}$$

$$= \tfrac{1}{2}\left(\overrightarrow{BA} + \overrightarrow{AC}\right)$$

$$= \tfrac{1}{2}\overrightarrow{BC}$$

Therefore, $DE = \tfrac{1}{2}BC$ and $DE \parallel BC$.

- Where was the addition law used twice?
- Vector proofs are often relatively short. What is the reason for this?

4.4 Exercises

A

1. In the diagram below, AB = DC and AB ∥ DC. Prove that DA = CB and DA ∥ CB by completing the following steps.

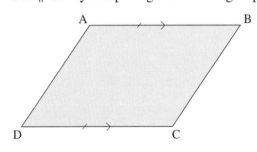

   a) Draw the diagram and join DB.

   b) It is given that AB = DC and AB ∥ DC. Write a single vector statement that is equivalent to these two statements.

   c) Use the triangle law to write two different expressions for the vector $\overrightarrow{DB}$.

   d) From the results of part c, deduce that $\overrightarrow{DA} = \overrightarrow{CB}$.

   e) Explain why DA = CB and DA ∥ CB.

2. In the diagram below, AO = OB and DO = OC.
   Prove that AC = DB and AC ∥ DB.

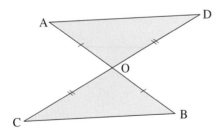

3. In parallelogram ABCD (below left), M and N are the midpoints of AB and DC, respectively. Prove that DM = NB and DM ∥ NB.

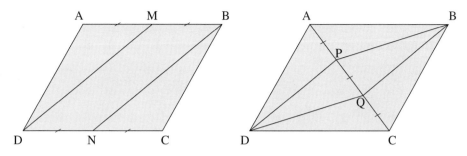

4. **Knowledge/Understanding** In parallelogram ABCD (above right), points P and Q trisect the diagonal AC. Prove that DPBQ is a parallelogram.

5. **Communication** If $\overrightarrow{AB} + \overrightarrow{BD} = \overrightarrow{BC}$, what type of quadrilateral is represented by ABCD? Explain how you know.

6. Use vectors to prove that if the diagonals of a quadrilateral bisect each other, the quadrilateral is a parallelogram.

7. **Application** Prove that the midpoints of the sides of a quadrilateral are the vertices of a parallelogram.

8. In △ABC (below left), points D and F trisect AB and points E and G trisect AC. Prove that:

   a) DE ∥ BC and DE = $\frac{1}{3}$BC

   b) FG ∥ BC and FG = $\frac{2}{3}$BC

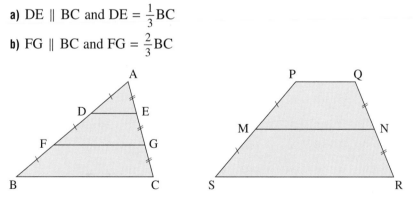

9. In trapezoid PQRS (above right), SR ∥ PQ, and SR = 3PQ. The midpoints of PS and QR are M and N, respectively. Prove that MN ∥ PQ and MN = 2PQ.

10. In the diagram below left, AB ∥ DE, AB = DE, and C is the midpoint of BD. Prove that A, C, and E are collinear, and that AC = CE.

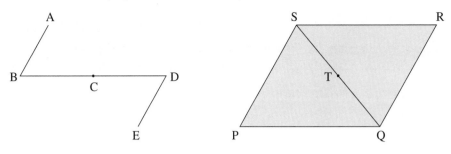

11. In parallelogram PQRS (above right), T is the midpoint of the diagonal QS. Prove that T is also the midpoint of diagonal PR.

12. Thinking/Inquiry/Problem Solving Refer to exercise 9. Suppose everything remains the same, but the condition SR = 3PQ is removed. Find out as much as you can about how segment MN is related to segment PQ. Use vectors to prove your results.

C

13. In a regular hexagon ABCDEF, prove that:

$$3\overrightarrow{AD} = \overrightarrow{AB} + \overrightarrow{AC} + \overrightarrow{AD} + \overrightarrow{AE} + \overrightarrow{AF}$$

There is a difference between conjecture and proof. A *conjecture* is a general statement based on an observed pattern. To *prove* such a statement is to prove it true for all cases, not just those considered when making the conjecture.

One *counterexample* is sufficient to prove a statement false.

Problem solving strategies to apply in proofs:
- Construct an appropriate line or line segment on a diagram.
- Write two expressions for the same thing, then equate them.
- Look for two different figures where the addition law of vectors can be used twice.

Coordinate Proofs

When using coordinate proofs, draw the figure and place coordinate axes strategically.

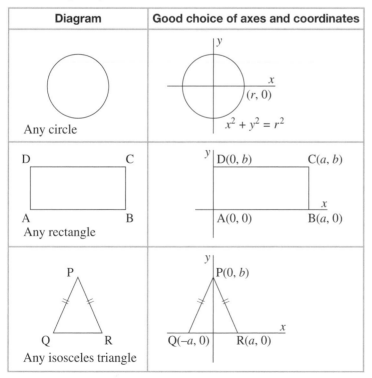

Diagram	Good choice of axes and coordinates
Any circle	$(r, 0)$ $x^2 + y^2 = r^2$
D C / A B Any rectangle	$D(0, b)$ $C(a, b)$ / $A(0, 0)$ $B(a, 0)$
P / Q R Any isosceles triangle	$P(0, b)$ / $Q(-a, 0)$ $R(a, 0)$

> **Vector Proofs**
> - When two vectors are equal, the line segments joining their endpoints are parallel and equal in length.
> - Apply the addition law twice, where possible, to obtain a statement of equality involving vectors.

1. In 1742, German mathematician Christian Goldbach conjectured that every even number greater than 2 is the sum of two prime numbers (for example, $18 = 13 + 5$). No one has been able to prove that this is true for all even numbers, and no one has ever found a counterexample. This problem is known as *Goldbach's Conjecture*. It is a famous unsolved problem in mathematics.

   a) Choose three other even numbers. Verify that each number can be written as the sum of two primes.

   b) To obtain a counterexample, what would you have to find?

2. Make a conjecture about the value of the expression $\sin^2 \theta + \cos^2 \theta$ as θ takes on various values. Prove your conjecture.

3. Find the sum of the shaded angles. State a general result suggested by these diagrams; then prove it.

   a)   b)

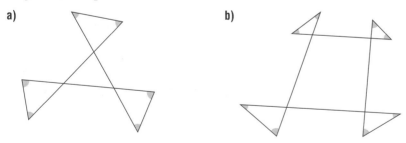

4. Make a conjecture about the product of two consecutive natural numbers. Prove your conjecture.

5. Given 3 points $(k, 3k)$, $\left(\frac{1}{3k}, \frac{1}{k}\right)$, and $(3k, 9k)$ in a plane, investigate this set of points for different values of k. Make a conjecture about the three points. Prove your conjecture.

6. Prove the Pythagorean Theorem.

7. In the diagram at the right, the radius of the circle is x cm. Determine expressions for the side lengths of both equilateral triangles.

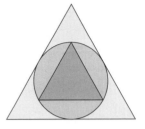

Use coordinate geometry to prove the following:

8. Prove that the perpendicular drawn from the centre of a circle to any chord bisects the chord.

9. In any triangle ABC, if AD is the median from A to BC, prove that:
$$AB^2 + AC^2 = 2BD^2 + 2AD^2$$

10. In the diagram at the right, ABCD is an isosceles trapezoid. DC ∥ AB and AP = QB. Prove that the slopes of the diagonals of the trapezoid are opposites.

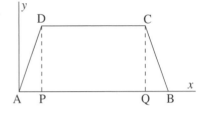

11. In △PQR, A, B, and C are the midpoints of the sides PQ, QR, and PR, respectively. Prove that $\overrightarrow{PB} + \overrightarrow{QC} - \overrightarrow{AR} = \overrightarrow{O}$.

12. Prove that if the diagonals of a quadrilateral bisect each other, then the quadrilateral is a parallelogram.

13. ABCD is a parallelogram. Prove that $\overrightarrow{AB} + \overrightarrow{CB} = \overrightarrow{DB}$.

14. Prove that the median drawn from the vertex of an isosceles triangle to the base is perpendicular to the base.

15. In the quadrilateral ABCD, the midpoints of the sides AB, BC, CD, and DA are P, Q, R, and S, respectively. Prove that PR and QS bisect each other.

16. PQRS is a trapezoid with PQ ∥ RS. Prove that
$$\overrightarrow{PS} + \overrightarrow{RQ} = \overrightarrow{PQ} + \overrightarrow{RS}.$$

1. **Communication** State whether the following statements are true or false. If they are false, give a counterexample.

   a) Two rectangles have the same area. Therefore, they have the same length and width.

   b) If two lines are not parallel, then the two lines will meet in a single point.

   c) If a quadrilateral has four equal sides, then the quadrilateral is a square.

2. Prove that the difference of the squares of any two odd natural numbers is divisible by 4.

3. **Knowledge/Understanding** Prove, using coordinates, that if the midpoints of the sides of a rectangle are joined, the quadrilateral formed is a rhombus.

4. **Application** In the diagram at right, an equilateral triangle and a square have a common base x units long. Determine the percent of the area of the square that is covered by the area of the triangle.

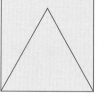

5. In parallelogram ABCD, AB $\parallel$ DC and AD $\parallel$ BC. Prove that:
   $$BD^2 + AC^2 = AD^2 + DC^2 + BC^2 + AB^2$$

6. **Thinking/Inquiry/Problem Solving** In the quadrilateral ABCD shown below, points E, F, G, and H are the midpoints of AB, AC, DC, and DB, respectively. Prove that EFGH is a parallelogram.

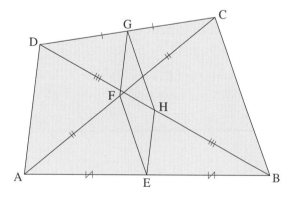

Performance Problems
for Proof

The problems in this section offer you the opportunity to solve some complex problems related to the topics you have studied. Some of these problems are challenging. You may find it helpful to work with others, to share ideas and strategies. You may be unable to complete a solution to some of the problems at the first attempt. Be prepared to research, to return to a problem again and again.

Curriculum Expectations

By the end of this section you will:

- Solve complex problems and present the solutions with clarity and justification.

- Solve problems of significance, working independently, as individuals and in small groups.

- Solve problems requiring effort over extended periods of time.

- Demonstrate significant learning and the effective use of skills in tasks such as solving challenging problems, researching problems, applying mathematics, creating proofs, using technology effectively, and presenting course topics or extensions of course topics.

In ancient Greece, about 440 B.C., Hippocrates of Chios found a way to calculate the areas of certain regions enclosed by circular arcs. These regions are called *lunes*. At that time, it was a very significant discovery that the area of a region bounded by curves could be calculated exactly, and that it could have the same area as a region bounded by straight lines.

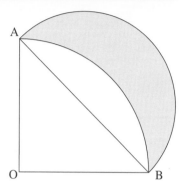

The two problems below are similar to the problems Hippocrates solved. You can use some formulas to find expressions for the areas of certain figures and combine them algebraically to solve the problems. However, there is an easier and more elegant way to solve the second problem that involves little or no calculation. Try to solve this problem both ways.

Problem 1

Right △AOB has legs of length r and a right angle at O. A quarter circle is constructed with centre O and radius r. A semicircle is constructed with diameter AB. Prove that the area of the shaded lune is equal to the area of △AOB.

Problem 2

C is any point on a circle with diameter AB. On sides AC and BC of △ABC, semicircles are drawn outside the triangle. Prove that the total area of the two shaded lunes is equal to the area of △ABC.

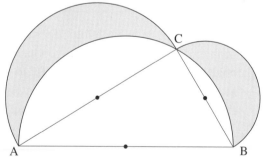

There are several interesting patterns involving the altitude to the hypotenuse in a right triangle. You will discover these patterns in the problems below.

Problem 3

In △ABC, ∠C = 90°. The lengths of AC and CB are 3 units and 4 units, respectively. Calculate the length, h, of the altitude CN.

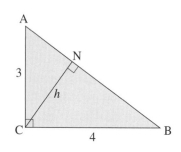

Problem 4

In problem 3, suppose the lengths of BC, CA, and AB are a, b, and c, respectively. Write an expression for h in terms of a, b, and c. Prove that your expression is correct.

Problem 5

Some proofs of the Pythagorean Theorem were given in Section 4.2. You can prove the Pythagorean Theorem yourself using similar triangles.

In the diagram at the right, altitude CN divides $\triangle ABC$ into two right triangles.

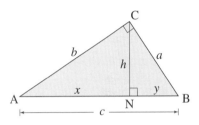

a) Prove that all three right triangles in the diagram are similar.

b) Use the results of part a to prove that:

    i) $a^2 = cy$ **ii)** $b^2 = cx$ **iii)** $h^2 = xy$

c) Prove that $c^2 = a^2 + b^2$.

Problem 6

Suppose C lies on a semicircle with diameter AB = 10 cm. Visualize C moving along the semicircle. As it moves, the lengths of a, b, h, x, and y change.

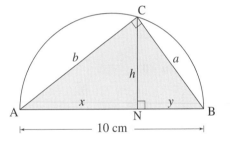

a) Determine the value(s) of x such that the triangle with side lengths a, b, and h is a right triangle.

b) Determine the value(s) of x such that the triangle with side lengths h, x, and y is a right triangle.

c) How do the triangles you found in parts a and b compare with $\triangle ABC$? Explain.

Problem 7

There are six variables on the diagram (top right): a, b, c, h, x, and y. Suppose you know the values of some of these variables. How many values would you need to know so that you could calculate the values of all the other variables? Support your answer with some numerical examples.

Challenge Problem 8

In problem 5b, there are 3 equations relating the variables. Three other equations result from applying the Pythagorean Theorem to the three right triangles. The equation $c = x + y$ is obvious from the diagram, and so is the equation $h = \dfrac{ab}{c}$ from problem 4. Together, these equations form a non-linear system of 8 equations in 6 variables. How many of these equations are independent? What is the least number of equations needed to derive the other equations?

Focus on ... The Pythagorean Diagram

The Pythagorean diagram has many interesting properties.

Problem 9

In the Pythagorean diagram, there are spaces between the squares on the three sides. We can draw a rectangle and two parallelograms to fill in these spaces, as shown. This diagram has many interesting properties.

Prove each property.

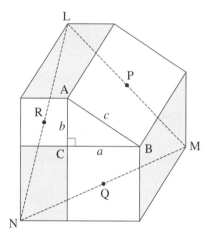

a) The areas of the rectangle and the two parallelograms are all equal.

b) The centres of the squares on the three sides are the midpoints of the sides of $\triangle LMN$.

c) The area of $\triangle LMN$ is $(a + b)^2$.

d) The area of $\triangle LMN$ is never less than 8 times the area of $\triangle ABC$.

Problem 10

Points P, Q, and R are the centres of the squares on the three sides of right $\triangle ABC$.

a) Prove that $PC \perp QR$ and $PC = QR$. The first result proves that PC is an altitude of $\triangle PQR$.

b) Prove that: **i)** $QA \perp RP$ and $QA = RP$

          ii) $RB \perp PQ$ and $RB = PQ$

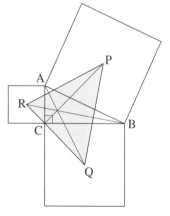

The first part of each result proves that the altitudes of $\triangle PQR$ through Q and R pass through A and B, respectively.

c) Prove that the altitudes of $\triangle PQR$ intersect at the same point.

Problem 11

Use *The Geometer's Sketchpad* to construct the diagram in problem 10. Points A and B must be free to move along vertical and horizontal lines so that $\angle C$ is always 90°. Drag points A and B and observe how $\triangle PQR$ changes.

a) Is it possible for $\triangle PQR$ to be a right triangle? an isosceles triangle? an equilateral triangle? If so, what kind of triangle is $\triangle ABC$, and how are the two triangles related in these situations?

b) Use the Calculate command to calculate the areas of the two triangles, and their ratio. Describe how the area of △PQR compares with the area of △ABC as you drag point A or B.

c) Describe any interesting results that you discovered. Explain why these results have only been illustrated and not proved.

d) Prove one of the results you discovered in part c.

Problem 12

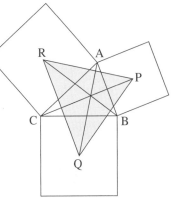

In problem 10, it is not necessary for △ABC to be a right triangle. P, Q, and R are the centres of the squares on the sides of any △ABC. Use *The Geometer's Sketchpad* to construct the diagram at the right. Construct △PQR. Drag point A to different positions on the screen. Find out as much as you can about the two triangles. For example, what happens when △ABC is equilateral? What happens if A, B, and C are collinear? Do the areas of the two triangles compare in the same way as when △ABC is a right triangle? Describe any interesting results you discovered. Prove one of these results.

Problem 13

Squares are constructed on the sides of any quadrilateral ABCD. Points P, Q, R, and S are the centres of the squares.

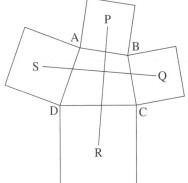

a) Prove that RP ⊥ SQ and RP = SQ. That is, the line segments joining the centres of squares opposite each other are perpendicular and equal in length.

b) Explain why the property of triangles in problem 12 is a special case of the property in part a.

Problem 14

Use *The Geometer's Sketchpad* to construct the diagram in problem 13. Construct quadrilateral PQRS. Drag points A and B to different positions on the screen. Find out as much as you can about the two segments and the two quadrilaterals. For example, what happens when ABCD is a parallelogram? What happens if two or more of the points A, B, C, and D are collinear? Describe any interesting results you discovered. Prove one or more of these results.

Challenge Problem 15

In the previous problems, you discovered several properties of the Pythagorean diagram, or diagrams related to the Pythagorean diagram. Find some other properties like these. Prove any properties you discover.

We can use properties of dot products to prove geometrical results using vectors. These results involve angles or perpendicularity.

- To prove that two line segments are perpendicular, show that a certain dot product equals 0.
- To prove that two angles are equal, work with the dot products of the vectors that form those angles.
- To work with lengths, use the property $\vec{a} \cdot \vec{a} = |\vec{a}|^2$.

Example

$\triangle ABC$ is an isosceles triangle in which $AB = AC$. Prove that the median AM is perpendicular to BC.

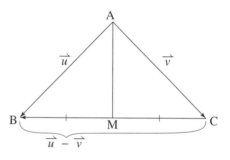

Proof

Let $\vec{u} = \overrightarrow{AB}$ and $\vec{v} = \overrightarrow{AC}$.

Since $|\vec{u}| = |\vec{v}|$, then $\vec{u} \cdot \vec{u} = \vec{v} \cdot \vec{v}$

$$\overrightarrow{CB} = \vec{u} - \vec{v}$$

$$\begin{aligned} \overrightarrow{AM} &= \overrightarrow{AC} + \overrightarrow{CM} \\ &= \vec{v} + 0.5(\vec{u} - \vec{v}) \\ &= 0.5(\vec{u} + \vec{v}) \end{aligned}$$

$$\begin{aligned} \overrightarrow{AM} \cdot \overrightarrow{CB} &= 0.5(\vec{u} + \vec{v}) \cdot (\vec{u} - \vec{v}) \\ &= 0.5(\vec{u} \cdot \vec{u} - \vec{v} \cdot \vec{v}) \\ &= 0 \end{aligned}$$

Therefore, the median AM is perpendicular to BC.

Notice the strategy that was used in the example.

- Represent two sides with vectors $\vec{u}$ and $\vec{v}$.
- Express other side(s) in terms of $\vec{u}$ and $\vec{v}$.
- Combine the expressions algebraically in an appropriate way to solve the problem, making sure to use the given information.

Give vector proofs for the next three problems.

Emilie du Châtelet (1706–1749)
Born: Paris, France

Du Châtelet was provided with a good education and excelled in languages. However, her true passion was mathematics. She developed a close friendship with Voltaire and the two devoted much time studying the work of Leibniz and Newton. Her major work was a translation of Newton's *Principia* into French.
Du Châtelet was very active in the social life of the French court, and throughout her life maintained her position in Paris society.

Problem 16

Prove the Semicircle Theorem.

Problem 17

△ABC is an isosceles triangle in which M is the midpoint of BC. Prove that M lies on the bisector of ∠A.

Problem 18

Prove the *Isosceles Triangle Theorem*: In an isosceles triangle, the angles opposite the equal sides are equal.

Other Problems

Problem 19

△ABC is an isosceles triangle in which AB = AC. Points D and E are the midpoints of sides AB and AC, respectively. Prove that the medians BD and CE are equal in length.

Problem 20

Prove that the sum of the squares of the diagonals of a parallelogram equals the sum of the squares of its sides.

Problem 21

Prove that the midpoint of the hypotenuse of a right triangle is equidistant from the three vertices.

Problem 22

Points P, Q, R, and S are the midpoints of the sides of square ABCD. Prove that the area of the shaded square is one-fifth the area of square ABCD.

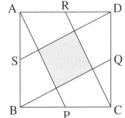

Problem 23

There are three different ways to draw two overlapping congruent right triangles standing on a common side. Which of the three shaded triangles has the greatest area?

 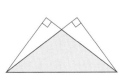 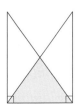

Problem 24

In △AOB (below left), H is the point of intersection of the altitudes from A and B. Let $\vec{a} = \overrightarrow{OA}$, $\vec{b} = \overrightarrow{OB}$, and $\vec{h} = \overrightarrow{OH}$.

a) Prove that $\vec{a} \cdot (\vec{b} - \vec{h}) = 0$.

b) Prove that $\vec{b} \cdot (\vec{a} - \vec{h}) = 0$

c) Using the results of parts a and b, prove that $\vec{h} \cdot (\vec{b} - \vec{a}) = 0$. Explain the geometrical significance of the result.

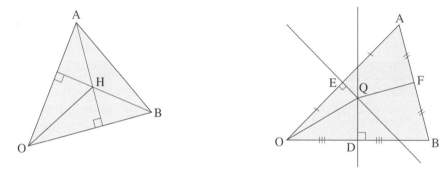

Challenge Problem 25

In △AOB (above right), Q is the point of intersection of the perpendicular bisectors of OA and OB. Let $\vec{a} = \overrightarrow{OA}$, $\vec{b} = \overrightarrow{OB}$, and $\vec{q} = \overrightarrow{OQ}$.

a) Prove that $\vec{a} \cdot \left(\vec{q} - \frac{1}{2}\vec{a} \right) = 0$.

b) Prove that $\vec{b} \cdot \left(\vec{q} - \frac{1}{2}\vec{b} \right) = 0$.

c) Let F be the midpoint of AB. Using the results of parts a and b, prove that QF is perpendicular to AB. Explain the geometrical significance of this result.

Challenge Problem 26

Vectors $\vec{a}$ and $\vec{b}$ are drawn tail-to-tail. Vector $\vec{c}$ is the reflection of $\vec{a}$ in the line containing vector $\vec{b}$. Express $\vec{c}$ as a linear combination of $\vec{a}$ and $\vec{b}$.

Deductive Reasoning

Curriculum Expectations

By the end of this chapter, you will:

- Demonstrate an understanding of the principles of deductive proof.
- Prove some properties of plane figures, using deduction.
- Prove some properties of plane figures, using indirect methods.
- Generate multiple solutions to the same problem.
- Solve problems by effectively combining a variety of problem-solving strategies.

In Chapter 4, we used a variety of methods to prove some properties of plane figures.

Angle Sum Theorem In Section 4.1, we used rotations to prove that the sum of the angles in a triangle is 180°. We also proved this theorem using the alternate-angle property of parallel lines.

Pythagorean Theorem In Section 4.2, we proved the Pythagorean Theorem by forming a square from four right triangles and the square on the hypotenuse. We also used similar triangles to prove that $a^2 + b^2 = c^2$, where a, b, and c are the lengths of the sides of a right triangle.

Side-Splitting Theorem In Section 4.3, we used coordinate geometry to prove that the line segment joining the midpoints of two sides of a triangle is parallel to the third side and half as long as that side. We gave an alternate proof of this theorem using vectors in Section 4.4.

These results were proved using *deductive reasoning*. In each case, we began with statements or properties that we accepted as true, and through logical reasoning, arrived at a conclusion. If we apply the principles of deductive reasoning correctly, we can be certain the conclusions we draw are true.

It is customary to reserve the term *deductive proof* for a method of proof developed by Euclid and other Greek mathematicians over 2000 years ago. This method involves starting with a set of basic assumptions, called *axioms*, and logically proving conclusions from them. Any of the conclusions reached can then be used to prove other results. Conclusions that are most useful for proving further results are called *theorems*. The theorems are arranged in a logical sequence where the proof of each one depends on theorems already proved.

Some examples of axioms are listed at the right. Other axioms involve congruent triangles.

Some Axioms

An axiom is considered so obvious that it is accepted as being true without being proved.

- Things that are equal to the same thing are equal to each other.
- If equals are added to equals, the sums are equal.
- Only one line can be drawn through two distinct points.
- There is only one line that bisects a given angle.
- Two distinct lines that intersect do so in exactly one point.

SSS Congruence Axiom

If three sides of one triangle are equal to three sides of another triangle, then the triangles are congruent.

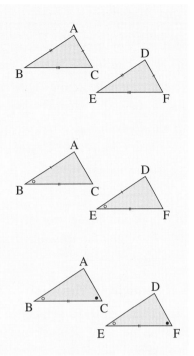

SAS Congruence Axiom

If two sides and the contained angle of one triangle are equal to two sides and the contained angle of another triangle, then the triangles are congruent.

ASA Congruence Axiom

If two angles and the contained side of one triangle are equal to two angles and the contained side of another triangle, then the triangles are congruent.

We can use deductive reasoning to prove an important theorem about isosceles triangles.

Isosceles Triangle Theorem

In an isosceles triangle, the angles opposite the equal sides are equal.

If AB = AC, then ∠B = ∠C.

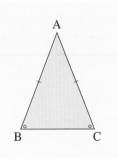

Proof using congruent triangles

In the diagram at the right, △ABC represents any isosceles triangle in which AB = AC. We must prove that ∠B = ∠C.

Draw a line through A which bisects ∠A and meets BC at D.

We are given that AB = AC. Since AD is a common side, and ∠BAD = ∠CAD, we can conclude that △BAD ≅ △CAD by SAS. It follows that ∠B = ∠C since these are corresponding angles of the congruent triangles.

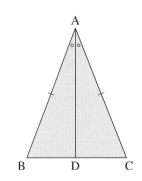

- Notice that the strategy of drawing a line segment is the key to proving the theorem this way. This line segment is the bisector of ∠A.
- Could we have proved the theorem by constructing the altitude from A to BC instead of the angle bisector? Explain.
- Could we have proved the theorem by constructing the median from A to BC instead of the angle bisector? Explain.
- What does "congruent" mean? What does the symbol ≅ mean?

In Chapter 4, we used both coordinate geometry and vectors to prove the Semicircle Theorem. We can use the Isosceles Triangle Theorem to give a third proof of the Semicircle Theorem.

Deductive proof of Semicircle Theorem

Construct a circle with centre O. Draw a diameter AB. Mark any point P on the circle. Join AP and PB. We must prove that ∠APB = 90°.

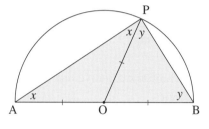

Join OP. Since OA and OP are radii of the circle, they have the same length. Hence, △OAP is isosceles. By the Isosceles Triangle Theorem, ∠OAP = ∠OPA. Let x degrees represent the measures of these angles. Similarly, △OBP is isosceles and ∠OBP = △OPB. Let y degrees represent the measures of these angles.

By the Angle Sum Theorem, the sum of the angles in △ABP is 180°. Hence,

$$x + y + (x + y) = 180°$$
$$2x + 2y = 180°$$
$$x + y = 90°$$

From the diagram, ∠APB = $x + y$
Therefore, ∠APB = 90°

It can be difficult to construct a set of axioms and prove geometric theorems from them in a logical sequence using deductive reasoning. Ideally, the number of axioms should be kept to a minimum. This means that considerable effort would be required to prove conclusions that may appear to be obvious. We will not attempt to do this in this book.

A

1. Explain the difference between an axiom and a theorem.

2. AB and CD are chords of equal length in a circle with centre O (below left).
   Prove that $\angle AOB = \angle COD$.

3. In the diagram (above right), $\angle B = \angle E$ and BC = EC. Prove that AB = DE
   and $\angle A = \angle D$.

4. a) If one of the angles in an isosceles triangle is 60°, what are the measures
   of the two other angles? Give a clearly worded and convincing explanation
   of your answer.

   b) In general, if one of the angles in an isosceles triangle is $x°$, what are the
   other two angles?

5. **Knowledge/Understanding** Use the Isosceles Triangle Theorem to prove
   that an equilateral triangle is equiangular.

B

6. Explain the difference between inductive reasoning and deductive reasoning.
   How are they similar? How are they different?

7. The SAS congruence axiom requires that the angle be contained by the
   two sides. Draw a diagram of two triangles to show why SSA is not a
   congruence axiom.

8. One special case of SSA occurs when the angle is a right angle. Explain
   why the following theorem is true.

   Hypotenuse-Side Theorem
   If the hypotenuse and one other side of a right triangle are equal to the
   hypotenuse and one side of another right triangle, then the triangles are
   congruent.

9. **Communication** In addition to axioms, definitions are another important part of deductive geometry. Defined terms can be explained using previously defined terms. For example, consider the definition of a rectangle.

A *rectangle* is a parallelogram with four right angles. This contains the word "parallelogram".

A *parallelogram* is a quadrilateral with both pairs of opposite sides parallel. This contains the word "quadrilateral".

Some Undefined Terms

- Point
- Line
- Angle
- Figure

A *quadrilateral* is a four-sided polygon. This contains the word "polygon".

A *polygon* is a closed figure formed from three or more line segments. This contains the word "figure".

A *figure* is …

point   line

Some words express notions so fundamental that they cannot be defined using other terms. Some examples are: point, line, angle, and figure. Although we can draw diagrams to show what they mean, we do not attempt to define them. They are undefined terms.

angle   figure

a) Decide which of the following words should be defined. If you think the word should be defined, give a definition.

degree	triangle	vertex
octagon	parallel	perpendicular
radius	plane	number

b) Find at least three geometric words that were used in Chapter 4, but which were not defined. Give definitions of these words.

10. In △ABC (below left), AB = AC. D is a point on BC such that AD bisects ∠BAC. Prove that AD is perpendicular to BC.

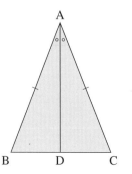

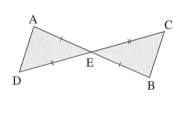

11. In the diagram (above right), point E bisects both AB and CD. Prove that ∠A = ∠B.

12. In the diagram (below left), P is on the bisectors of both ∠AMN and ∠MNC. Prove that ∠P = 90°.

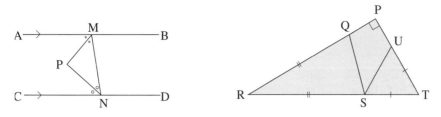

13. In the diagram (above right), RQ = RS and TU = TS. Prove that ∠QSU = 45°.

14. In the diagram (below left), AB = AC and AB ∥ DE. Prove that BC bisects ∠ACE.

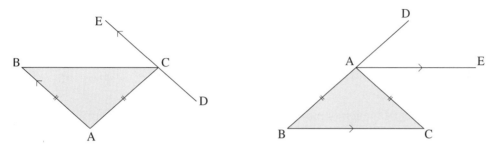

15. In the diagram (above right), AB = AC and AE ∥ BC. Prove that AE bisects ∠CAD.

16. In the diagram (below left), AB = DE and ∠ABC = ∠DEC. Prove that AE = DB.

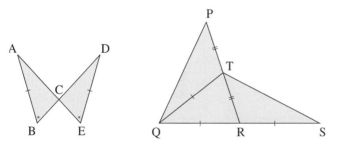

17. In the diagram (above right), R is the midpoint of QS, T is the midpoint of PR, and QT = QR. Prove that ∠PTQ = ∠TRS and PQ = TS.

18. The quadrilateral (top left of the following page) is sometimes called a *kite*. Observe that a kite has two distinct pairs of congruent, adjacent sides. Prove these properties of a kite:

a) One pair of opposite angles is equal.

b) One diagonal bisects the angles through which it passes.

c) The diagonals intersect at right angles.

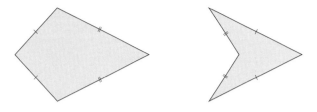

19. The quadrilateral (above right) is sometimes called a *dart*. Like a kite, a dart has two distinct pairs of congruent, adjacent sides. However, in a dart, one of the interior angles is greater than 180°.

   a) Do the properties in exercise 18 hold for a dart?

   b) Do your proofs in exercise 18 apply to a dart? If your answer is yes, explain. If your answer is no, make the necessary changes.

20. **Thinking/Inquiry/Problem Solving** In the diagram at the right, BC is a diameter of a circle with centre O. Point A is on the circle. OD and OE bisect chords AB and AC. Prove that OD is perpendicular to OE.

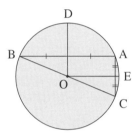

21. Prove that the midpoint of the hypotenuse of a right triangle is equidistant from the three vertices.

22. **Application** Many puzzles involve deductive reasoning. Solve the three puzzles below. Explain your solutions.

   a) One card below has a one-digit number on one side and a geometric figure on the other side. Which cards should you pick up and turn over to find out if every card with an even number on one side has a square on the other side?

   b) All the labels on the boxes at the right are incorrect. You may select only one fruit from each box. How can you relabel the boxes correctly?

   c) You are marooned on an island, where there are only liars and truth-tellers. You meet a couple and the husband says, "My wife told me that she is a liar." Is he a liar or a truth-teller?

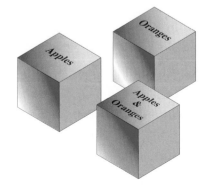

The proofs we have written so far have all been direct proofs. In a direct proof, we begin with a statement we accept as true, and make one deduction after another until we reach the desired conclusion. Sometimes it is difficult or impossible to prove directly that a result is true. In such cases, we may be able to prove the result using an *indirect proof.*

For example, consider the following statement and its proof.

Statement: A triangle cannot have two obtuse angles.

Proof

Either a triangle cannot have two obtuse angles, or it can have two obtuse angles.

Suppose $\triangle ABC$ has two obtuse angles.

Since an obtuse angle is greater than $90°$, the sum of the two obtuse angles is greater than $180°$. Hence, the sum of the three angles in the triangle is greater than $180°$. This is impossible because the Angle Sum Theorem states that the sum of the angles in a triangle is $180°$.

Therefore, a triangle cannot have two obtuse angles.

Notice how we proved the statement. We assumed it was not true, and we reached a conclusion that contradicts a known fact. This means that our assumption that the statement is not true is incorrect. The only logical possibility is that the statement is true.

> **Maria Agnesi (1718–1799)**
> Born: Milan, Italy
>
> Born to a wealthy and literate family, Agnesi received an enriched education. She was encouraged to participate in philosophical and mathematical discussions with the distinguished intellectual guests at her home. At age nine, Agnesi delivered a discourse in defence of higher education for women to an academic gathering.
> Agnesi's greatest contribution to mathematics was a text of differential and integral calculus. In it, she discusses a cubic curve now known as the "Witch of Agnesi." Inspired by her work, a Canadian has composed an instrumental work of the same name.

An indirect proof has 4 steps:

Step 1. Begin the proof with the statement we are trying to prove and the opposite statement.

Step 2. Assume that the statement that we are required to prove is false, and that the opposite statement is true.

Step 3. Show that this assumption leads to a contradiction.

Step 4. Since there is a contradiction, the assumption in Step 2 must be false. Therefore, we can conclude that the statement to be proved is true.

In Grade 11, you learned that a tangent to a circle is a line that intersects the circle in only one point. This point is called the *point of tangency*.

The following theorem states an important property of tangents to a circle. We can prove this theorem using an indirect proof.

Tangent-Radius Theorem

A tangent to a circle is perpendicular to the radius at the point of tangency.

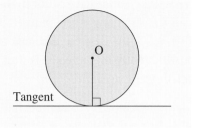

Tangent

Proof

Suppose that line *l* is a tangent to a circle at A.

Either *l* is perpendicular to OA or *l* is not perpendicular to OA.

Assume that *l* is not perpendicular to OA.

Then there must be some other point, B, on *l* such that *l* is perpendicular to OB.

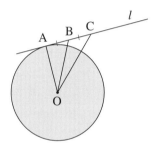

Let C be a point on *l* so that CB = BA, where C is on the opposite side of B from A.

In △OBC and △OBA, OB is a common side.

$$\angle OBC = \angle OBA$$
$$= 90°$$
$$CB = BA$$

Therefore, △OBC ≅ △OBA by SAS.
Since the triangles are congruent OC = OA.
Since OA is a radius, OC must also be a radius. Hence, C lies on the circle.

For both A and C to lie on the circle, *l* must intersect the circle at two points. This is impossible because *l* is a tangent to the circle.

The assumption that *l* is not perpendicular to OA must be false. Therefore, *l* is perpendicular to OA.

A very significant proof involves the number $\sqrt{2}$. In ancient Greece, Pythagoras and his followers thought that all numbers could be expressed as fractions in the form $\frac{m}{n}$ where *m* and *n* are natural numbers. They also knew that the length of the diagonal of the unit square is $\sqrt{2}$. But they were able to prove that $\sqrt{2}$ cannot be expressed in the form $\frac{m}{n}$. The Pythagoreans were perplexed by this development because it seemed to be counterintuitive to them. They did not know about irrational numbers, yet they proved that $\sqrt{2}$ is not a rational number.

Student Reference

Rational and Irrational numbers

Theorem

$\sqrt{2}$ is an irrational number.

Proof

Either $\sqrt{2}$ is rational or it is irrational.

Assume that $\sqrt{2}$ is a rational number.

Then there are natural numbers m and n such that $\sqrt{2} = \frac{m}{n}$.

Square both sides:

$$(\sqrt{2})^2 = \left(\frac{m}{n}\right)^2$$

$$2 = \frac{m^2}{n^2}$$

$$2n^2 = m^2$$

Since a perfect square has an even number of prime factors, m^2 has an even number of prime factors and $2n^2$ has an odd number of prime factors. Therefore, this equation is impossible. The assumption that $\sqrt{2}$ is a rational number is incorrect. Therefore, $\sqrt{2}$ is irrational.

Something to Think About

- Is it possible for the lengths of all sides of a right triangle to be natural numbers?
- Why does a perfect square contain an even number of prime factors?

5.2) Exercises

A

1. For each statement, write the first two steps of an indirect proof.

   a) △ABC and △DEF are not congruent.

   b) A line segment has only one right bisector.

   c) In an isosceles triangle, the angles opposite the congruent sides are congruent.

   d) A line segment has only one midpoint.

   e) If two lines intersect, then the opposite angles are congruent.

   f) AB = CD

2. State which of the following pairs of statements form a contradiction.

   a) Lines l_1 and l_2 are parallel.
      Lines l_1 and l_2 do not intersect.

   b) $l_1 \perp l_2$
      l_1 and l_2 are not perpendicular.

   c) $\angle A = \angle B$
      $\angle A > \angle B$

   d) $\angle A$ and $\angle B$ are congruent
      $\angle A$ and $\angle B$ are supplementary

   e) $\angle A$ and $\angle B$ are obtuse angles
      $\angle A$ and $\angle B$ are supplementary

   f) $\triangle ABC$ is isosceles
      $\triangle ABC$ is equilateral

3. In $\triangle PQR$ at the right, $\angle Q = 50°$ and $\angle R = 60°$. Use the method of indirect proof to explain why $PQ \neq PR$.

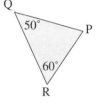

4. Use indirect proof to prove that a triangle cannot have two right angles.

B

5. Communication The outline of an indirect proof is given below. Copy the proof in your notebook and complete it. Justify all statements in the proof.

In the diagram at the right, lines l_1 and l_2 are perpendicular to the same line m. Prove that $l_1 \parallel l_2$.

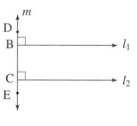

Proof

Either _____.

Suppose that l_1 is not parallel to l_2.

Since l_1 is not parallel to l_2, they intersect at some point A. Let B and C be the points of intersection of l_1 and l_2 respectively with m.

$\angle ABD =$ _____

$\angle ACB =$ _____

$\angle ABD = \angle$_____ $+ \angle$_____

$\angle ABD > 90°$

But, _____.

Therefore, _____.

Hence, _____.

Use indirect proof in the following exercises.

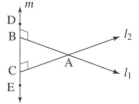

6. A line l and a point P not on the line are given at the right. Prove that it is impossible for two different lines through P to be perpendicular to l.

7. **Knowledge/Understanding** In $\triangle PQR$, $\angle P > 40°$ and $\angle Q = 2\angle P$. Prove that $\triangle PQR$ cannot be an isosceles triangle.

8. In $\triangle ABC$, AM is the median from A to BC, and $\angle AMC = 60°$. Prove that $AB \neq AC$.

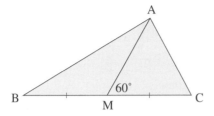

9. In $\triangle PQR$, PS is the altitude from P to QR, and $QS \neq RS$. Prove that $PQ \neq PR$.

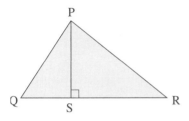

10. Prove that the bisector of any angle in a scalene triangle cannot be perpendicular to the opposite side.

11. **Thinking/Inquiry/Problem Solving** Prove that if two angles in a triangle are equal, then the sides opposite those angles are equal.

12. Prove that it is impossible for a scalene triangle to have two equal angles.

13. Prove that each number is irrational.

   a) $\sqrt{3}$ b) $2\sqrt{2}$ c) $\sqrt{2} + 1$

14. **Application** The ages of Anjanee, Blair, and Concetta are three consecutive numbers. Only *one* of the following statements is true.

   • Blair is 2 years older than Anjanee.
   • Blair is 1 year older than Concetta.
   • Anjanee is 1 year older than Concetta.
   • Concetta is 1 year younger than Anjanee.

   Prove than Anjanee is the oldest of the three. Justify your reasoning.

C

15. Prove that two lines perpendicular to the same plane do not intersect.

Consider the following statement:
If a quadrilateral is a square, then it has 4 right angles.

In mathematics, we frequently make statements that are in *"if... then..."* form. In an *"if... then..."* statement, the "if" part is called the *hypothesis* and the "then" part is called the *conclusion*.

When we interchange the hypothesis and conclusion of an *"if... then..."* statement, we obtain a new statement called the *converse*.

Statement

If a quadrilateral is a square, then it has 4 right angles.

Converse

If a quadrilateral has 4 right angles, then it is a square.

The converse of a true statement may or may not be true. In this case, the converse is not true because a rectangle has 4 right angles, but it is not necessarily a square. Therefore, a rectangle is a counterexample proving that the converse statement above is false.

On page 261, we proved that if a triangle has two equal sides, then it has two equal angles. In exercise 5 on page 276, you will prove that the converse is true. When a statement and its converse are both true, we can combine them into a single statement using the words *"... if and only if ..."*, or *"iff"* for short.

Statement

If a triangle has two equal sides, then it has two equal angles.

Converse

If a triangle has two equal angles, then it has two equal sides.

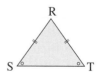

Combined statement

A triangle has two equal angles if and only if it has two equal sides.

In Section 4.2, we proved the Pythagorean Theorem. The converse of this theorem is also true.

Converse of Pythagorean Theorem

In $\triangle ABC$, if $c^2 = a^2 + b^2$ then $\angle C = 90°$.

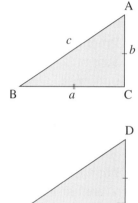

Proof using congruent triangles

Construct $\triangle DEF$ such that $\angle F = 90°$, $DF = AC$, and $EF = BC$.

Apply the Pythagorean Theorem to $\triangle DEF$:

$$DE^2 = DF^2 + EF^2$$
$$= AC^2 + BC^2$$
$$= AB^2$$

Therefore, $DE = AB$.

Since the three sides of $\triangle ABC$ are equal to the corresponding three sides of $\triangle DEF$, $\triangle ABC \cong \triangle DEF$. It follows that $\angle F = \angle C$ since these are corresponding angles of the congruent triangles.

Therefore, $\angle C = 90°$.

Something to Think About

- How could the Pythagorean Theorem be written using the words "… if and only if …"?

In an earlier grade, you discovered that if a transversal intersects two parallel lines, then the alternate angles are equal. Conversely, if a transversal intersects two lines, and the alternate angles are equal, then the lines are parallel. These statements form the basis for the following theorem.

Alternate-Angles Theorem

Suppose a transversal intersects two lines l_1 and l_2. The lines are parallel if and only if the alternate angles are equal.

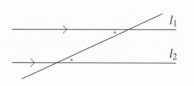

We can prove the Alternate-Angles Theorem using an indirect proof. In the proof, we make use of the Exterior Angle Theorem. You proved this theorem in exercise 10 on page 225. We also make use of the axiom that for any given line l and a point P not on l, there exists in the plane of l and P, exactly one line through P parallel to l. This is *Playfair's axiom*.

Proof of Alternate-Angles Theorem

Draw lines l_1 and l_2. Draw transversal t that intersects l_1 at A and l_2 at B. The alternate interior angles are $\angle 1$ and $\angle 2$.

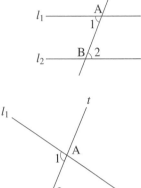

We must show that $l_1 \parallel l_2$ if and only if $\angle 1 = \angle 2$. Since this involves a statement and its converse, we must prove two things.

1. **Proof that if $\angle 1 = \angle 2$, then $l_1 \parallel l_2$**

   Suppose $\angle 1 = \angle 2$.
   Either $l_1 \parallel l_2$, or l_1 is not parallel to l_2.
   Suppose that l_1 is not parallel to l_2, and that, therefore, l_1 and l_2 meet at some point P.
   Consider $\triangle ABP$. By the Exterior Angle Theorem, $\angle 1 = \angle 2 + \angle P$. Hence, $\angle 1 > \angle 2$.
   But this contradicts the given information that $\angle 1 = \angle 2$.
   Therefore, the assumption that l_1 is not parallel to l_2 is incorrect. Hence, $l_1 \parallel l_2$.

2. **Proof that if $l_1 \parallel l_2$, then $\angle 1 = \angle 2$**

   Suppose $l_1 \parallel l_2$.
   Either $\angle 1 = \angle 2$ or $\angle 1 \neq \angle 2$.
   Assume that $\angle 1 \neq \angle 2$.
   Construct line m, through A, such that $\angle 3 = \angle 2$. Then, according to the first proof, $m \parallel l_2$.
   Since $l_1 \parallel l_2$, we have two different lines through A that are parallel to l_2.
   This contradicts Playfair's axiom.
   Therefore, the assumption that $\angle 1 \neq \angle 2$ is incorrect.
   Hence, $\angle 1 = \angle 2$.

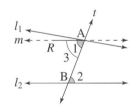

Something to Think About

- In the first proof, we assumed that l_1 and l_2 meet on the right side of the transversal. Should the proof include the case where they meet on the left side of the transversal?

A theorem that follows directly from another theorem, and is deducible from that theorem is called a *corollary*. The following theorem is a corollary of the Alternate-Angles Theorem. The proof is left to the exercises.

Corresponding-Angles Theorem

A transversal intersects two lines l_1 and l_2. The lines are parallel if and only if the corresponding angles are equal.

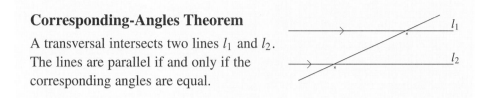

5.3) Exercises

A

1. Write each statement in "*if… then…*" form. State the hypothesis and conclusion of each statement.

   a) A triangle is equilateral if it is mapped onto itself under a rotation of 120°.

   b) Vertically opposite angles are congruent.

   c) An equilateral triangle has three equal sides.

   d) A right triangle has exactly one 90° angle.

   e) The longest side of a triangle is opposite to the largest angle.

   f) Every square is a rectangle.

   g) If a point lies on the perpendicular bisector of a line segment, then it is equidistant from the ends of that line segment.

   h) If an angle is opposite to the longest side of a triangle, then it is the largest angle in the triangle.

   i) If two triangles are congruent, then they have the same area.

2. Write the converse of each statement in exercise 1. Decide whether the converse is true. If it is not true, provide a counterexample.

3. **Communication** Rewrite each "if … then" statement in exercise 1 that has a true converse in exercise 2 as an "… if and only if …" statement.

B

4. **Knowledge/Understanding** Write an example of each of the following.

   a) A true statement that has a false converse.

   b) A true statement that has a true converse.

   c) A false statement that has a true converse.

   d) A false statement that has a false converse.

5. Prove the converse of the Isosceles Triangle Theorem.

6. The perpendicular bisector of a line segment is the line that is perpendicular to the line segment and passes through its midpoint.

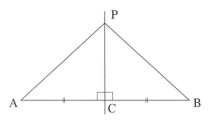

a) Prove that any point P on the perpendicular bisector of line segment AB is equidistant from the endpoints A and B.

b) State and prove the converse of the statement in part a.

7. If you construct the perpendicular bisectors of the sides of any triangle, you will find that they intersect at a common point. We say that they are *concurrent*. The point of intersection of the perpendicular bisectors of the sides of a triangle is called the *circumcentre*, O, of the triangle.

a) Prove that the perpendicular bisectors of the sides of any △ABC are concurrent.

b) Prove that a circle with centre O can be drawn passing through the vertices of the triangle. This circle is called the *circumcircle*. Its centre is called the *circumcentre*.

8. Thinking/Inquiry/Problem Solving

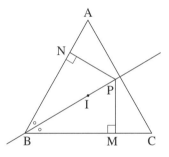

a) Prove that any point P on the bisector of any ∠ABC is equidistant from the arms AB and AC.

b) State and prove the converse of the statement in part a.

c) Prove that the bisectors of the angles of any △ABC are concurrent. The point of intersection is called the *incentre*, I.

d) Prove that a circle with centre I can be drawn passing through the points where the altitudes intersect the sides of the triangle. This circle is called the *incircle*.

9. Prove the Corresponding-Angles Theorem.

10. Application Prove that the diagonals of a parallelogram are perpendicular if and only if the parallelogram is a rhombus.

11. Prove that a triangle has three equal altitudes if and only if the triangle is equilateral.

12. Prove the converse of the Semicircle Theorem.

13. Prove the converse of the Side-Splitting Theorem.

14. Prove the converse of the Tangent-Radius Theorem.

15. In their work with logic, the ancient Greeks encountered some strange paradoxes such as this one: *This sentence is false.*

Is this sentence true or is it false? Suppose it is true. Then by what it says, it must be false. Suppose it is false. Then what it says is false, so it must be true!

Here are some other paradoxes like this one:

a) Is the third sentence true or is it false?
   1. This book has 1000 pages.
   2. This page is in Chapter 2.
   3. Sentences 1, 2, and 3 are all false.

b) Are these sentences true or are they false?
   1. Sentence 2 is true.
   2. Sentence 1 is false.

c) In a booklet of test questions, a page was found that contained only the sentence below. Is the page blank?
This page is intentionally left blank.

**Kurt Gödel
(1906–1978)**
Born: Brno,
Czech Republic

Until the 20th century, mathematicians considered paradoxes like these to be merely riddles. However, in 1931 Gödel used a similar paradox to prove that mathematics contains "undecidable" statements that can never be proved. Hence, there may be true statements that can never be proved. Gödel proved a theorem something like the following:
This theorem cannot be proved.

5.4 Generating Multiple Solutions

Karl Friedrich Gauss (1777–1855) was one of the greatest mathematicians of all time. At age 24, he published a treatise on the theory of numbers that contained three different proofs of an important theorem that had baffled other mathematicians. Gauss later gave five other proofs of the same theorem. In so doing, he proved, in eight different ways, a theorem that other mathematicians had been unable to prove even once.

Problems in mathematics can frequently be solved in different ways. If you can give more than one solution to a problem, you will enhance your problem solving skills and gain a deeper insight into the nature of mathematics. Since you obviously expect to get the same result if you solve a problem in more than one way, you will also appreciate that mathematics is consistent. This means that it is impossible to prove that something is true and also to prove that it is not true.

In Chapter 4, we often gave more than one proof of a theorem. In Section 5.1, we gave only one proof of the Isosceles Triangle Theorem. Here are two other proofs of this theorem. In each diagram, △ABC represents any triangle in which AB = AC. We must prove that ∠B = ∠C.

Proof using congruent triangles

Draw the median from A to the midpoint, M, of BC. Thus, BM = CM. Since we are given that AB = AC, and AM is a common side, we can conclude that △ABM ≅ △ACM by SSS.

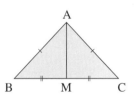

It follows that ∠B = ∠C since these are corresponding angles of the congruent triangles.

Proof using symmetry

Draw a line *l* which bisects ∠A and intersects BC at D. Then *l* is a line of symmetry, and everything on one side of *l* has a corresponding congruent part on the other side of *l*. Therefore, ∠B = ∠C.

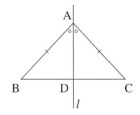

A

1. Mentally determine each answer in two different ways.

   a) $3 \times 6 + 3 \times 4$ **b)** $20(12 + 10)$

   c) $5 \times 4 \times 2$ **d)** $\frac{1}{2} \times \frac{2}{3} \times \frac{3}{4}$

2. Solve this problem in as many different ways as you can.

   Certain candies come in packages of 4. Two people purchased 12 packages for treats during a 4-day car trip. If the candies are shared equally, how many does each person get each day?

3. **Communication** Any triangle is congruent to itself. Explain how this observation can be used to prove the Isosceles Triangle Theorem.

B

4. **Knowledge/Understanding** Prove, in two different ways, that the midpoints of adjacent sides of a rectangle are the vertices of a rhombus (below left).

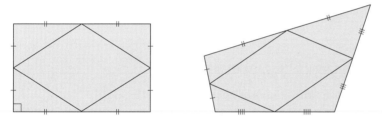

5. The midpoints of the adjacent sides of a quadrilateral are the vertices of a parallelogram (above right). You used vectors to prove this result in exercise 7 on page 245. Give two other proofs of this result.

6. The largest square in this diagram has side length s. Write expressions for the side length and the area of each smaller square. Solve this problem in two ways.

7. A parallelogram is a quadrilateral in which both pairs of opposite sides are parallel. Prove the following properties of a parallelogram in as many different ways as you can.

   a) The opposite sides of a parallelogram are equal in length.

   b) The opposite angles of a parallelogram are equal.

   c) The diagonals of a parallelogram bisect each other.

8. The diagrams show two rectangles ABCD. In the first, there is a point P on DC such that ∠APB = 90°. On the second, there is no such point P. Determine how to tell, for any given rectangle ABCD, if there is a point P on DC such that ∠APB = 90°.

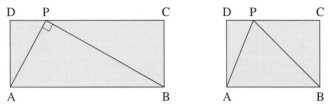

In exercises 9 and 10, solve each problem in two ways.

9. Triangle ABC and △DBC are isosceles triangles with the same base BC (below left). Prove that ∠ABD = ∠ACD.

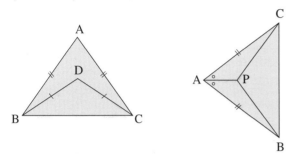

10. In the diagram (above right), prove that △PBC is isosceles.

11. In exercise 5 on page 276, you proved the converse of the Isosceles Triangle Theorem. Prove the converse in a different way.

12. In exercise 6 on page 276, you proved the converse of the Semicircle Theorem. Prove the converse in a different way.

13. **Thinking/Inquiry/Problem Solving** Solve this problem in two ways.

On the Pythagorean diagram, a new triangle is constructed whose sides are formed by the diagonals of the squares. Prove that the new triangle is a right triangle.

14. **Application** In the puzzle below, 78 flowers are enclosed in a 13 by 6 rectangle. The rectangle is cut apart along the solid lines and the pieces rearranged. Only 77 flowers remain!

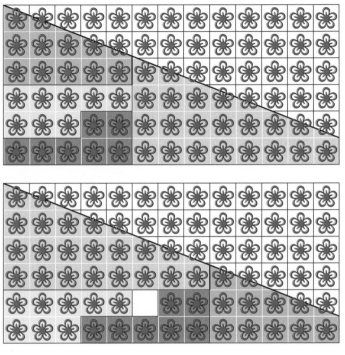

   a) Explain, in two different ways, why there is a space instead of a flower in the second diagram.

   b) What happened to the other flower?

C

15. The length of chord AB (below left) is equal to the radius of the circle. P is any point on the major arc AB. Prove that $\angle P = 30°$.

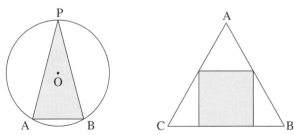

16. Triangle ABC is an equilateral triangle with sides 6 cm (above right). Calculate the area of the coloured square.

17. Recall that three or more lines that intersect at a common point are called *concurrent*. Certain lines or line segments associated with a triangle are significant because they are concurrent. For example, the altitudes all intersect at a point called the *orthocentre*. You can prove this in different ways.

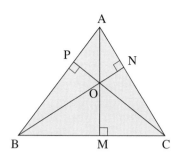

AM, BN, and CP are the altitudes of any △ABC. Three different proofs that the altitudes are congruent are outlined below. Complete each proof.

A proof using coordinates

Introduce a system of coordinates such that BC is on the *x*-axis and AM lies along the *y*-axis.

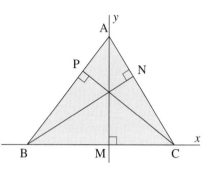

a) Let BN be the altitude from B to AC. Determine the equation of the line BN. What is the *y*-intercept of this line?

b) Let CP be the altitude from C to AB. Determine the *y*-intercept of this line.

c) Compare the *y*-intercepts in parts a and b, and complete the proof that the altitudes of △ABC are concurrent.

A proof using properties of a circle

Let the altitudes BN and CP intersect at H. Join AH, and extend to meet BC at M. Prove that AM is perpendicular to BC by following these steps.

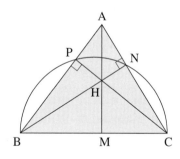

a) Explain why B, P, N, and C lie on a semicircle. Use some circle properties to write some equal angles.

b) Prove that A, P, H, and N lie on a circle.

c) Complete the proof that the altitudes of △ABC are concurrent.

A proof using perpendicular bisectors

Through each vertex of △ABC draw a line parallel to the opposite side. This creates △PQR as shown.

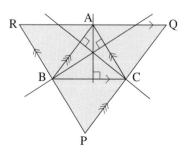

a) How are the perpendicular bisectors of the sides of △PQR related to the altitudes of △ABC?

b) Complete the proof that the altitudes are concurrent.

5.5) Posing and Solving Problems

George Polya, a former professor of mathematics at Stanford University, gained worldwide recognition for his skills as a teacher. In the quotation at the right, Polya is suggesting that when we have solved a problem we may think of related problems. These may often be obtained by generalizing some condition of the problem, or changing some part of the problem to make a new problem.

> "(No) problem whatever is completely exhausted. There remains always something to do ..."
> *George Polya*

For example, consider the Semicircle Theorem. If a complete circle is drawn with diameter AB, then we notice that ∠APB is constant as P rotates around the circle (except when P is at A or B). We might ask what happens if AB is a chord of the circle and not a diameter. If we draw a diagram with P in different positions, we will find that when P is on one side of AB, ∠APB appears constant and less than 90˚. When P is on the other side of AB, ∠APB appears constant and is greater than 90˚.

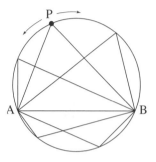

We say inscribed angle ∠APB is subtended by chord AB.

A chord that is not a diameter divides a circle into two arcs. The longer arc is called the *major arc*, and the smaller one is called the *minor arc*.

Angles in a Circle Theorem

Inscribed angles on the same side of a chord AB of a circle are equal.

If P is on major arc AB, ∠APB = ∠ARB. ∠APB, ∠ARB < 90˚

If Q is on minor arc AB, ∠AQB = ∠ASB. ∠AQB, ∠ASB > 90˚

Conversely, if A, B, C, and D are four points such that C and D are on the same side of AB and ∠ACB = ∠ADB, then A, C, D, and B lie on a circle. They are *concyclic*.

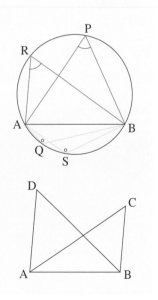

We can prove this theorem deductively as follows.

Proof using isosceles triangles

Construct a circle with centre O. Mark any points A and B on the circle that are not endpoints of a diameter.

Case 1: P on major arc AB

Mark point P on the major arc AB. Join AP and PB. First prove that ∠APB is constant for all positions of P on the major arc.

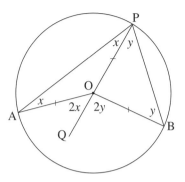

Join AO and OB. Join PO and extend to point Q. Then △OAP and △OBP are isosceles. By the Isosceles Triangle Theorem, the angles opposite the equal sides in these triangles are equal. Let x and y represent the measures of these angles. Since ∠APB = $x + y$, we must prove that $x + y$ is constant.

By the Exterior Angle Theorem, ∠AOQ = $2x$ and ∠QOB = $2y$. Therefore,

$$2x + 2y = \angle AOQ + \angle QOB$$
$$2x + 2y = \angle AOB$$
$$x + y = \frac{1}{2}\angle AOB$$
$$\angle APB = \frac{1}{2}\angle AOB$$

Since ∠AOB is constant for all positions of P on major arc AB, ∠APB is constant. Further, since ∠AOB < 180°, ∠APB < 90°.

Case 2: P on minor arc AB

The proof of this case and the converse is left to the exercises.

Observe that inscribed angle ∠APB is one-half of the central angle ∠AOB subtended by chord AB.

Something to Think About

- Why is ∠AOB constant for all positions of P on major arc AB?
- Does the proof in Case 1 above apply to all positions of P on major arc AB? Explain.
- How does the proof of the Angles in a Circle Theorem compare with the proof of the Semicircle Theorem on page 262?

The above example shows how we can sometimes create a new result by changing some condition of a theorem or a problem we have already proved. We have done this before. For example, in exercise 7 on page 225 we extended the Angle-Sum Theorem to polygons.

A square piece of cardboard has sides 10 cm. Four isosceles triangles are cut off from the corners to form a regular octagon.

a) Calculate the side lengths of the regular octagon.

b) Create three other problems that are suggested by this one.

Solution

a) Define x as shown in the diagram.
Using the Pythagorean Theorem, $CE = \sqrt{2}x$.
Since the octagon is a regular octagon, $BC = \sqrt{2}x$.

$$AB + BC + CD = 10$$
$$x + \sqrt{2}x + x = 10$$
$$x = \frac{10}{2 + \sqrt{2}}$$

Therefore, $CE = \sqrt{2}x$

$$= \frac{10\sqrt{2}}{2 + \sqrt{2}}$$
$$\doteq 4.14$$

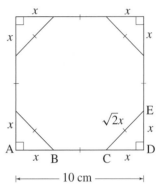

The side lengths of the regular octagon are approximately 4.14 cm.

b) *Problem 1*

Generalize the problem for any size of square. The answer expresses the length of the sides of the octagon as a function of the length of the sides of the square.
Suppose the sides of the square are s cm. Determine an expression for the side lengths of the regular octagon.

Problem 2

Ask a question about areas instead of lengths.
What percent of the cardboard is wasted to make the octagon?

Problem 3

Ask a similar question about a different figure.
A piece of cardboard in the shape of an equilateral triangle has sides 10 cm. Three equilateral triangles are cut off to form a regular hexagon. Calculate the side lengths of the regular hexagon.

The solutions of the problems created in the *Example* are left to the exercises.

B

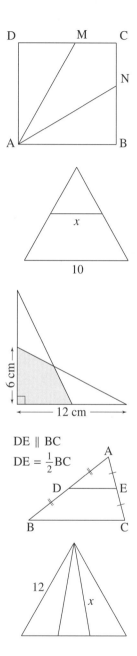

1. Solve the three problems in the *Example* on page 285.

2. Recall the following exercise from Section 4.2.

   ABCD is a square with sides 6 cm. If AM and AN divide the square into three regions with equal areas, find the lengths of AM and AN.

   Create two other problems that are suggested by this one. Then solve each problem.

3. **Knowledge/Understanding** An equilateral triangle with sides 10 cm is divided into two regions by a line segment parallel to one of the sides.

   a) If the regions have equal areas, determine the length of the line segment.

   b) Create two other problems that are suggested by this one. Then solve each problem.

4. A card 12 cm long and 6 cm wide is cut along a diagonal to form two congruent triangles. The triangles are arranged as shown.

   a) Find the area of the region where the triangles overlap.

   b) Without changing the dimensions of the card, create another problem that is suggested by this one. Then solve the problem.

5. Recall the Side-Splitting Theorem from Section 4.3.

   Create another problem suggested by this theorem. Then solve the problem.

6. **Thinking/Inquiry/Problem Solving** An equilateral triangle has sides 12 cm. It is divided into three triangles of equal area by two line segments passing through one of the vertices. Determine the lengths of these lines.

7. Create two other problems suggested by exercise 6. Then solve each problem.

8. **Application** In *Something to Think About* on page 284, you should have noted that the proof of the Angles in a Circle Theorem does not apply for all positions of P on major arc AB. It applies only when O is in the interior of ∠APB. If not, the diagram is different from the one on page 284.

a) Draw a diagram similar to the one on page 284 with P located so that O is not in the interior of ∠APB.

b) Prove the Angles in a Circle Theorem in this case.

9. Prove Case 2 of the Angles in a Circle Theorem.

10. Communication A and B are any two points on a circle. P and Q are points on the two arcs of the circle determined by A and B. According to the Angles in a Circle Theorem, ∠APB and ∠AQB are both constants.

What problem does this situation suggest? Solve the problem.

11. Quadrilateral PQRS is inscribed in a circle (below left). Side PQ is parallel to side SR. The diagonals intersect at T. Prove that △TSR and △TPQ are isosceles.

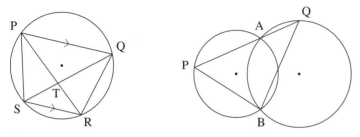

12. Two circles intersect at A and B (above right). A line is drawn through A to intersect the circles at P and Q.

a) Prove that for all possible positions of line PAQ, ∠PBQ is constant.

b) What special case occurs when the radii of the circles are equal? Explain why it occurs.

c) What special case occurs when each circle passes through the centre of the other circle? Explain why it occurs.

13. Prove the converse of the Angles in a Circle Theorem.

C

14. Equilateral triangles are constructed on the sides of any △ABC, as shown at the right. Prove that the segments AD, BE, and CF all have the same length.

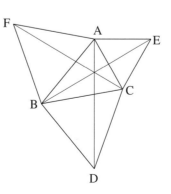

15. Create a problem suggested by exercise 14. Solve the problem.

Note for exercise 14

The Pythagorean Theorem relates squares on the sides of a right triangle. A wide variety of related problems can be created by starting with figures other than a right triangle and constructing figures on their sides. In this case, we have equilateral triangles on the sides of any triangle.

A *deductive proof* derives a result by logical reasoning from axioms accepted as true.

An *indirect proof* shows that if a result to be proved is assumed false, then this must lead to a contradiction.

The *converse of a statement* written as *"if p, then q"* is the statement *"if q, then p."*

1. An isosceles triangle has two equal sides. Prove that the median to the third side is also the altitude.

2. Two concentric circles are drawn with centre O. OPQ and OMN are straight line segments as illustrated in the diagram (below left). Prove that PQ = MN.

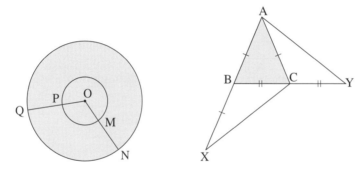

3. Triangle ABC is isosceles with AB = AC. AB is extended its own length to X, and BC is extended its own length to Y as shown in the diagram (above right). Prove that XC = AY.

4. The perpendicular bisector PQ is drawn to a given line segment AB with point Q on AB. PQ is extended an equal distance on the other side of line AB. Prove that the figure formed by joining the ends of the line segments is a rhombus.

5. In the diagram at the right, PA bisects ∠P, and BC is the perpendicular bisector of PA. Prove that AB ∥ RP.

6. If n is an integer such that n^2 is even, prove that n is even.

7. Prove that each number is irrrational.

    a) $\sqrt{5}$ **b)** $\sqrt{10}$

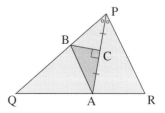

8. In $\triangle ABC$, P is a point on BC such that $BP \neq PC$ and PA bisects $\angle A$. Prove that $AB \neq AC$.

9. Suppose a transversal intersects two lines l_1 and l_2. Use an indirect method to prove the following statement. If the corresponding angles are equal then l_1 and l_2 are parallel.

10. State the converse of each statement. Also determine whether each statement and its converse is true, or false. Explain your reasoning but do not provide a detailed proof.

a) If a right triangle has a 30° angle, then it also has a 60° angle.

b) If a line intersects a plane in a single point, then the line is perpendicular to the plane.

c) If $\overrightarrow{a} \cdot (\overrightarrow{b} \times \overrightarrow{c}) = 0$, then the three vectors are coplanar.

d) If a number is a multiple of 6, then it is a multiple of 3.

e) If the sum of the lengths of two line segments is greater than the length of a third line segment, then a triangle can be formed from the three line segments.

11. Prove the following statement:
Two exterior angles of a triangle are equal if and only if the triangle is isosceles.

12. In quadrilateral PQRS, PQ = QR and the diagonal QS bisects $\angle Q$. Prove that PS = RS.

13. Line segments AB and CD bisect each other at M. Prove that AC = BD.

14. Create a problem suggested by exercise 13.

15. Prove that if two altitudes of a triangle are congruent, then the triangle is isosceles.

16. Use the method of indirect proof. If m and n are integers and their product mn is odd, prove that both m and n are odd.

17. Prove that if a radius of a circle bisects a chord, then it is perpendicular to the chord.

18. State, then prove the converse of exercise 17.

1. In $\triangle ABC$, P and Q are the respective midpoints of AB and AC. Suppose PQ is extended to R so that $PQ = QR$. Prove that $RC \parallel AB$.

2. **Communication** Some people might say that the ASA Congruence Axiom should be called the ASA or AAS Congruence Axiom.

   a) Explain why two triangles are congruent if two angles and a non-contained side of one triangle are equal to two angles and a non-contained side of another triangle.

   b) Do you agree that the axiom should be renamed? Explain.

3. The line segment AB intersects CD so as to bisect CD and $DB > AC$. Prove that BD is not parallel to AC.

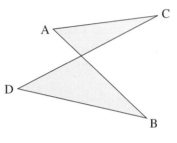

4. **Knowledge/Understanding** State the converse of each statement. Decide if the converse is true. If it is not true, provide a counterexample. If it is true, write the statement using "… if and only if …".

   a) If two triangles are congruent, then the corresponding angles are congruent.

   b) If a triangle has one obtuse angle, then the other two angles must be acute.

   c) If the diagonals of a parallelogram are perpendicular, then the paralellogram is a rhombus.

5. **Thinking/Inquiry/Problem Solving** Prove in two different ways that the diagonals of a rectangle are congruent.

6. **Application** A storeowner claims that an expensive radio has been stolen from her store. She is convinced that Anna, Bina, Carlos, or Djarat has stolen the radio. Each person made a statement, but only one of the four statements was true.

   Anna said, "I didn't take it."
   Bina said, "Anna is lying."
   Carlos said, "Bina is lying."
   Djarat said, "Bina took it."

   Who told the truth? Who took the radio? Write a proof to justify your choice.

7. Prove that a quadrilaterial is a parallelogram if and only if its diagonals bisect each other.

8. Prove that the number $\sqrt{2} + \sqrt{5}$ is irrational.

Performance Problems
for Deductive Reasoning

The problems in this section offer you the opportunity to solve some complex problems related to the topics you have studied. Some of these problems are challenging. You may find it helpful to work with others, to share ideas and strategies. You may be unable to complete a solution to some of the problems at the first attempt. Be prepared to research, to return to a problem again and again.

Curriculum Expectations

By the end of this section you will:

- Solve complex problems and present the solutions with clarity and justification.
- Solve problems of significance, working independently, as individuals and in small groups.
- Solve problems requiring effort over extended periods of time.

- Demonstrate significant learning and the effective use of skills in tasks such as solving challenging problems, researching problems, applying mathematics, creating proofs, using technology effectively, and presenting course topics or extensions of course topics.

Focus on ... Cyclic Quadrilaterals

A quadrilateral whose vertices lie on a circle
is called a *cyclic quadrilateral*.

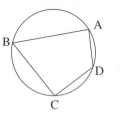

Problem 1

Prove the *Cyclic Quadrilateral Theorem*: The opposite angles of a
cyclic quadrilateral are supplementary. That is, in the diagram at the
right, prove that $\angle A + \angle C = 180°$ and $\angle B + \angle D = 180°$.

Problem 2

Opposite sides of cyclic quadrilateral ABCD are extended to meet
at E. Prove that $\triangle EAD \sim \triangle ECB$.

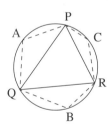

Problem 3

PQRS is a cyclic quadrilateral in which PQ = PS and RQ = RS.

a) Draw a diagram of this quadrilateral.

b) Prove that $\triangle PQR$ and $\triangle PSR$ are right triangles.

Problem 4

In the diagram, $\triangle PQR$ is inscribed in a circle. A, B, and C are any
three points on the three arcs determined by the sides of $\triangle PQR$.
Prove that $\angle A + \angle B + \angle C = 360°$.

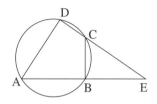

Problem 5

Prove a similar result to the one in problem 4 for a cyclic quadrilateral.

Problem 6

Prove the converse of the Cyclic Quadrilateral Theorem: If the opposite angles
of a quadrilateral are supplementary, then the quadrilateral is cyclic.

Problem 7

From a point, P, outside a circle, two tangents can be drawn. The line segments joining P to the points of contact are called *tangent segments*. Prove the *Equal Tangents Theorem*: The tangent segments from an external point to a circle are equal in length.

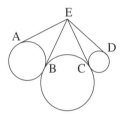

Problem 8

In the diagram, the four segments with endpoint E are tangent segments. Prove that ABCD is a cyclic quadrilateral.

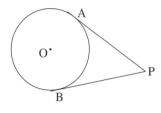

Problem 9

Tangents PS and PT intersect a circle at S and T. Points A and B lie on segments PS and PT, respectively, such that AB is a tangent to the circle at U. Prove that the perimeter of △PAB is equal to 2PS.

In the diagram, according to the Tangent-Radius Theorem, ∠PTC = 90°. According to the Semicircle Theorem, ∠A = 90°. Therefore, ∠PTC = ∠A. Suppose P moves along the circle to Q as shown on the second diagram. Both ∠QTC and ∠A are less than 90°, and it is reasonable to expect that they are equal. You will prove this in the next problem.

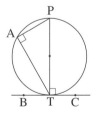

Problem 10

Prove the *Tangent-Chord Theorem*: The angle between a tangent to a circle and a chord of the circle is equal to the inscribed angle on the opposite side of the chord. That is, ∠QTC = ∠A.

Problem 11

A line is tangent to a circle at B. Points A and C are on the line on opposite sides of B. A chord MN is parallel to the tangent.

a) Draw a diagram to illustrate this situation.

b) Prove that △MBN is isosceles.

Problem 12

AB and AC are two equal chords in a circle. PA and PB are tangent segments to the circle.

a) Draw a diagram to illustrate this situation.

b) Prove that ∠APB = ∠BAC.

Challenge Problem 13

One leg of a right triangle is a diameter of a circle. Prove that the tangent at the point of intersection of the circle and the hypotenuse bisects the other leg of the triangle.

Sun-Yung Alice Chang (1948–)
Born: Ci-an, China

Born in China and raised in Taiwan, Chang received her undergraduate degree from the National Taiwan University in 1970. She earned a doctorate in mathematics at the University of California, Berkeley. Since then, Chang has taught at several institutions in the USA and is now a professor at UCLA. Chang's research interests include problems in geometric analysis. She has received numerous honours and awards for her outstanding contribution to mathematics research. A champion of women's rights, Chang would like to see more women join her profession.

Focus on ... The Nine-Point Circle

There are 9 significant points associated with a triangle that always lie on a circle. These points are:

- the midpoints of the sides: D, E, F
- the feet of the altitudes: P, Q, R
- the midpoints of the segments joining the orthocentre, H, to the three vertices: X, Y, Z

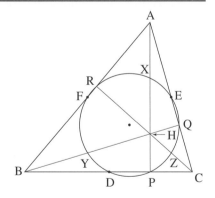

Problem 14

a) Prove that quadrilaterals FEZY and DEXY are rectangles.

b) Explain why the result of part a proves that D, E, F, X, Y, and Z all lie on the same circle.

c) Why do the points P, Q, and R also lie on this circle?

d) Complete a proof that D, E, F, P, Q, R, X, Y, and Z lie on a circle. This circle is called the *nine-point circle* of the triangle.

Challenge Problem 15

Prove that the centre of the nine-point circle of any triangle is the midpoint of the line segment joining the orthocentre, H, and the circumcentre, O.

Twenty-three centuries ago, Euclid posed this problem. "What are the dimensions of a rectangle with the property that when you divide it into a square and a rectangle, the smaller rectangle has the same shape as the original rectangle?"

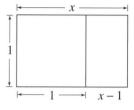

For the two rectangles in the diagram to have the same shape, their length:width ratios must be equal.

$$\frac{x}{1} = \frac{1}{x-1}$$

This equation reduces to $x^2 - x - 1 = 0$. The positive root is $x = \frac{1 + \sqrt{5}}{2}$, or $x \doteq 1.618033989...$. This number is called the *golden ratio*, and it is often represented by the Greek letter ϕ (phi). A rectangle whose length:width ratio is ϕ is called a *golden rectangle*. Both rectangles in the diagram are golden rectangles.

The golden ratio occurs in a wide variety of problems (including problem 6 on page 253).

Problem 16

Square ABCD with sides 2 units long is constructed in a semicircle with radius r and diameter PQ.

a) Determine the radius of the circle.

b) Show that rectangle ABQR is a golden rectangle.

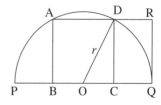

Problem 17

The diameter AB of a circle is extended to a point P outside the circle. The tangent segment PT has length equal to the diameter AB. Prove that B divides AP in the golden ratio.

Problem 18

ABCDE is a regular pentagon with sides of length 1. Diagonals AD and BE intersect at F. Let x represent the lengths of the diagonals.

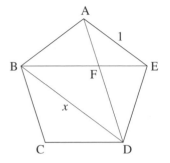

a) Prove that $\triangle AEF \sim \triangle DBF$.

b) Prove that the ratio of the length of a diagonal to the length of a side is the golden ratio.

c) Prove that the diagonals intersect each other in the golden ratio.

Problem 19

Use the results of problem 19. Prove that $\cos 36° = \dfrac{\sqrt{5}+1}{4}$.

Problem 20

T is any point on a circle with centre O, and P is a point on the tangent at T such that PT = 2OT. With centre P, a second circle is drawn tangent to the given circle to intersect PT at N.

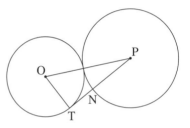

a) Prove that N divides PT in the golden ratio.

b) Use the result of part a to construct a regular pentagon with one side PN using only a ruler and compass.

Challenge Problem 21

In $\triangle ABC$, the ratio of the sides is AB:BC:CA = 3:4:5. The bisector of $\angle A$ intersects BC at O. A circle with centre O and radius OB intersects AO at P and Q. Prove that P divides QA in the golden ratio.

Focus on ... Prime Numbers

The proof that $\sqrt{2}$ is irrational in Section 5.2 is a famous proof in the history of mathematics. Another famous proof is Euclid's proof that there are an infinite number of prime numbers. The proof uses the indirect method, and goes like this.

Assume that the number of primes is finite. Therefore, there must be a prime, p, which is the largest prime. Multiply all the primes together, and add 1. This forms the following number.

$$n = (2 \times 3 \times 5 \times 7 \times \ldots \times p) + 1 \qquad ①$$

Now n cannot be a prime number because it is greater than p, which we assumed is the largest prime. So n must be a composite number. Hence:

n is divisible by some prime number ②

According to ①, n is not divisible by any prime number. This contradicts statement ②. This means that the assumption that the number of primes is finite is not correct. Therefore, there are an infinite number of prime numbers.

Problem 22

About 200 years ago, German mathematician Lejeune Dirichlet proved the following theorem.

> *Dirichlet's Theorem:* Let a and d be any two natural numbers with no common factor. Then the infinite arithmetic sequence $a, a + d, a + 2d,$ $a + 3d, \ldots$ contains infinitely many prime numbers.

Use this result to prove that there are infinitely many prime numbers whose final digits are 1, 3, 7, and 9.

Other Problems

Problem 23

Quadrilateral PQRS is inscribed in a circle and PQ ∥ RS. Diagonals RP and SQ intersect at T.

a) Draw a diagram to illustrate this situation.

b) Prove that △TRS and △TPQ are isosceles.

Problem 24

Opposite sides of cyclic quadrilateral ABCD are extended to meet at E (see diagram at right). Prove that △EAC ∼ △EDB.

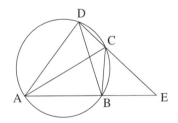

Problem 25

Two tangents are drawn from an external point P to points A and B on a circle with centre O. Prove that PAOB is a cyclic quadrilateral.

Problem 26

PM is a tangent segment to a circle with centre O. Segment OP intersects the circle at N. If MO = MN, prove that N bisects OP.

Problem 27

State and prove the converse of the result in problem 27.

Problem 28

Two parallel lines are tangent to a circle with centre O. Another tangent to the circle intersects these lines at Q and S. Prove that $\triangle$OQS is a right triangle.

Problem 29

Prove that the area of any $\triangle$ABC is given by the formula $A = rs$, where r is the radius of the inscribed circle, and s is the semi-perimeter, $s = \frac{1}{2}(a + b + c)$.

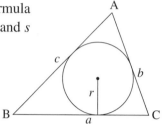

Problem 30

In problem 20, it is not necessary for P to lie on the line containing the diameter. In the diagram, the tangent PT and the chord AB have equal lengths. Prove that B divides AP in the golden ratio.

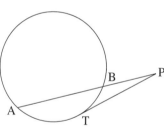

Challenge Problem 31

Give an example of two triangles, $\triangle$ABC and $\triangle$PQR, in which the three angles of $\triangle$ABC are equal to the three angles of $\triangle$PQR, and two sides of $\triangle$ABC are equal to two sides of $\triangle$PQR, but $\triangle$ABC and $\triangle$PQR are not congruent.

Challenge Problem 32

Quadrilateral ABCD is cyclic, with perpendicular diagonals AC and BD intersecting at E. Point M is the midpoint of CD. Prove that the line through M and E is perpendicular to AB.

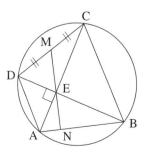

Challenge Problem 33

In △ABC, the bisectors of ∠B and ∠C meet AC and AB at M and N respectively. If segments BM and CN have the same length, prove that △ABC is isosceles.

Challenge Problem 34

In this problem there are two challenges. The first is to obtain an equation in r. The second is to solve the equation, but you can do that using technology.

In a semicircle, three connected chords have lengths 1, 2, and 3 respectively. Find the radius of the semicircle.

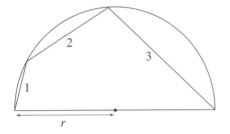

Challenge Problem 35

This problem looks simple, and it can be solved in many different ways. However, one mathematician noted that "the number of blind alleys the problem leads to is extraordinary."

The diagram contains three squares. Prove that $x + y = z$.

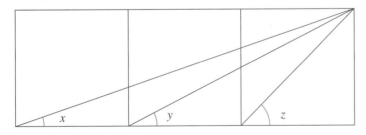

DISCRETE MATHEMATICS

**Performance Problems for
Discrete Mathematics**

Curriculum Expectations

By the end of this chapter, you will:

- Solve problems, using the additive and multiplicative counting principles.

- Evaluate expressions involving factorial notation, using appropriate methods.

- Express the answers to permutation and combination problems, using standard combinatorial symbols.

- Solve problems involving permutations and combinations, including problems that require the consideration of cases.

- Explain solutions to counting problems with clarity and precision.

6.1 The Fundamental Counting Principle

We are constantly confronted with making choices. In doing so, it is often useful to know the possibilities available to us. When the number of possibilities is small, we can list them all and count them one by one. We must list the possibilities systematically to avoid leaving out a possibility or listing one twice.

Suppose a cafeteria has a lunch special consisting of an egg or ham sandwich (E or H) with milk, juice, or coffee (M, J, or C).

We can determine the number of lunch specials by making a systematic list.

EM	EJ	EC
HM	HJ	HC

Alternatively, we can draw a *tree diagram*. Starting from a point, we draw 2 line segments, one for each choice of sandwich. From each of these segments, we draw 3 more line segments, one for each choice of beverage.

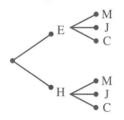

From the list and tree diagram, we see that there are 6 possible lunch specials we could order.

The tree diagram suggests a method for counting the number of possible lunch specials without listing each one. When we order a lunch special, we have two separate actions to take.

Choose a sandwich   **Choose a beverage**
2 choices   3 choices

For *each* choice of sandwich, there are 3 choices for a beverage. Thus, there are $2 \times 3 = 6$ possible lunch specials.

The preceding example illustrates a general principle of counting called the *Fundamental Counting Principle*. This principle is also known as the Multiplication Principle.

> Tree diagrams and lists are only useful when the number of possibilities is small. In this chapter, we will learn how to count possibilities without individually listing each one.

The Fundamental Counting Principle

If an action can be done in m ways and for each way, a second action can be done in n ways, then the two actions can be performed, in that order, in mn ways.

The Fundamental Counting Principle can be extended to situations involving more than 2 actions.

Example 1

A store sells 6 different computers, 4 different monitors, 5 different printers, and 3 different multimedia packages. How many different computer systems are available?

Solution

To order a computer system, 4 separate actions must be taken.

Choose a computer	**Choose a monitor**	**Choose a printer**	**Choose a multimedia package**
6 choices	4 choices	5 choices	3 choices

Use the Fundamental Counting Principle.
$6 \times 4 \times 5 \times 3 = 360$
There are 360 computer systems available.

Something to Think About

- In calculating the number of computer systems available, why are the numbers multiplied instead of added?

Example 1 illustrates a generalization of the Fundamental Counting Principle. To find the number of ways a series of successive actions can be performed, multiply the number of ways each action can be made.

Ada Lovelace (1815–1852)
Born: London, England

Lovelace, the daughter of poet Lord Byron, was destined to be a mathematician and scientist. Lovelace collaborated in the development of a calculating machine, called the Analytical Engine. She predicted that such a machine would be able to compose music, produce graphics, and would have practical and scientific application. Lovelace described a plan for how the Analytical Engine could generate a series of numbers, which is now regarded as the first computer program. The US Department of Defense named a software language "Ada" in her honour.

Example 2

A Canadian postal code consists of 6 characters. The first, third, and fifth characters are letters. The remaining characters are numbers. How many postal codes are possible?

Solution

Draw 6 boxes, one to represent each character in a postal code.

There are 26 possible choices for a letter (A–Z), and 10 possible choices for a number (0–9). Write the number of choices in each box.

L	N	L	N	L	N
26	10	26	10	26	10

Use the Fundamental Counting Principle.
$26 \times 10 \times 26 \times 10 \times 26 \times 10 = 17\ 576\ 000$

There are 17 576 000 possible choices for a postal code.

Sometimes there are restrictions on the choices we can make. In such cases, deal with the restrictions first.

Example 3

A president, secretary, and treasurer are to be chosen from among four people: Asha, Bill, Curt, and Dena. No person can hold more than one office, and the treasurer must be a woman.

a) Determine the number of ways the offices can be filled.

b) Draw a tree diagram to verify the answer to part a.

Solution

a) Draw 3 boxes to represent the position of president, secretary, and treasurer. Since there is a restriction on the choice of treasurer, consider this position first.

If the treasurer must be a woman, either Asha or Dena must be chosen. Thus, there are 2 choices for the treasurer.

Now consider the choices for president. Anyone can be chosen except for the person chosen as treasurer. Thus, there are 3 choices for the president.

Finally, consider the choices for secretary. Anyone can be chosen except for the two already chosen as treasurer and president. Thus, there are 2 choices for secretary.

T	P	S
2	3	2

Use the Fundamental Counting Principle.
$2 \times 3 \times 2 = 12$

There are 12 ways the positions can be filled.

b)

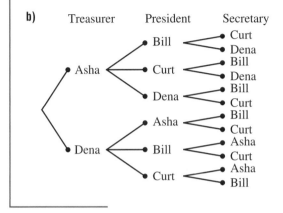

Something to Think About

- Why is the analysis more difficult if we fill the positions for president or secretary first? Explain using a tree diagram.
- Can we use the Fundamental Counting Principle if we fill the positions for president or secretary first? Explain.

Example 4

In each case, how many odd 3-digit numbers can be formed using the digits 0 to 9?

a) Repeated digits are allowed.

b) Repeated digits are not allowed.

Solution

Draw three boxes, one to represent each digit.

□ □ □

Consider the restrictions first.
Since the number is odd, the last digit must be odd. Therefore, the last digit can be a 1, 3, 5, 7, or 9.
A number cannot begin with the digit 0.

a) The last digit can be selected in 5 ways.
Since 0 cannot be the first digit, the first digit can be selected in 9 ways.

There are no restrictions on the middle digit. It can be selected in 10 ways. Use the Fundamental Counting Principle.

$9 \times 10 \times 5 = 450$

There are 450 numbers that can be formed.

b) The last digit can be selected in 5 ways.

Repeated digits are not allowed, so the first digit can be any digit except for 0 and the number chosen as the last digit. Thus, the first digit can be selected in 8 ways.

8	8	5
$\neq 0$		odd

The second digit can be any digit except for the two already chosen. Thus, the second digit can be selected in 8 ways. Use the Fundamental Counting Principle.

$8 \times 8 \times 5 = 320$

There are 320 numbers that can be formed.

We can verify the answer in *Example 4a* by noting that there are 999 integers between 1 and 999. However, 99 of these numbers (1–99) are 1- or 2-digit numbers; so, the remaining $999 - 99 = 900$ numbers must be 3-digit numbers. Half of these numbers, 450 numbers, must be odd.

6.1 Exercises

A

1. A student has 4 different shirts (S1, S2, S3, and S4), 2 different pairs of pants (P1 and P2), and 3 different pairs of shoes (H1, H2, and H3).

   a) Use a tree diagram to list and count the total number of possible outfits.

   b) Use the Fundamental Counting Principle to verify your answer to part a.

2. Use a systematic list to list and count the number of 3-digit numbers that can be formed using the digits 1, 2, and 3 if repeated digits are not allowed. Verify your answer using the Fundamental Counting Principle.

B

3. **Knowledge/Understanding** A lunch special offers a choice of 4 sandwiches, 3 salads, 5 desserts, and 2 beverages. How many different meals are possible when one item is chosen from each category?

4. A pizza can be ordered with 3 choices of size, 4 choices of crust, and 6 choices of toppings. How many different one-topping pizzas can be ordered?

5. How many different ways are there to spell out each word vertically?

a)
```
NNNN
 I I I
 AA
  G
 AA
 RRR
AAAA
```

b)
```
  F
 AA
LLL
LLLL
SSSSS
```

c)
```
  O
 NN
TTT
AAAA
RRR
 I I
  O
```

6. How many even 2-digit numbers are there?

7. In each case, how many odd 2-digit numbers can be made using the digits 1, 2, 3, 4, 5, 6, 7, and 8?

a) Repetitions are allowed.

b) Repetitions are not allowed.

8. In each case, how many 3-digit numbers greater than 500 can be made using the digits 1, 3, 5, 7 and 9?

a) Repetitions are allowed.

b) Repetitions are not allowed.

9. A home security system has an entry code consisting of 4 digits (0–9) that must be entered in the correct sequence. The digits can be repeated in the code.

a) How many different entry codes are possible?

b) If it takes a burglar 5 s to try a code, how long would it take to try every possible code?

10. Refer to exercise 9.

a) How many entry codes are possible if digits cannot be repeated in the code?

b) How many entry codes contain repeated digits?

11. A true-false test has 5 questions. Suppose that a student guesses the answer to each question.

a) How many possible answers are there for each question?

b) How many different ways are there to complete the test?

12. A multiple-choice test has 5 questions, with 4 possible answers for each question. Suppose a student guesses the answer to each question. How many different ways are there to complete the test?

13. A car licence plate consists of 6 characters. Each character can be any of the letters from A to Z, or any numeral from 0 to 9.

  a) How many licence plates are possible?

  b) Explain why the answer to part a is different from the number of licence plates that would be produced.

14. Application In a hotel in Hong Kong, a room key is a card. The card has positions for holes that form a 5 by 10 array. Each position in the array is either punched with a hole or left blank.

  a) How many different keys are possible?

  b) Suppose all the keys were distributed equally among all the people on Earth. How many keys would there be for each person?

15. Communication The book *Cent Mille Milliards de Poèmes* consists of 10 sonnets written in French. Each sonnet is cut into 14 strips, one for each line. The strips can be mixed so a sonnet can be created using any one of the 14 available strips for each line. It is said that so many sonnets are possible that you could probably read a sonnet that no one has ever read before, or will ever read again. Explain. Illustrate with calculations.

16. Thinking/Inquiry/Problem Solving William, Xavier, Yasmin, and Zenobia have tickets for four seats in a row at a concert.

  a) Use a tree diagram or systematic list to count the number of ways they can seat themselves.

  b) In how many of these ways is William in the left-most seat?

  c) In how many of these ways are Xavier and Yasmin seated next to each other?

  d) Explain how the answers to parts a, b, and c could have been calculated using the Fundamental Counting Principle.

17. The final score in a hockey game is 5 to 2. How many different scores are possible at the end of the second period? Solve the problem in 2 ways.

  a) List and count the possible scores.

  b) Use the Fundamental Counting Principle.

18. The dial on a 3-number combination lock contains markings to represent the numbers from 0 to 59. How many combinations are possible in each case?

a) The first and second numbers must be different, and the second and third numbers must be different.

b) The first and second numbers differ by 3.

C

19. Azadeh has a penny, nickel, dime and quarter in her pocket. How many different sums of money can she form using any or all of these coins? Solve the question in 2 different ways.

20. In a competition between players A and B, the first player to win 2 games in a row or a total of 3 games wins. Draw a tree diagram to show the possible outcomes of the competition.

a) How many ways can the competition be played?

b) How many ways can the competition be played if player A wins the first game?

c) How many ways can the competition be played if no player wins 2 games in a row?

6.2 Permutations Involving Different Objects

Permutations Involving Different Objects

1. Two letters, A and B, can be written in two different orders: AB and BA. These are the *permutations* of A and B.

   a) List all the permutations of 3 letters A, B, and C. How can you be certain that you have listed all of them, and that you have not counted any permutation more than once? How many permutations are there? Verify your answer using the Fundamental Counting Principle.

   b) List all the permutations of 4 letters A, B, C, and D. How many permutations are there? Verify your answer using the Fundamental Counting Principle.

   c) Predict the number of permutations of 5 letters A, B, C, D, and E.

   d) Suppose you know the number of letters. How can you determine the number of permutations?

2. Instead of arranging letters in order, we can arrange objects that are different. Explain your answer to each question.

   a) How many different ways can 5 people be arranged in a line?

   b) How many different ways can 5 different books be arranged on a shelf?

   c) How many permutations are there of the letters of the word PROVE?

3. Products such as $5 \times 4 \times 3 \times 2 \times 1$ occur frequently when working with permutations. These are tedious to write, so we use *factorial notation*. When a factorial sign ! follows a natural number n, it means the product of all the natural numbers from n down to 1. For example, $5! = 5 \times 4 \times 3 \times 2 \times 1$, or 120. This is read as "5 factorial".

   > Natural numbers are the positive integers, that is, the numbers 1, 2, 3, ...

   a) Write each factorial as a product.
      i) 3!   ii) 7!

   b) Write each expression in factorial notation.
      i) $9 \times 8 \times 7 \times 6 \times 5 \times 4 \times 3 \times 2 \times 1$
      ii) $6 \times 5 \times 4 \times 3 \times 2 \times 1$

iii) $4 \times 3 \times 2 \times 1 \times 3 \times 2 \times 1$

iv) $\dfrac{7 \times 6 \times 5 \times 4 \times 3 \times 2 \times 1}{4 \times 3 \times 2 \times 1}$

c) Your calculator should have a factorial key or menu item. For example, to determine 5! on the TI-83 Plus graphing calculator, press: 5 [MATH] [▶] [▶] [▶] 4 [ENTER].

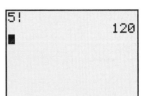

d) Evaluate each factorial in parts a and b.

4. For each question, write the answer using factorial notation. Evaluate the answers in parts a to c.

a) How many permutations can be formed using all the letters in the word MATH?

b) How many ways can 6 children be seated in a row?

c) How many ways can 10 different samples of work be arranged in a mathematics portfolio?

d) Suppose n different objects are to be arranged. How many ways can this be done? Explain.

Many student lockers are secured with a 3-number combination lock. Knowing the 3 numbers is not sufficient to open the lock. The numbers must be used in the correct sequence. The order of the numbers is important.

An arrangement of a set of objects is a permutation.
In a permutation, the order is important.

Example 1

How many permutations can be formed using all 8 letters in the word QUESTION?

Solution

Draw 8 boxes, one for each letter in the arrangement.

There are 8 possible choices for the first box, 7 remaining choices for the second box, 6 choices for the third box, and so on. There is only 1 choice for the last box.

Use the Fundamental Counting Principle.
$8 \times 7 \times 6 \times 5 \times 4 \times 3 \times 2 \times 1 = 8! = 40\ 320$

The number of permutations is 40 320.

Bhama Srinivasan (1935–)
Born: Madras, India

Srinivasan received her BA and MSc degrees in India, then moved to England to pursue her PhD in mathematics. She has taught in many different countries and currently teaches at the University of Illinois in Chicago.
Srinivasan has served as president of the Association for Women in Mathematics and has been on the editorial boards of numerous mathematical journals. Her research involves the application of geometry in finite group theory.

In *Example 1*, we calculated the number of permutations of 8 objects. This is denoted by $P(8, 8)$. By the Fundamental Counting Principle, $P(8, 8) = 8!$.

Your calculator may have a $_nP_r$ key or a menu item. For example, to determine $P(8, 8)$ on a TI-83 Plus calculator, press: 8 [MATH] [▶] [▶] [▶] 2 8 [ENTER] to get the result 40 320.

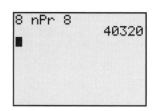

Take Note

Permutation of n Different Objects

The number of permutations of n different objects is an arrangement of all of the objects *in a definite order*. This is denoted by $P(n, n)$ where:

$$P(n, n) = n \times (n - 1) \times (n - 2) \times \ldots \times 3 \times 2 \times 1$$
$$= n! \text{ where } n \text{ is a natural number}$$

Sometimes we wish to arrange some, not all, of a set of objects.

Example 2

How many 3-letter permutations can be formed from the letters in the word QUESTION?

Solution

Draw 3 boxes. Visualize placing the letters in the boxes.

☐ ☐ ☐

There are 8 choices for the first box, 7 for the second box, and 6 choices for the third box.

$8 \times 7 \times 6 = 336$

The number of 3-letter permutations is 336.

In *Example 2*, we calculated the number of permutations of 8 objects taken 3 at a time. This is denoted by $P(8, 3)$.

Notice that $P(8, 3) = 8 \times 7 \times 6$. It is the product of the first 3 factors of 8!.

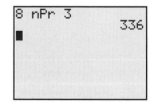

We can also write $P(8, 3)$ using factorial notation.

$$P(8, 3) = 8 \times 7 \times 6$$
$$= 8 \times 7 \times 6 \times \frac{5 \times 4 \times 3 \times 2 \times 1}{5 \times 4 \times 3 \times 2 \times 1}$$
$$= \frac{8 \times 7 \times 6 \times 5 \times 4 \times 3 \times 2 \times 1}{5 \times 4 \times 3 \times 2 \times 1}$$
$$= \frac{8!}{5!}$$
$$= \frac{8!}{(8 - 3)!}$$

In general, we can arrange n objects taken r at a time in $\frac{n!}{(n-r)!}$ ways. This is denoted by $P(n, r)$.

Visualize r boxes, one for each object to be arranged.

Box Number   1   2   3   4 $r - 1$ r

| n | $n-1$ | $n-2$ | $n-3$ | ... | $n-(r-2)$ | $n-(r-1)$ |

The first box can be filled with any one of the n objects in n ways. The second box can be filled with any one of the remaining $(n - 1)$ objects in $(n - 1)$ ways. The third box can be filled with any one of the remaining $(n - 2)$ objects in $(n - 2)$ ways.

Continue the pattern.

The rth box can be filled with the remaining $(n - [r - 1])$ objects in $(n - [r - 1])$ or $(n - r + 1)$ ways.

Thus, by the Fundamental Counting Principle,

$$P(n, r) = n \times (n - 1) \times (n - 2) \times ... \times (n - r + 1)$$

We can write this expression more compactly using factorial notation.

$$P(n, r) = n \times (n - 1) \times (n - 2) \times ... \times (n - r + 1) \frac{(n - r) \times (n - r - 1) \times ... \times 3 \times 2 \times 1}{(n - r) \times (n - r - 1) \times ... \times 3 \times 2 \times 1}$$
$$= \frac{n \times (n - 1) \times (n - 2) \times ... \times (n - r + 1) \times (n - r) \times (n - r - 1) \times ... \times 3 \times 2 \times 1}{(n - r) \times (n - r - 1) \times ... \times 3 \times 2 \times 1}$$
$$= \frac{n!}{(n - r)!}$$

Take Note

Permutation of n Objects Taken r at a Time

The number of permutations of n different objects taken r at a time is the number of arrangements of r of the n objects *in a definite order*. This is denoted by $P(n, r)$ where:

$$P(n, r) = n \times (n - 1) \times (n - 2) \times ... \times (n - r + 1)$$
$$= \frac{n!}{(n - r)!}, \text{ where } 0 \leq r \leq n$$

The symbol $_nP_r$ or $n_{(r)}$ is sometimes used instead of $P(n, r)$. The symbol $_nP_r$ appears on calculator keys or menu items.

A special case of these formulas occurs when $r = n$. The first formula becomes $P(n, n) = n \times (n - 1) \times (n - 2) \times \ldots \times 1$, or $n!$.

The second formula becomes $P(n, n) = \frac{n!}{0!}$.

Thus we have $n! = \frac{n!}{0!}$. This will only be true if $0! = 1$.

For the formula $P(n, r) = \frac{n!}{(n - r)!}$ to have meaning when $r = n$, we define $0! = 1$.
Use your calculator to verify this definition.

Take Note

Definition of n!

For any natural number n,
$$n! = n \times (n - 1) \times (n - 2) \times \ldots \times 3 \times 2 \times 1$$

Also $0! = 1$.

6.2) Exercises

A

1. a) List and count all the permutations of the letters A, B, C, and D taken 2 at a time.

 b) List and count all the permutations of the letters A, B, C, and D taken 3 at a time.

2. How many permutations are there of all the letters in each word?

 a) FRY   **b)** FISH   **c)** FIRST

3. Refer to each word in exercise 2.

 a) How many 2-letter permutations are there?

 b) How many 3-letter permutations are there?

4. How many permutations are there of the words in this sentence?
 I DO NOT WANT LUNCH

5. Knowledge/Understanding In how many ways can 7 different fruits be distributed among each number of children, if each child is to receive exactly one fruit?

 a) 7 children   **b)** 4 children

6. There are 10 different books. How many ways can 4 of these books be arranged on a shelf?

B

7. a) Evaluate.

    i) $P(1, 1)$

    ii) $P(2, 1)$, $P(2, 2)$

    iii) $P(3, 1)$, $P(3, 2)$, $P(3, 3)$

    iv) $P(4, 1)$, $P(4, 2)$, $P(4, 3)$, $P(4, 4)$

    v) $P(5, 1)$, $P(5, 2)$, $P(5, 3)$, $P(5, 4)$, $P(5, 5)$

b) Write your answers to part a in a triangle of numbers similar to the shape at the right. The triangle can be continued indefinitely by adding rows. Find as many patterns in this triangle as you can. Describe each pattern.

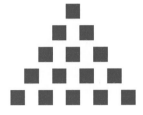

8. a) What is the value of 3!?

b) How can you use the value of 3! to find 4!? Write an equation that expresses 4! in terms of 3!.

c) How can you use the value of 4! to find 5!? Write an equation that expresses 5! in terms of 4!.

d) Write an equation that expresses 6! in terms of 5!.

e) Write an equation that expresses $(n + 1)!$ in terms of n!. Prove this result.

9. a) Write 6! in terms of 5!. Use this result to calculate $\dfrac{6!}{5!}$.

b) Write 6! in terms of 4!. Use this result to calculate $\dfrac{6!}{4!}$.

c) Write 6! in terms of 3!. Use this result to calculate $\dfrac{6!}{3!}$.

d) Write each expression without using a factorial symbol.

    i) $\dfrac{n!}{(n-1)!}$ **ii)** $\dfrac{n!}{(n-2)!}$ **iii)** $\dfrac{n!}{(n-3)!}$

10. Write each expression without using a factorial symbol.

  a) $\dfrac{(n+2)!}{n!}$ **b)** $\dfrac{(n-3)!}{n!}$ **c)** $\dfrac{(n+1)!}{(n-1)!}$

  d) $\dfrac{(n+4)!}{(n+2)!}$ **e)** $\dfrac{(n-r+1)!}{(n-r)}$ **f)** $\dfrac{(n-r+1)!}{(n-r-2)!}$

11. Evaluate each expression. Attempt to find the answer without using a calculator. Use a calculator if the answer cannot be found easily.

  a) 3!   **b)** 4!   **c)** 5!

  d) 9!   **e)** 52!   **f)** $\dfrac{11!}{10!}$

  g) $\dfrac{8!}{6!}$ **h)** $\dfrac{5!}{2!}$ **i)** $\dfrac{10!}{5!}$

  j) $P(7, 2)$ **k)** $P(5, 5)$ **l)** $P(10, 3)$

  m) $P(9, 6)$ **n)** $P(14, 3)$ **o)** $\dfrac{10!}{2!8!}$

  p) $\dfrac{52!}{5!47!}$ **q)** $\dfrac{6!}{3!3!}$

12. The 20 members of a math club are to select an executive committee consisting of a president, vice-president, treasurer, and secretary. No person may hold more than one office. In how many ways can this be done?

13. Use the digits 1, 3, 5, 7, and 9 with no repetitions.

   a) How many 3-digit numbers can be formed?

   b) How many 4-digit numbers can be formed?

14. A model train has an engine, a caboose, a tank car, a flat car, a boxcar, a refrigerator car, and a stock car. How many ways can all the cars be arranged between the engine and the caboose?

15. An ordinary deck of 52 cards is resting on a table. Suppose the first 4 cards on the top of the deck are turned over and placed in a row from left to right.

   a) Determine the total number of possible arrangements.

   b) How many arrangements contain only spades?

16. **Application** For a dance recital, 4 beginner groups, 7 intermediate groups, and 3 advanced groups are to perform. The program is set up so that all the beginner groups perform first, then the intermediate groups, and then the advanced groups. How many orders are possible?

17. Which of the following expressions are not defined? For each expression you choose, explain why it is not defined.

   a) $P(9, 6)$ b) $P(6, 6)$ c) $P(6, 9)$

   d) $P(-6, 3)$ e) $P(6, 2.5)$ f) $P(6, 0)$

18. **Communication** Choose values of n and r in $P(n, r)$. Pose a problem for which your value of $P(n, r)$ is the solution. Solve your problem.

19. **Thinking/Inquiry/Problem Solving** Solve each equation for n. State any restrictions on n.

   a) $\dfrac{(n + 1)!}{(n - 1)!} = 20$ b) $P(n, 2) = 72$

   c) $P(n + 1, 2) = 30$ d) $P(n + 1, 3) = 12P(n - 1, 2)$

   e) $P(n, 4) = 20P(n, 2)$ f) $2P(n, 2) = P(2n, 2) - 50$

20. Solve each equation for r. State any restrictions on r.

   a) $P(6, r) = 30$ b) $P(6, r) = 120$ c) $P(6, r) = 360$ d) $P(6, r) = 720$

C

21. Which is larger, $n!$ or 2^n? Explain.

22. Prove or disprove the following statement.

   For every $n \geq 1$, $\dfrac{(3n)!}{(3!)^n}$ is an integer.

Permutations Involving Identical Objects

1. Consider the words FUEL and FULL. Both words have 4 letters. However, FUEL has 4 different letters while FULL has 2 identical letters.

   a) How many permutations are there of the letters in the word FUEL?

   b) Would there be the same number of permutations of the letters in the word FULL? Explain.

2. Think of the letters in FULL as F, U, L_1, and L_2 so that the letters are all different.

   a) List all the permutations of these 4 letters.

   b) Create a table with the following headings.

Permutations in the Order L_1L_2	Permutations in the Order L_2L_1

   c) In the first column, write all the permutations from part a that contain the Ls in the order L_1L_2. In the second column, write the corresponding permutation that contains the Ls in the order L_2L_1. For example, three entries in the table will be:

Permutations in the Order L_1L_2	Permutations in the Order L_2L_1
FUL_1L_2	FUL_2L_1
FL_1UL_2	FL_2UL_1
FL_1L_2U	FL_2L_1U
⋮	⋮

3. a) Refer to the table. If the subscripts on the Ls are removed, are the permutations in each row the same or different?

   b) The question in part a can be asked another way. Does rearranging the Ls without changing their position give the same permutation or a different permutation?

c) Add a third column to your table with the heading **Permutations of FULL**. Complete this column.

d) How many permutations are there of the letters in FULL? How does this compare to the number of permutations of 4 different letters? Explain.

e) Evaluate $\frac{4!}{2!}$. Explain why this expression gives the number of permutations of the letters in FULL.

The *Investigation* illustrates that there are fewer permutations of a number of objects if some of them are identical than there are if all of them are different.

Example 1

Determine the number of permutations of all the letters in each word.

a) LULL   **b)** PEPPERS

Solution

a) LULL

If the 4 letters were different, there would be 4! permutations. However, in many of these permutations, the 3 Ls are in the same position but permuted among themselves.
The 3 Ls can be permuted in 3! or 6 ways. So the 4! permutations occur in groups of 6, which are in fact the same permutation. Since we counted 6 times as many permutations as there are, divide 4! by 3!.
There are $\frac{4!}{3!}$, or 4 permutations of the letters in LULL.

> The four permutations of LULL are:
>
> **ULLL, LULL, LLUL, and LLLU.**

b) PEPPERS

If the 7 letters were different, there would be 7! permutations. However, in many of these permutations, the 3 Ps are in the same position but permuted among themselves, and the 2 Es are in the same position but permuted among themselves.
The 3 Ps can be permuted in 3! or 6 ways. Similarly, the 2 Es can be permuted in 2! or 2 ways. So the 7! permutations occur in groups of 6×2 or 12, which are in fact the same permutation. Since we counted 12 times as many permutations as there are, divide 7! by 3! and by 2!.
There are $\frac{7!}{3!2!}$, or 420 permutations of the letters in PEPPERS.

We can generalize the method of *Example 1* to obtain the following result.

Permutations With Identical Objects

The number of permutations of n objects, of which a objects are alike, another b objects are alike, another c objects are alike, and so on is:

$$\frac{n!}{a!b!c!\dots}$$

Example 2

How many permutations of the letters in the word BEGINNING begin with B?

Solution

The B can be placed as the first letter in only one way. There are 8 remaining letters: 1 E, 2 Gs, 2 Is, and 3 Ns.

Thus, the required number of arrangements is $\frac{8!}{2!2!3!}$, or 1680.

Example 3

Mario's home is 3 blocks north and 6 blocks west from his school. In how many ways can Mario make the journey from home to school if he always travels either south or east?

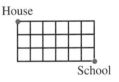

Solution

Let S represent a south-going route past one block. Let E represent an east-going route past one block.

One possible route is SSSEEEEEE. In general, for each possible route from his house to school, Mario must travel 3 blocks south and 6 blocks east.

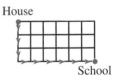

Thus, the problem is equivalent to the number of arrangements of 9 letters, 3 of which are S and 6 of which are E.

Therefore, Mario can make the trip in $\frac{9!}{3!6!}$, or 84 ways.

A

1. Determine each of the following.

a) $\dfrac{5!}{2!2!}$ b) $\dfrac{8!}{3!2!}$ c) $\dfrac{12!}{3!3!2!}$ d) $\dfrac{10!}{2!2!4!}$

2. a) How many permutations are there of all the letters in the word PEEP?

b) List the permutations of PEEP.

3. How many permutations are there of all the letters in each word?

a) ASPARAGUS   b) SCISSORS

c) MISSISSAUGA   d) PARALLEL

B

4. How many 9-digit numbers can be formed from 2 ones, 3 twos, and 4 threes?

5. Knowledge/Understanding How many different signals, each consisting of 8 flags hung in a vertical line, can be formed from 3 identical blue flags, 3 identical white flags, and 2 identical red flags?

6. Communication Consider the words QUESTION and NONSENSE. Explain why the number of permutations of all the letters in QUESTION is 24 times that of the number of permutations of the letters in NONSENSE.

7. Five different coins are tossed once each. How many ways can exactly 3 coins be heads and 2 coins be tails?

8. A soccer team has a record of 12 wins, 6 losses, and 2 ties. In how many different orders could this record have occurred?

9. A true-false test has 5 questions. A student takes the test and randomly guesses the answer to each question. How many answer keys are possible in each situation?

a) All 5 answers are T.

b) Four answers are T and 1 answer is F.

c) Three answers are T and 2 answers are F.

d) Two answers are T and 3 answers are F.

e) One answer is T and 4 answers are F.

f) All 5 answers are F.

10. Add your answers to the 6 parts of exercise 9. Explain why the sum is the same as the answer to exercise 11 on page 307.

11. How many arrangements of the letters in the word GEOMETRY begin with G and end with Y?

12. **Application** An airline pilot reported her itinerary for 7 days. She spent 1 day in Vancouver, 1 day in Regina, 2 days in Ottawa, and 3 days in Yellowknife.

a) How many different itineraries are possible?

b) How many itineraries are possible if she spent the first day in Regina and the last day in Vancouver?

c) How many itineraries are possible if she spent the first and last day in Ottawa?

13. On each grid, explain how many different paths A can take to get to B. Only south and east travel directions can be used.

a)

b)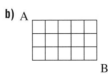

c) How many different paths would there be for each size of grid?
   i) 10 by 10   ii) x by x
   iii) 8 by 12   iv) x by y

14. On each grid, how many different paths are there from A to B? Only south and east travel directions can be used.

a)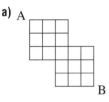

b)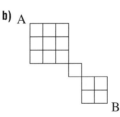

15. **Thinking/Inquiry/Problem Solving** Visualize grids made of cubes in three dimensions.

a) How many paths are there from A to B if each path must be as short as possible and follow the edges of the grid? Explain.

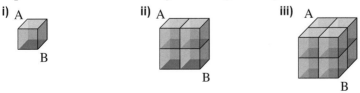

i) A   B   ii) A   B   iii) A   B

b) How many different paths would there be for each size of grid?
   i) 10 by 10 by 10   ii) x by x by x
   iii) 8 by 10 by 12   iv) x by y by z

6.4 Permutations with Restrictions

In this section, we will calculate the number of permutations possible when specific conditions must be met.

Example 1

A bag contains 3 identical blue marbles and 2 identical red marbles. Four marbles are taken out of the bag and arranged in a row from left to right. Determine the number of possible arrangements.

Solution

An arrangement can have either 1 red marble or 2 red marbles. Since these two situations cannot occur at the same time, consider each separately.

Case 1: 1 red marble
If there is 1 red marble and 3 blue marbles, the number of possible arrangements is $\frac{4!}{1!3!} = 4$.

Case 2: 2 red marbles
If there are 2 red marbles and 2 blue marbles, the number of possible arrangements is $\frac{4!}{2!2!} = 6$.

$$\text{Total number of arrangements} = 4 + 6$$
$$= 10$$

The number of possible arrangements is 10.

When two actions cannot occur at the same time, we say they are *mutually exclusive*. We use the following counting principle to count the number of ways two mutually exclusive actions can occur.

Take Note

The Addition Principle

If two actions are mutually exclusive, and one can be done in m ways and the other in n ways, then there are $m + n$ ways in which the first or second action can be performed.

Something to Think About

- How does the Addition Principle differ from the Fundamental Counting Principle?

When working with permutations, the formula alone may not be sufficient to count the number of possible arrangements.

Example 2

Consider the 5-letter arrangements of the letters in the word EXPANDS.

a) How many arrangements contain only consonants?

b) How many arrangements begin with E and end with S?

c) How many arrangements contain the letter N?

d) In how many arrangements do the vowels appear together in the order AE?

Solution

There are 7 letters, of which 5 are consonants and 2 are vowels.
Draw 5 boxes, one for each letter.

a) There are 5 boxes to fill and 5 consonants available.

$P(5, 5) = 5!$
$\qquad = 120$

The total number of arrangements is 120.

b) After the E and S are placed, there are 3 boxes to be filled and 5 letters available.

$P(5, 3) = \dfrac{5!}{2!}$
$\qquad = 60$

The total number of arrangements is 60.

c) After the N is selected, it can be placed in any of the 5 boxes. For each of these choices, there are 4 boxes left to be filled and 6 letters available.

$5 \times P(6, 4) = 5 \times \dfrac{6!}{2!}$
$\qquad\quad = 1800$

The total number of arrangements is 1800.

d) Since the A and E must appear together, treat them as a single unit. There are 4 positions in which they can be placed. For each of these positions, there are 3 boxes left to be filled and 5 letters available.

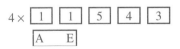

$4 \times P(5, 3) = 4 \times \dfrac{5!}{2!}$
$\qquad\quad = 240$

The total number of arrangements is 240.

- How does the analysis of each part of *Example 2* change if EXPANDS is changed to EXPENDS? Support your explanations with the appropriate calculations.

Example 3

A group of 6 friends attends a movie. All friends sit in the same row of six seats.

a) How many ways can the group sit together?

b) How many ways can the group sit together if two people in the group must sit next to each other?

c) How many ways can the group sit together if two people refuse to sit next to each other?

Solution

a) $P(6, 6) = 6!$
$= 720$

The number of ways 6 different people can be placed in 6 different seats is 720.

b) Treat the two people who must sit next to each other as one unit. Now there are 5 objects to arrange, this unit and the four remaining people in the group. The number of arrangements of 5 objects taken all at a time is:

$P(5, 5) = 5!$
$= 120$

There are another 120 arrangements with the position of the people in the unit reversed.

$120 + 120 = 240$

The total number of arrangements is 240.

c) From part a, there are 720 possible seating arrangements.
From part b, there are 240 arrangements with 2 specific people next to each other.

$720 - 240 = 480$

The number of arrangements where two specific people are not seated together is 480.

Example 3c illustrates that in some instances it is easier to count indirectly than directly.

The 3 letters A, B, and C can be arranged in 3!, or 6 ways.

ABC	BCA	CAB
ACB	CBA	BAC

However, if these letters are arranged in a circle, no letter is first or last. Thus, only the position of the letters relative to each other is important. Since the relative positions are the same in arrangements where one is a rotation of the other, the following 3 arrangements are the same.

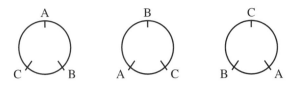

Similarly, the following 3 arrangements are also the same.

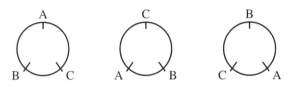

Observe, that for every 3 different arrangements in a line, there is only one corresponding arrangement in a circle. Thus, 3 objects can be arranged in a circle in $\frac{3!}{3}$, or 2 ways. Observe that $\frac{3!}{3} = 2!$.

We could also reason this way. Since only the position of the letters relative to another is important, it does not matter where on the circle the first letter is located. Suppose the position of A is fixed. Then, there are $(3 - 1)!$, or $2!$ ways to arrange the remaining 2 letters.

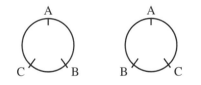

Take Note

Circular Permutations

The number of ways a set of n objects can be arranged in a circle is:
$$\frac{n!}{n} = (n - 1)!$$

In exercise 8 on page 326, you will redo *Example 3* when the six friends are seated around a circular table instead of in a row.

A

1. **a)** In how many ways can 5 people be arranged in a line?

   b) In how many ways can 5 people be arranged in a circle?

2. Five groups are to perform at the school show. How many different ways can the groups be scheduled to perform if one particular group must perform first?

3. Suppose the numbers 1, 2, 3, 4, 5 and 6 are arranged in random order. In how many arrangements do 3 and 4 appear together and in the order 34?

B

4. **Knowledge/Understanding** How many ways can a 5-person family be arranged in a line for a photograph if the mother and father must stand together?

5. Four men and 3 women are to be seated in a row of 7 chairs.

   a) How many ways can they be seated if the men and women alternate?

   b) How many ways can they be seated if the men all sit together and the women all sit together?

6. **Communication** Explain in 2 different ways why 12 football players can be arranged in a circular huddle in 11! ways.

7. How many ways can 4 boys and 4 girls be seated around a circular table so that the boys and girls alternate?

8. Redo *Example 3* with the 6 friends seated around a circular table.

9. How many seating arrangements are possible at a 5-person circular table if 7 people are available?

10. **Application** If any 7 digits can be used to form a telephone number, how many 7-digit telephone numbers have at least 1 repeated digit?

11. A box contains 4 identical black balls and 3 identical white balls. Five balls are taken out of the box and arranged in a row. How many possible arrangements are there?

12. How many ways can 8 books be arranged on a shelf if 4 of the books belong to a numbered set and are to be kept together in numerical order?

13. **Thinking/Inquiry/Problem Solving** How many 3-letter arrangements are there of the letters in the word PUPPY?

14. How many numbers greater than 300 000 can be formed using all the digits 1, 3, 4, 4, 5, and 5?

15. Consider the possible arrangements of all the letters in the word PARALLEL.

   a) How many arrangements are there?

   b) In how many arrangements do the 3 Ls appear together?

   c) How many arrangements end in PR?

   d) In how many arrangements are the 2 As separated by at least 1 letter?

16. Consider the possible arrangements of all of the letters in the word CANADIAN.

   a) How many arrangements begin with the letter A?

   b) How many arrangements begin with two As?

   c) How many arrangements begin with just 1 A?

   d) How many arrangements begin with just 2 As?

17. How many numbers can be formed using all of the digits 1, 2, 3, 4, 5, 6, and 7 if the odd digits must be in ascending order and the even digits in descending order?

C

18. How many even numbers can be formed using all of the digits 1, 1, 2, 4, 6, and 6?

19. Find the number of 4-letter words that can be formed from the letters in the word QUESTION under each condition:

   a) At least 1 consonant must be used.

   b) At least 1 consonant and 1 vowel must be used.

   c) No two vowels can be together.

6.5) Combinations

In many situations, when we make a selection from a group of objects, the order in which we make the selection is not important.

For example, suppose you have to do any 3 of 4 questions on a test. In this situation, we only care about which 3 questions you choose. The order in which you choose the questions is not important.

Call the 4 questions A, B, C, and D. From Section 6.2, we know that the number of *ordered* selections of 3 questions is given by:

$$P(4, 3) = \frac{4!}{(4 - 3)!}$$

$$= 4 \times 3 \times 2$$

$$= 24$$

These 24 permutations are listed below.

							Questions Chosen
ABC	ACD	BAC	BCA	CAB	CBA	→	A, B, C
ABD	ADB	BAD	BDA	DAB	DBA	→	A, B, D
ACD	ADC	CAD	CDA	DAC	DCA	→	A, C, D
BCD	BDC	CBD	CDB	DBC	DCB	→	B, C, D

Notice that each choice of 3 questions, for example, A, B, and C, appears 3!, or 6 times, on the list.

Therefore, the number of possible choices is equal to the $P(4, 3)$ orderings possible divided by the 3! different orderings for each choice.

$$\text{Number of choices} = \frac{P(4, 3)}{3!}$$

$$= \frac{4!}{(4 - 3)!3!}$$

$$= \frac{4!}{1!3!}$$

$$= 4$$

Example 1

To play Lotto 649, you must select 6 different numbers from 1 to 49. The order of the numbers does not matter. How many ways can this be done?

Solution

The number of ways to select 6 numbers from 1 to 49 and order them is $P(49, 6)$.

Any selection of 6 numbers can be ordered in 6! ways.

Thus, the number of ways to select the 6 numbers without regard to order is $\frac{P(49, 6)}{6!}$.

$$\frac{P(49, 6)}{6!} = \frac{49!}{43!6!}$$
$$= 13\ 983\ 816$$

There are 13 983 816 ways to select the 6 numbers in Lotto 649.

We could have solved *Example 1* in another way.

Visualize the 49 numbers in a line as shown.

1 2 3 4 5 6 7 8 9 10 11 12 13 14 15 16 17 18 19 20 21 22 23 24 25 26 27 28 29 30 31 32 33 34 35 36 37 38 39 40 41 42 43 44 45 46 47 48 49

N N N Y N N N N N N Y N N N N N N Y N N N N N N N Y N N N N N N N N N N N N N N Y N N Y N N N N N

Denote each number selected by Y (yes) and each number not selected by N (no). For example, the line shown above represents the selection 4, 11, 18, 26, 41, and 44. For each selection, there must be 6 Ys and 43 Ns. Hence, the number of possible selections is the number of ways that 6 Ys and 43 Ns can be arranged. When we use the result of Section 6.3, the number of ways is $\frac{49!}{6!43!}$. This agrees with the answer from *Example 1*.

A selection from a group of objects without regard to order is a *combination*. The symbol $C(49, 6)$ represents the number of combinations of 49 different objects taken 6 at a time.

Evaluating $C(49, 6)$ using a calculator

Your calculator may have a $_nC_r$ key or menu item. For example, to determine $C(49, 6)$ on the TI-83 Plus graphing calculator, press: 49 [MATH] [▶] [▶] [▶] 3 6 [ENTER]

Hence, $C(49, 6) = 13\ 983\ 816$

The symbol $\binom{n}{r}$ is often used instead of $C(n, r)$. The symbol $_nC_r$ appears on calculator keys or menu items.

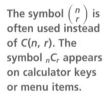

Evaluating $C(49, 6)$ using factorials

If your calculator does not have a $_nC_r$ key or menu item, it should have a factorial key.
Key in: 49 [x!] [÷] 6 [x!] [÷] 43 [x!] [=] to display 13 983 816.

Evaluating $C(49, 6)$ using arithmetic

$$C(49, 6) = \frac{49!}{6!43!}$$
$$= \frac{49 \times 48 \times 47 \times 46 \times 45 \times 44}{6 \times 5 \times 4 \times 3 \times 2 \times 1}$$
$$= 13\ 983\ 816$$

Observe the pattern. The numerator and denominator start with 49 and 6 respectively, and each have 6 factors.

Combinations

A combination of n different objects taken r at a time is a selection of r of the n objects *without regard to order*.

The total number of such combinations is denoted by $C(n, r)$ where:

$$C(n, r) = \frac{n!}{r!(n - r)!}, \text{ where } 0 \leq r \leq n$$

The symbol $C(n, r)$ is read as "n choose r".

Example 2

A standard deck of 52 playing cards consists of 4 suits (spades, hearts, diamonds, and clubs) of 13 cards each.

BLACK														
	Spades	A	K	Q	J	10	9	8	7	6	5	4	3	2
	Clubs	A	K	Q	J	10	9	8	7	6	5	4	3	2
RED	Hearts	A	K	Q	J	10	9	8	7	6	5	4	3	2
	Diamonds	A	K	Q	J	10	9	8	7	6	5	4	3	2

A DECK OF 52 CARDS

a) How many different 5-card hands can be formed?

b) How many different 5-card red hands can be formed?

c) How many different 5-card hands can be formed containing at least 3 black cards?

Solution

a) $C(52, 5) = \dfrac{52!}{5!47!}$

$\qquad = 2\ 598\ 960$

The number of combinations of 5 cards chosen from 52 cards is 2 598 960.

b) There are two red suits (hearts and diamonds) for a total of 26 red cards.

$C(26, 5) = \dfrac{26!}{5!21!}$

$\qquad = 65\ 780$

The number of combinations of 5 cards chosen from 26 cards is 65 780.

c) There could be 3, 4, or 5 black cards. Consider each case separately.

Case 1: 3 black cards and 2 red cards

3 black cards can be chosen in $C(26, 3)$ ways, and for each of these ways 2 red cards can be chosen in $C(26, 2)$ ways.

The total number of combinations is:

$$C(26, 3) \times C(26, 2) = \frac{26!}{3!23!} \times \frac{26!}{2!24!}$$
$$= 845\ 000$$

Case 2: 4 black cards and 1 red card

4 black cards can be chosen in $C(26, 4)$ ways, and for each of these ways the 1 red card can be chosen in $C(26, 1)$ or 26 ways.

The total number of combinations is:

$$C(26, 4) \times 26 = \frac{26!}{4!22!} \times 26$$
$$= 388\ 700$$

Case 3: 5 black cards

5 black cards can be chosen in $C(26, 5)$ ways, which is

$$\frac{26!}{5!21!} = 65\ 780$$

$845\ 000 + 388\ 700 + 65\ 780 = 1\ 299\ 480$

Thus, the number of combinations is 1 299 480.

6.5 Exercises

A

1. Consider the letters A, B, C, and D.

   a) List all the different 2-letter permutations of these 4 letters.

   b) List all the different 2-letter combinations of these 4 letters.

   c) How is the number of 2-letter permutations related to the number of 2-letter combinations? Explain.

2. From a group of 5 student representatives (A, B, C, D, and E), 3 will be chosen to work on the dance committee.

   a) How many committees are possible?

   b) List all possible committees.

3. How many different 10-question examinations can be formed from a test bank containing 25 questions?

4. In a Scratch & Win promotion, participants scratch any 3 spots on a card containing 9 spots. The person who has 3 matching spots wins the prize shown under the spots. How many different ways are there to scratch 3 spots?

B

5. Refer to exercise 2. Each committee must have a chairperson. How many committees are possible? Solve the problem in two ways.

6. Knowledge/Understanding A committee consists of 10 people.

a) How many ways can a subcommittee of 3 people be selected from the committee?

b) How many ways can an executive subcommittee consisting of 3 people (chairperson, treasurer, and secretary) be selected from the committee?

c) Explain why the answers to parts a and b are different.

7. a) How many ways can a committee of 6 students be chosen from 10 students?

b) How many ways can a committee of 4 students be chosen from 10 students?

c) Explain why the answers to parts a and b are the same.

8. Communication

a) Evaluate.

i) $C(0, 0)$
ii) $C(1, 0), C(1, 1)$
iii) $C(2, 0), C(2, 1), C(2, 2)$
iv) $C(3, 0), C(3, 1), C(3, 2), C(3, 3)$
v) $C(4, 0), C(4, 1), C(4, 2), C(4, 3), C(4, 4)$
vi) $C(5, 0), C(5, 1), C(5, 2), C(5, 3), C(5, 4), C(5, 5)$

b) Write your answers to part a in a triangle of numbers similar to the shape above right. Find as many patterns in this triangle as you can. Describe each pattern.

c) Use patterns to write two more rows of the triangle.

9. Thinking/Inquiry/Problem Solving From Section 6.3, we know that 4 As, 3 Bs, 2 Cs, and 1 D can be arranged in $\frac{10!}{4!3!2!}$ ways. The method of Section 6.3 uses permutations to develop this formula. Explain how the result could also have been obtained using combinations.

10. Simplify, without using the triangle in exercise 8 or a calculator.

a) $C(10, 0)$ **b)** $C(10, 1)$ **c)** $C(10, 2)$ **d)** $C(11, 2)$ **e)** $C(12, 2)$

f) $C(10, 3)$ **g)** $C(11, 3)$ **h)** $C(12, 3)$ **i)** $C(10, 4)$ **j)** $C(11, 4)$

11. Write an expression for each number of combinations. State any restrictions on n.

a) $C(n, 0)$ **b)** $C(n, 1)$ **c)** $C(n, 2)$ **d)** $C(n, 3)$ **e)** $C(n, 4)$

12. Five boys and five girls were nominated for a homecoming celebration at a local school. How many ways can a king, a queen, and a court of two students be selected from those nominated?

13. From a deck of 52 cards, how many 5-card hands can be formed in each case?

a) There are only aces or face cards.

b) There are only cards numbered 2, 3, 4, 5, 6, 7, 8, 9, and 10.

c) There are only clubs.

d) There are only red cards.

14. From a deck of 52 cards, the 12 face cards are removed. From these face cards, 4 are chosen. How many combinations that have at least two queens are possible?

15. From a deck of 52 cards, how many different 5-card hands can be formed in each case?

a) with exactly 3 spades

b) with at least 3 spades

c) with at most 3 spades

16. **Application** To play in the Super 7 lottery, you must choose 7 different numbers from 1 to 47. To play in the Lotto 649 lottery, you must choose 6 different numbers from 1 to 49. To win each jackpot, the numbers chosen must match the numbers drawn by the lottery corporation.

a) Without doing any calculations, which lottery do you think has more combinations of possible winning numbers? Explain.

b) How many combinations of possible winning numbers does each lottery have?

c) How many more combinations of possible winning numbers does one lottery have than the other?

17. Sacha invites 6 of her friends to a party.

a) In how many ways can they be selected from among 10 friends?

b) How many ways can they be selected if two of the 10 friends are not on speaking terms and will not attend the party together?

18. A 3-member committee is to be chosen from the 6 young women and 8 young men of the student council. One member of the committee will be chosen as the spokesperson. How many ways can the committee be formed if it must have at least 1 person of each gender?

19. Solve each equation for the indicated variable. State any restrictions on the variable.

a) $C(n, 2) = 10$
b) $C(8, r) = 28$
c) $C(n, 4) = 35$
d) $C(n, 4) = 70$
e) $C(6, r) = 15$
f) $C(10, r) = 120$

20. Eight points are marked on a circle.

a) How many triangles can be formed using any 3 of the 8 points?

b) How many line segments can be formed using any 2 of the 8 points?

c) Suppose the points are joined in order to form an octagon. How many diagonals does the octagon have?

21. There are 8 boys and 12 girls in a drama club. How many ways can a committee of 5 be selected in each case?

a) There must be exactly 2 boys and 3 girls.

b) There must be at least 2 boys.

22. The ballot for a student council election contains 3 candidates for president, 3 for secretary, and 2 for treasurer. A ballot is valid if a student votes for at least one position. How many ways can the ballot be marked?

23. Three different numbers are chosen from 1, 2, 3, 4, 5, 6, 7, 8, 9, and 10. How many ways can the numbers be chosen so that no 2 of the 3 numbers are consecutive?

24. Five-card poker is played by choosing 5 cards from a standard deck of 52 cards. From *Example 2a*, we know that 2 598 960 different hands are possible. The table on the following page shows the various 5-card hands that can be formed. Verify the number of ways each hand can occur.

Recall that in a standard deck of cards, there are 13 different kinds of cards (2s, 3s, 4s, 5s, 6s, 7s, 8s, 9s, 10s, jacks, queens, kings, aces) with 4 cards of each kind (one of each suit: hearts, diamonds, spades, clubs).

Type of hand	Description	Number of ways
Royal flush	Ace, king, queen, jack, and 10 of one suit	4
Straight flush	5 consecutive cards of one suit (excluding a royal flush)	36
Four of a kind	4 cards of one kind and 1 other card	624
Full house	3 cards of one kind and 2 cards of a second kind	3744
Flush	Any 5 cards of the same suit, but not in sequence	5108
Straight	5 consecutive cards, but not all of the same suit	10 200
Three of a kind	Exactly 3 cards of one kind and 2 different cards	54 912
Two pairs	1 pair each of two different kinds and one card of a third kind	123 552
One pair	2 cards of one kind and 1 card each of three different kinds	1 098 240
No pair	Any hand not included above	1 302 540

25. Recall that a factor of a natural number n is any number that divides n with no remainder, including 1 and n. How many factors of each number are there?

a) 36   **b)** 360   **c)** 3600

26. How many 5-letter combinations are there in the letters of the word KINGSTON?

27. The English alphabet consists of 21 consonants and 5 vowels.

a) In how many ways can 4 consonants and 2 vowels be selected?

b) How many "words" consisting of 4 consonants and 2 vowels can be formed?

c) How many of the words in part b begin with R?

d) How many of the words in part c contain E?

28. On May 17, 1998, the Powerball Lottery in Oregon had a main jackpot of $195 million U.S. In this lottery, participants choose 5 different numbers from 1 to 49 and 1 number from 1 to 42. The order of the numbers is unimportant. How many different ways are there to choose the numbers?

Counting Tools

Fundamental Counting Principle

- If a first action can be done in a ways and for each of these ways, a second action can be done in b ways, then these actions can be performed, in this order, in $a \times b$ ways.

Addition Principle

- If two actions cannot occur at the same time (are mutually exclusive), and one can be done in m ways and the other in n ways, then there are $m + n$ ways in which the first or second action can be performed.

Factorial notation

- The product of the first n natural numbers is called n factorial, or $n!$, where:
$n! = n \times (n - 1) \times (n - 2) \times \ldots \times 3 \times 2 \times 1$
Also $0! = 1$.

Permutations

- A permutation is an *ordered* arrangement of objects.
- The number of permutations of n different objects taken n (all) at a time is $P(n, n) = n!$.
- The number of permutations of n different objects taken r at a time is
$P(n, r) = \dfrac{n!}{(n - r)!}$, where $0 \leq r \leq n$.
- The number of permutations of n objects, of which a objects are alike, another b objects are alike, another c objects are alike, and so on is $\dfrac{n!}{a!b!c! \ldots}$.
- The number of permutations of n objects arranged in a circle is $\dfrac{n!}{n} = (n - 1)!$.

Combinations

- A combination is an *unordered* arrangement of objects.
- A combination of n different objects taken r at a time is $C(n, r) = \dfrac{n!}{r!(n - r)!}, 0 \leq r \leq n$.

Guidelines for choosing a counting method

- If repetition is allowed, use the Fundamental Counting Principle.
- If repetition is not allowed, and order is important use permutations.
- If repetition is not allowed, and order is not important use combinations.
- To count mutually exclusive events, use the Addition Principle.

1. A pen is available in 4 colours (red, black, blue, green), 3 different writing tips (medium, fine, extra fine), and 2 types of ink (regular, gel). How many different choices of pens are available?

2. Use the digits 2, 3, 6, 8, and 9. Repeated digits are not allowed.

   a) How many 3-digit numbers can be formed?

   b) How many even 3-digit numbers can be formed?

   c) How many 3-digit numbers greater than 350 can be formed?

3. A postal code consists of a letter, a digit, a letter, a digit, a letter, and a digit. The letters D, F, I, O, Q, and U are never used. In addition, W and Z are not used as the first letters of postal codes. Repetition of letters and digits is allowed.

   a) How many different postal codes are possible?

   b) Suppose the post office removed the restrictions on the letters. How many extra postal codes would be available?

4. An automated teller machine (ATM) requires a 4-digit personal identification number (PIN). The first digit can be 0. In each case, how many such PIN numbers are possible?

   a) Repetitions are allowed.

   b) Repetitions are not allowed.

5. Alice, Bob, and Carol are having dinner at a restaurant. There are 5 dinner specials available. Specials 1 and 2 are vegetarian. Specials 1 and 5 contain nuts. Each orders a dinner special.

   a) In how many different ways can they order dinner?

   b) In how many different ways can they order dinner if Bob is vegetarian and Carol is allergic to nuts?

6. The dial on a 3-number combination lock contains markings to represent the numbers from 0 to 59. How many combinations are possible in which the first and second numbers differ by at least 3?

7. a) How many arrangements are there of all the letters in the word NUMBER?

   b) How many arrangements begin with N and end with R?

8. There are 8 horses in a race. How many possibilities are there for the win, place, and show results (the first three finishers)?

9. There are 7 empty seats on a bus and 4 people come on board. How many ways can they be seated?

10. A sports club with 30 members wishes to pick a president, a vice-president, a secretary, and a treasurer. Assume that no person can hold two offices. How many ways can the selections be made?

11. How many ways can 5 different math books, 3 different history books, and 2 different science books be arranged on a shelf if books of the same subject are to be kept together?

12. Refer to the books in exercise 11. How many ways can 2 books from different subjects be selected?

13. Four-letter arrangements are to be formed from the word PROBLEMS.

    a) How many arrangements are possible?

    b) How many arrangements do not contain a vowel?

    c) How many arrangements contain the letter M?

    d) How many arrangements contain B and L together in the order BL?

14. Solve for n or r. State any restrictions.

    a) $P(n, 3) = 210$ b) $P(n, 4) = 360$

    c) $P(5, r) = 20$ d) $P(8, r) = 336$

15. Write the following expressions without using a factorial symbol. State any restrictions.

    a) $\dfrac{(n + 3)!}{(n + 1)!}$ b) $\dfrac{(n - 1)!}{(n + 1)!}$ c) $\dfrac{(n - r + 3)!}{(n - r)!}$

16. How many 9-digit numbers can be formed from 3 eights, 2 fours, 2 twos, and 2 ones?

17. A soccer team has a record of 7 wins, 6 losses, and 2 ties. In how many different orders could this record have occurred?

18. How many different ways can the letters in the word NIPISSING be arranged?

19. How many different routes are possible from the point (0, 0) to the point (3, 2) if you travel in a positive direction along a coordinate grid with integer coordinates?

20. Use the digits 2, 3, 4, 7, 8, and 9 to form a 3-digit number. Repetitions are not permitted.

    a) How many 3-digit numbers can be formed?

    b) How many of these numbers are less than 400?

    c) How many of these numbers are even? odd?

21. A car licence plate can consist of up to 6 characters. Each character can be any letter from A to Z, or any numeral from 0 to 9. How many licence plates are possible?

22. In each case, how many ways can 3 boys and 2 girls sit in a row?
    a) The boys and girls are to alternate.
    b) The three boys are to sit together.

23. Three Canadians, 4 Americans, and 2 Mexicans attend a trade conference. In how many ways can they be seated in a row if people of the same nationality are to be seated next to each other?

24. Redo exercise 23 if the delegates sit at a round table.

25. Explain how you can determine whether a counting problem involves permutations or combinations. Support your explanation with an example.

26. A football team has 6 basic plays. How many arrangements of 3 different plays could be called?

27. How many ways can a Winter Carnival committee of 6 people be selected from 8 boys and 10 girls in each case?
    a) There are no restrictions.
    b) There are exactly 4 boys on the committee.
    c) There are at least 4 girls on the committee.

28. A poker hand consists of 5 cards dealt from an ordinary deck of 52 cards.
    a) How many possible poker hands are there?
    b) How many different hands are there consisting of 3 kings and 2 queens?
    c) The hand in part b is an example of a full house, 3 cards of 1 kind and 2 of another. How many different full houses are there?

29. Ten points are marked on a circle.
    a) How many triangles can be formed using these points?
    b) Suppose one of the points is labelled as A. How many triangles contain point A as a vertex?

30. How many 7-letter permutations are there of the letters in the word OKANAGAN?

1. Suppose you have a penny, nickel, dime, and quarter in your pocket. You select two coins at random. List and count how many different sums of money can be formed.

2. **Knowledge/Understanding**

   a) A book club offers a choice of 5 books from a list of 30. In how many ways can this be done?

   b) At a movie festival, a team of judges is to select the first, second, and third place finishers from the 18 films entered. How many ways can this be done?

   c) How many permutations can be formed using all the letters of the word ANTARCTICA?

3. **Application** Suppose 5-digit licence plates are to be made using the digits 0 to 9.

   a) How many licence plates are possible if the first digit cannot be 0 and repetition of digits is not allowed?

   b) How many licence plates are possible if the first digit cannot be 0 and repetition of digits is allowed?

   c) In how many arrangements in part b do repetitions occur?

4. **Communication**

   a) Write an equation that relates $P(n, r)$ to $C(n, r)$.

   b) Explain the relationship in part a.

5. Three men, 2 women, and a child are seated at a round table.

   a) How many different seating arrangements are possible?

   b) How many different seating arrangements are possible if the child must sit between the 2 women?

6. **Thinking/Inquiry/Problem Solving** How many 5-letter permutations consisting of two vowels and three consonants can be formed from the letters A, E, I, O, B, H, R, Q, and Z?

Curriculum Expectations

By the end of this chapter, you will:

- Prove relationships between the coefficients in Pascal's triangle, by mathematical induction and directly.

- Describe the connections between Pascal's triangle, values of $C(n, r)$, and values for the binomial coefficients.

- Solve problems, using the binomial theorem to determine terms in the expansion of a binomial.

- Use sigma notation to represent a series or a sum of series.

- Demonstrate an understanding of the principle of mathematical induction.

- Prove the formulas for the sums of series using mathematical induction.

- Prove the binomial theorem, using mathematical induction.

7.1 Pascal's Triangle

In exercise 8 on page 332, you wrote some values of $C(n, r)$ in a triangular pattern. This triangular array of numbers has intrigued mathematicians for centuries. Chu Shih-Chieh, a Chinese mathematician of the thirteenth century, called it the "Precious Mirror of the Four Elements". We call it *Pascal's triangle* in honour of French mathematician Blaise Pascal (1623–1662) who developed and applied many of its properties.

The pattern continues.

The top row of Pascal's triangle is counted as the 0th row, and the 1 at the beginning of each row is counted as the 0th entry of that row. We begin counting at 0 so that in the nth row, the rth entry is the number of combinations of n objects taken r at a time, $C(n, r) = \dfrac{n!}{r!(n - r)!}$. So, in the 4th row, the 0th entry is $C(4, 0) = 1$, the 1st entry is $C(4, 1) = 4$, the 2nd entry is $C(4, 2) = 6$, the 3rd entry is $C(4, 3) = 4$, and the 4th entry is $C(4, 4) = 1$.

Take Note

Pascal's Triangle

Pascal's triangle contains all the combinatorial coefficients.
The coefficient $C(n, r) = \dfrac{n!}{r!(n - r)!}$ is entry r in row n, where $n = 0, 1, 2, \ldots$ and $0 \leq r \leq n$.

In exercise 8 of page 332, you found some patterns in Pascal's triangle. Here are two important patterns you probably discovered, and another pattern you might have not discovered.

The Symmetrical Pattern

The numbers in each row are "symmetric" in that numbers to the left of the middle are identical to those to the right of the middle. Hence the numbers in each row read the same from left to right or from right to left.

Symmetrical Pattern

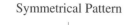

$$
\begin{array}{ccccccccccccc}
& & & & & & 1 & & & & & & \\
& & & & & 1 & & 1 & & & & & \\
& & & & 1 & & 2 & & 1 & & & & \\
& & & 1 & & 3 & & 3 & & 1 & & & \\
& & 1 & & 4 & & 6 & & 4 & & 1 & & \\
& 1 & & 5 & & 10 & & 10 & & 5 & & 1 & \\
1 & & 6 & & 15 & & 20 & & 15 & & 6 & & 1
\end{array}
$$

$$C(n, r) = C(n, n - r)$$

In the 6th row, the first 15 is $C(6, 2)$ and the second 15 is $C(6, 4)$. We know that $C(6, 2) = C(6, 4)$ since each expression equals 15. Here are two proofs of this result.

Numerical proof

$$
\begin{aligned}
C(6, 4) &= \frac{6 \times 5 \times 4 \times 3}{4 \times 3 \times 2 \times 1} \\
&= \frac{6 \times 5 \times \cancel{4} \times \cancel{3}}{\cancel{4} \times \cancel{3} \times 2 \times 1} \\
&= \frac{6 \times 5}{2 \times 1} \\
&= C(6, 2)
\end{aligned}
$$

We can also use factorials to prove that $C(6, 2) = C(6, 4)$.
See exercise 7 on page 347.

Combinatorial proof

Suppose a committee of 2 is to be selected from 6 eligible people. This can be done in $C(6, 2)$ ways. An alternate but equivalent approach is to select the 4 people who are *not* on the committee. This can be done in $C(6, 4)$ ways. Therefore, $C(6, 2)$ and $C(6, 4)$ must be equal.

In general, $C(n, r) = C(n, n - r)$; the proofs are left to the exercises.

Florence Nightingale (1820–1910)
Born: Florence, Italy

Nightingale was born in Italy, but raised in England. She developed an interest in social issues and studied the application of statistical methods to social science data. Nightingale gained her nursing experience while travelling through Europe and Egypt. In 1854, at the start of the Crimean war, she became nursing administrator of English military hospitals. Nightingale collected data on the deaths of soldiers and used them to calculate mortality rates, which she represented using polar area diagrams. Nightingale revealed how the unsanitary conditions of the hospitals killed more soldiers than the battlefields.
In 1858, Nightingale became the first woman elected to the Royal Statistical Society.

The Recursive Pattern

In each row, each number except the first and last is the sum of the two numbers immediately above it.

Recursive Pattern

```
            1
         1     1
      1     2     1
   1     3     3     1
1     4     6     4     1
```
$$1 + 5 + 10 + 10 + 5 + 1$$
```
1     6    15    20    15    6     1
```

$$C(n, r) = C(n - 1, r - 1) + C(n - 1, r)$$

For example, in the 6th row, the second 15 is the sum of the numbers 5 and 10 in the 5th row: $C(6, 4) = C(5, 3) + C(5, 4)$.

We can prove that $C(6, 4) = C(5, 3) + C(5, 4)$ in two ways.

Numerical proof

$$C(5, 3) + C(5, 4) = \frac{5 \times 4 \times 3}{3 \times 2 \times 1} + \frac{5 \times 4 \times 3 \times 2}{4 \times 3 \times 2 \times 1}$$

The common denominator is $4 \times 3 \times 2 \times 1$.

$$C(5, 3) + C(5, 4) = \frac{(5 \times 4 \times 3 \times 4) + (5 \times 4 \times 3 \times 2)}{4 \times 3 \times 2 \times 1}$$

Each term in the numerator has a common factor of $5 \times 4 \times 3$.

$$C(5, 3) + C(5, 4) = \frac{5 \times 4 \times 3 \times (4 + 2)}{4 \times 3 \times 2 \times 1}$$
$$= \frac{6 \times 5 \times 4 \times 3}{4 \times 3 \times 2 \times 1}$$
$$= C(6, 4)$$

We can also use factorials to prove that $C(6, 2) = C(6, 4)$. See exercise 7 on page 347.

Combinatorial proof

$C(6, 4)$ represents the number of committees of 4 people that can be selected from 6 people: A, B, C, D, E, and F. Select a single person, say A. Observe that 2 types of committees can be formed: those that contain A, and those that do not contain A.

If A is on the committee, the other 3 committee members must be chosen from the remaining 5 people; there are $C(5, 3)$ ways to do this.

If A is not on the committee, all 4 committee members must be chosen from the remaining 5 people; there are $C(5, 4)$ ways to do this.

This is a remarkable argument: simple and convincing, yet difficult to discover. "Argument from a physical analogy" is an important type of mathematical proof.

Since these 2 possibilities are mutually exclusive and there are no other possibilities, the number of ways to choose the committee is $C(5, 3) + C(5, 4)$. Therefore, $C(6, 4) = C(5, 3) + C(5, 4)$.

In general, $C(n, r) = C(n - 1, r - 1) + C(n - 1, r)$. This relationship is called *Pascal's formula*. The proofs are left to the exercises.

The Diagonal Pattern

In Pascal's triangle, the partial sums of any diagonal appear in the next diagonal. Since the numbers and their sum form an L-shape, this pattern is sometimes called a "hockey-stick pattern".

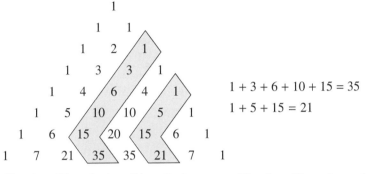

$1 + 3 + 6 + 10 + 15 = 35$

$1 + 5 + 15 = 21$

$$C(r, r) + C(r + 1, r) + C(r + 2, r) + \ldots + C(n, r) = C(n + 1, r + 1)$$

For example, the sum of the first 5 numbers in diagonal 2 is entry 3 in row 7. That is:

$$1 + 3 + 6 + 10 + 15 = 35$$

This can be written in combinatorial notation as:

$$C(2, 2) + C(3, 2) + C(4, 2) + C(5, 2) + C(6, 2) = C(7, 3)$$

We can prove that $C(2, 2) + C(3, 2) + C(4, 2) + C(5, 2) + C(6, 2) = C(7, 3)$ in two ways.

Proof using Pascal's formula $C(n, r) = C(n - 1, r - 1) + C(n - 1, r)$

$$\begin{aligned}
C(7, 3) &= C(6, 2) + C(6, 3) \\
&= C(6, 2) + C(5, 2) + C(5, 3) \\
&= C(6, 2) + C(5, 2) + C(4, 2) + C(4, 3) \\
&= C(6, 2) + C(5, 2) + C(4, 2) + C(3, 2) + C(3, 3)
\end{aligned}$$

But $C(3, 3) = C(2, 2) = 1$

Therefore, $C(7, 3) = C(6, 2) + C(5, 2) + C(4, 2) + C(3, 2) + C(2, 2)$

Combinatorial proof

$C(7, 3)$ represents the number of committees of 3 people that can be selected from 7 people: A, B, C, D, E, F, and G.

Select a single person, say A. If A is on the committee, the other 2 committee members must be chosen from the remaining 6 people; there are $C(6, 2)$ ways to do this.

This leaves us with the committees that do not contain A. Consider the committees that contain B. The other 2 committee members must be chosen from the remaining 5 people; there are $C(5,2)$ ways to do this.

This leaves us with the committees that do not contain A or B. Consider the committees that contain C. The other 2 committee members must be chosen from the remaining 4 people; there are $C(4,2)$ ways to do this.

This leaves us with the committees that do not contain A or B or C. Consider the committees that contain D. The other two committee members must be chosen from the remaining 3 people; there are $C(3,2)$ ways to do this.

This leaves us with the committees that do not contain A or B or C or D. There is only 1 possible committee: the one containing E, F, and G. Observe that if we choose any member, say E, the other two committee members must be chosen from the remaining 2 people in $C(2,2)$ ways, or 1 way.

Since these 5 possibilities are mutually exclusive and there are no other possibilities, the number of ways to choose the committee is
$C(6,2) + C(5,2) + C(4,2) + C(3,2) + C(2,2)$.
Thus, $C(2,2) + C(3,2) + C(4,2) + C(5,2) + C(6,2) = C(7,3)$

Something to Think About

- Does this combinatorial argument apply only to the partial sums of diagonal 2, or can it also be applied to the partial sums of other diagonals? Explain.
- There are many interesting patterns in the diagonals of Pascal's triangle. You will explore and prove these patterns throughout the chapter.

7.1 Exercises

Draw Pascal's triangle to the 10th row. Refer to the triangle to complete these exercises.

A

1. Use Pascal's triangle to evaluate each of the following.

   a) $C(0,0)$ b) $C(3,2)$ c) $C(5,3)$

   d) $C(6,3)$ e) $C(9,3)$ f) $C(10,7)$

2. **Knowledge/Understanding** State another expression in the form $C(n,r)$ that is equal to each of the following.

   a) $C(7,5)$ b) $C(9,4)$ c) $C(11,7)$ d) $C(20,6)$

e) $C(4, 2) + C(4, 3)$ **f)** $C(6, 5) + C(6, 6)$ **g)** $C(11, 8) + C(11, 9)$

h) $C(20, 6) + C(20, 7)$

3. Some rows in Pascal's triangle contain an odd number of entries. Other rows contain an even number of entries. How do you know whether the number of entries in a given row is odd or even? Explain.

4. In any given row of Pascal's triangle, explain why the numbers increase toward the middle and then decrease towards the end.

5. In exercise 7 of page 315, you wrote some values of $P(n, r)$ in a triangular pattern. Explain why this triangle is not as useful as Pascal's triangle.

6. a) What is the second number in the 50th row of Pascal's triangle?

b) How can you determine the second number in any row of Pascal's triangle? Explain.

B

7. Redo the numerical proofs on pages 343 and 344 using factorials.

8. Prove that $C(7, 5) = C(7, 2)$ in these two ways:

a) numerically, using factorials

b) by reasoning, using the meaning of combinations

9. Prove the symmetrical pattern in Pascal's triangle, $C(n, r) = C(n, n - r)$, in these two ways:

a) algebraically, using factorials to show that the two expressions are equal

b) by reasoning, using the meaning of combinations

10. Prove that $C(7, 5) = C(6, 4) + C(6, 5)$ in these two ways:

a) numerically, using factorials

b) by reasoning, using the meaning of combinations

11. Prove Pascal's formula, $C(n, r) = C(n - 1, r - 1) + C(n - 1, r)$, in these two ways:

a) algebraically, using factorials

b) by reasoning, using the meaning of combinations

12. Communication Explain in these two ways why the numbers in the first diagonal of Pascal's triangle are the natural numbers:

a) using the formula for $C(n, r)$

b) using the meaning of combinations

13. Application In each pinball situation shown, a ball is equally likely to fall to the left or to the right after hitting a divider. How many different paths are there to each exit?

a)

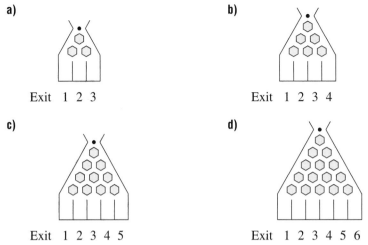

Exit 1 2 3

b)

Exit 1 2 3 4

c)

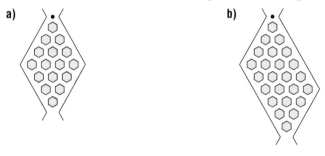

Exit 1 2 3 4 5

d)

Exit 1 2 3 4 5 6

14. In any pinball situation similar to those in exercise 13, explain why the total number of paths from top to bottom is a power of 2.

15. In each pinball situation below, determine the number of different paths a ball could take when it falls from top to bottom. Explain.

a)

b)

16. On a coordinate grid, visualize starting at (0, 0) and using a pencil to move to any point in the first quadrant according to these rules:

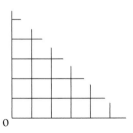

- You must always move along the grid lines, without taking your pencil off the paper.
- You must always move either up or to the right.

a) How many different ways can you move to each point?

   i) (1, 0), (0, 1)
   ii) (2, 0), (1, 1), (0, 2)
   iii) (3, 0), (2, 1), (1, 2), (0, 3)
   iv) (4, 0), (3, 1), (2, 2), (1, 3), (0, 4)

b) Explain why the results of part a are the numbers in Pascal's triangle.

17. The sum of the first 4 terms in diagonal 3 of Pascal's triangle is entry 4 in row 7.

a) Express this relationship using combinatorial notation.

b) Explain this relationship using a combinatorial model.

18. On pages 345 and 346, we looked at the partial sums of the second diagonal of Pascal's triangle. This same sequence of numbers occurs in a diagonal that runs the other way, from left to right.

a) Express this relationship using combinatorial notation.

b) Explain this relationship.

19. The diagram at the right shows a regular hexagon and its diagonals.

a) How many line segments are on the diagram?

b) How many of these line segments are diagonals?

20. Thinking/Inquiry/Problem Solving

a) How many interior diagonals are there in a regular polygon with 20 sides? Explain.

b) What is the general formula for the number of interior diagonals in a regular polygon with n sides? Explain.

C

21. a) Add the numbers in each row of Pascal's triangle from row 0 to row 6. What do you notice?

b) What does the sum of the numbers in the 5th row represent, in terms of choosing items from a set of 5?

c) Explain why the sum of the numbers in part b is 2^5.

d) Explain why the sum of the numbers in the nth row is 2^n.

Patterns in Binomial Powers

You already know how to expand the square of a binomial:

$(a + b)^2 = a^2 + 2ab + b^2$

When we expand other powers of $a + b$, a number of patterns emerge. These patterns can be generalized to derive a formula for the expansion of $(a + b)^n$ for any natural number n.

$(a + b)^0 = 1$
$(a + b)^1 = a + b$
$(a + b)^2 = a^2 + 2ab + b^2$
$(a + b)^3 = a^3 + 3a^2b + 3ab^2 + b^3$
$(a + b)^4 = a^4 + 4a^3b + 6a^2b^2 + 4ab^3 + b^4$
$(a + b)^5 = a^5 + 5a^4b + 10a^3b^2 + 10a^2b^3 + 5ab^4 + b^5$

1. Find as many patterns as you can in the results. Describe each pattern.

2. Predict the expansion of $(a + b)^6$.

 a) How many terms are in the expansion?

 b) What is the exponent of a in the first term? What is the exponent of a in the last term? What happens to the exponent of a from term to term?

 c) What is the exponent of b in the first term? What is the exponent of b in the last term? What happens to the exponent of b from term to term?

 d) In any term, what is the sum of the exponents of a and b?

 e) What are the coefficients of the terms in the expansion? How do you know?

 f) Write the expansion of $(a + b)^6$.

3. Predict each expansion.

 a) $(a + b)^7$ **b)** $(a + b)^8$

4. a) How is the expansion of $(a - b)^2$ similar to the expansion of $(a + b)^2$? How is it different?

 b) Use the expansions of $(a + b)^3$, $(a + b)^4$, and $(a + b)^5$. Predict the expansions of $(a - b)^3$, $(a - b)^4$, and $(a - b)^5$.

In the *Investigation*, you discovered that the coefficients in the expansion of $(a + b)^n$ are numbers in the *n*th row of Pascal's triangle. For this reason, the combinatorial coefficients in Pascal's triangle are also called *binomial coefficients*.

	Binomial expansion	Coefficients of expansion

$(a + b)^0 = $ $\qquad\qquad\qquad 1 \qquad\qquad\qquad\qquad\qquad\qquad 1$

$(a + b)^1 = $ $\qquad\qquad\qquad a + b \qquad\qquad\qquad\qquad\qquad 1 \quad 1$

$(a + b)^2 = $ $\qquad\qquad a^2 + 2ab + b^2 \qquad\qquad\qquad 1 \quad 2 \quad 1$

$(a + b)^3 = $ $\qquad a^3 + 3a^2b + 3ab^2 + b^3 \qquad\qquad 1 \quad 3 \quad 3 \quad 1$

$(a + b)^4 = $ $\quad a^4 + 4a^3b + 6a^2b^2 + 4ab^3 + b^4 \qquad 1 \quad 4 \quad 6 \quad 4 \quad 1$

$(a + b)^5 = a^5 + 5a^4b + 10a^3b^2 + 10a^2b^3 + 5ab^4 + b^5 \qquad 1 \quad 5 \quad 10 \quad 10 \quad 5 \quad 1$

We can use combinations to explain why the binomial coefficients appear in Pascal's triangle.

For example, consider the expansion of $(a + b)^2$.

$$(a + b)^2 = (a + b)(a + b) \qquad ①$$
$$= aa + ab + ba + bb \quad ②$$
$$= a^2 + 2ab + b^2$$

Observe that:

- Each term in ② is the product of 2 factors. In each term, either an *a* or a *b* is taken from each binomial factor in ①.

- The first term is a^2, which is formed by choosing the *a* from both binomial factors.

- The second term contains *ab*, and is formed by choosing the *a* from one factor and the *b* from the other factor. Since there are 2 ways to do this, the second term is *2ab*.

- The third term is b^2, which is formed by choosing the *b* from both binomial factors.

  Hence, $(a + b)^2 = a^2 + 2ab + b^2$

  The coefficients are the numbers in the 2nd row of Pascal's triangle.

We can use similar reasoning to expand a binomial power such as $(a + b)^4$.

$$(a + b)^4 = (a + b)(a + b)(a + b)(a + b)$$
$$= aaaa + aaab + aaba + aabb + abaa + abab + abba$$
$$+ abbb + baaa + baab + baba + babb + bbaa + bbab$$
$$+ bbba + bbbb$$
$$= a^4 + 4a^3b + 6a^2b^2 + 4ab^3 + b^4$$

- Each term is the product of 4 factors. In each term, an *a* or a *b* is taken from each binomial factor.

- The first term is a^4. It is formed by choosing the a from each of the 4 binomial factors. There is only one way to do this.

- The second term contains a^3b. It is formed by choosing the b from any one of the 4 binomial factors and the three a's from the remaining 3 factors. The b can be chosen in $C(4, 1)$ ways, and for each way, the three a's can be chosen in only 1 way. Hence, the coefficient of a^3b is 4, and the second term is $4a^3b$.

- The third term contains a^2b^2. It is formed by choosing b from any two of the 4 binomial factors, and a from the remaining 2 factors.
  The 2 b's can be selected in $C(4, 2)$ ways, and for each of these ways, the two a's can be chosen in only 1 way. Hence, the coefficient of a^2b^2 is 6, and the third term is $6a^2b^2$.

- Similarly, the fourth term is $4ab^3$, and the fifth term is b^4.

Therefore, $(a + b)^4 = C(4, 0)a^4 + C(4, 1)a^3b + C(4, 2)a^2b^2 + C(4, 3)ab^3 + C(4, 4)b^4$

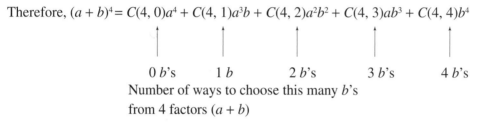

$$0\ b\text{'s} \qquad 1\ b \qquad 2\ b\text{'s} \qquad 3\ b\text{'s} \qquad 4\ b\text{'s}$$
Number of ways to choose this many b's
from 4 factors $(a + b)$

This simplifies to $(a + b)^4 = a^4 + 4a^3b + 6a^2b^2 + 4ab^3 + b^4$.
The coefficients are the numbers in the 4th row of Pascal's triangle.

We can apply this reasoning to obtain the expansion of any binomial power of the form $(a + b)^n$, where n is a natural number. This is the *binomial theorem*. A combinatorial proof using the reasoning on page 351 and above has been left to the exercises (see exercise 7). An alternate proof is given in Section 7.5.

Take Note

The Binomial Theorem

For any natural number n and all real numbers a and b:

$$(a + b)^n = C(n, 0)a^n + C(n, 1)a^{n-1}b + C(n, 2)a^{n-2}b^2 + C(n, 3)a^{n-3}b^3 + \dots$$
$$+ C(n, r)a^{n-r}b^r + \dots + C(n, n - 1)ab^{n-1} + C(n, n)b^n$$

Something to Think About

- The coefficients in the expansion of $(a + b)^4$ can be expressed in terms of the possible number of ways to choose the number of b's in the terms of the expansion. Could we have counted the number of ways to choose different numbers of a's instead? Explain.

Example 1

Expand.

a) $(x + 1)^6$ b) $(2x - 3)^3$

Solution

a) Use the binomial theorem. Substitute $a = x$, $b = 1$, and $n = 6$.

$$(x + 1)^6 = C(6, 0)x^6 + C(6, 1)x^5(1) + C(6, 2)x^4(1)^2 + C(6, 3)x^3(1)^3$$
$$+ C(6, 4)x^2(1)^4 + C(6, 5)x(1)^5 + C(6, 6)(1)^6$$
$$= x^6 + 6x^5 + 15x^4 + 20x^3 + 15x^2 + 6x + 1$$

b) Use the binomial theorem. Substitute $a = 2x$, $b = -3$, and $n = 3$.

$$(2x - 3)^3 = (2x + (-3))^3$$
$$= C(3, 0)(2x)^3 + C(3, 1)(2x)^2(-3) + C(3, 2)(2x)(-3)^2 + C(3, 3)(-3)^3$$
$$= 8x^3 + 3(4x^2)(-3) + 3(2x)(9) - 27$$
$$= 8x^3 - 36x^2 + 54x - 27$$

Example 2

Find the coefficient of x^3y^5 in the expansion of $(x + 2y)^8$.

Solution

$(x + 2y)^8$ is the product of 8 factors of $(x + 2y)$.

The term x^3y^5 is formed by choosing $2y$ from any five of 8 binomial factors, and x from the remaining 3 factors.

The five $2y$'s can be selected in $C(8, 5)$ ways, and for each of these ways, the three x's can be chosen in only 1 way.

Thus, the required term is:

$$C(8, 5)x^3(2y)^5 = 56x^3(32y^5)$$
$$= 1792x^3y^5$$

We can solve *Example 2* in another way.

In the expansion of $(a + b)^n$, the term containing b^r is called the *general term* of the expansion. Notice that this term is the $(r + 1)$th term of the expansion.

$$(a + b)^n = C(n, 0)\,a^n + C(n, 1)a^{n-1}b + C(n, 2)a^{n-2}b^2 + \ldots + C(n, r)\,a^{n-r}b^r + \ldots + C(n, n-1)ab^{n-1} + C(n, n)b^n$$

$$t_1 \qquad\qquad t_2 \qquad\qquad t_3 \qquad \ldots \qquad t_{r+1} \qquad \ldots \qquad t_n \qquad\qquad t_{n+1}$$

The General Term of a Binomial Expansion

The general term in the expansion of $(a + b)^n$ is:

$$t_{r+1} = C(n, r)a^{n-r}b^r$$

In *Example 2*, the general term of $(x + 2y)^8$ is:

$$t_{r+1} = C(8, r)x^{8-r}(2y)^r$$
$$= C(8, r)(2)^r x^{8-r} y^r$$

The term $x^3 y^5$ corresponds to $r = 5$. Thus, the required term is:

$$t_6 = 56(32)x^3 y^5$$
$$= 1792x^3 y^5$$

We can use the general term to find a particular term in a binomial expansion without writing the entire expansion.

Example 3

Determine the 7th term in the expansion of $(x - 2)^{10}$.

Solution

The general term is $t_{r+1} = C(10, r)(x)^{10-r}(-2)^r$.

To determine t_7, substitute 6 for r.

$$t_7 = C(10, 6)(x)^4(-2)^6$$
$$= 210x^4(64)$$
$$= 13\,440x^4$$

7.2 Exercises

Ⓐ

1. Expand using Pascal's triangle. Simplify each term.

   a) $(a + 2)^3$ **b)** $(y - 5)^4$ **c)** $(4t + 1)^5$

   d) $(x - y)^3$ **e)** $(2a + b)^4$ **f)** $(x - 7)^5$

2. a) Explain how the term $a^5 b^3$ is formed in the expansion of $(a + b)^8$.

   b) What is the coefficient of $a^5 b^3$?

3. In the binomial expansion of $(a + b)^n$, a term involving a^3b^4 occurs.

   a) What is the value of n?

   b) What is the coefficient of a^3b^4?

   c) Which term in the expansion is this?

4. In the expansion of $(a + b)^6$, explain why the coefficient of a^4b^2 is the same as the coefficient of a^2b^4.

5. a) How many terms are there in the expansions of $(a + b)^9$ and $(a + b)^{10}$?

   b) Which expansion in part a has one middle term? Which expansion has two middle terms?

   c) When does the expansion of $(a + b)^n$ have one middle term? When does it have two middle terms?

B

6. **Communication** Use the reasoning on pages 351 and 352 to explain the expansion of $(a + b)^3$.

7. Use the reasoning on pages 351 and 352 to give a combinatorial proof of the binomial theorem.

8. Expand using the binomial theorem. Simplify each term.

   a) $(x + 2)^6$ b) $(x - 3)^4$ c) $(1 + x^2)^6$ d) $(2 - x)^5$

   e) $(a - 2b)^4$ f) $(2a + 3b)^3$ g) $\left(x + \dfrac{1}{x}\right)^5$ h) $(3a + 2b^2)^5$

9. Write the first four terms in each expansion. Simplify each term.

   a) $(1 + \sqrt{x})^{10}$ b) $(x + 2)^{12}$ c) $(2 - x)^8$ d) $(1 - 2x)^9$

10. **Knowledge/Understanding** Find the first three terms and the 7th term in the expansion of $(a + 2b)^{12}$. Simplify.

11. Determine the indicated term in each expansion.

    a) the 8th term in the expansion of $(x - 2)^{10}$

    b) the 4th term in the expansion of $(x + 5y)^8$

    c) the 10th term in the expansion of $(1 - 2a)^{12}$

    d) the 11th term in the expansion of $(2a^3 + 1)^{13}$

    e) the middle term in the expansion of $(1 - x^2)^8$

12. Find the coefficient of x^2y^6 in the expansion of $\left(2x - \dfrac{y}{2}\right)^8$.

13. Find the coefficient of x^3 and of x^6 in each expansion.

    a) $(1 - 3x)^8$ b) $(1 + 2x)^{12}$ c) $(1 - x^2)^{10}$

14. In the expansion of $\left(x + \dfrac{1}{x^2}\right)^6$, determine:

a) the constant term

b) the coefficient of x^{-6}

c) whether there is a term involving x^4
Explain.

In the constant term, the exponent of x is 0.

15. Expand and simplify.

a) $(x + y)^4 + (x - y)^4$

b) $(x + y)^4 - (x - y)^4$

16. Application Use the binomial theorem to expand the trinomial $(a + b + c)^3$.

17. a) In *Example 1a*, the sum of the coefficients in the expansion of $(x + 1)^6$ is $1 + 6 + 15 + 20 + 15 + 6 + 1 = 64$, or 2^6. Use the binomial theorem to prove this result.

b) Prove that, in general, the sum of the coefficients in the expansion of $(x + 1)^n$ is 2^n.

18. Thinking/Inquiry/Problem Solving

a) Expand $(1 - 2x)^3$ and $\left(1 + \dfrac{1}{x}\right)^5$.

b) Find, in the expansion of $(1 - 2x)^3 \left(1 + \dfrac{1}{x}\right)^5$:

i) the constant term

ii) the coefficient of x

19. When the terms of the expansion of $(x^2 + 1)^n$ are written in ascending powers of x, the coefficient of the third term is 9316. Determine n.

C

20. Find the coefficient of x^{17} in the expansion of $(1 + x^5 + x^7)^{20}$.

21. In the binomial expansion of $(1 + x)^n$, the coefficients of the fifth, sixth, and seventh terms are consecutive terms of an arithmetic sequence. Determine the first three terms of the expansion.

22. The first three terms of the expansion of $(1 + ax + bx^2)^4$ are 1, $8x$, and $32x^2$ respectively. Determine a and b.

7.3 Sigma Notation

In mathematics, we often use symbols to shorten expressions that are tedious to write. To express the sum of the squares of the first 10 natural numbers, we write

$$1 + 4 + 9 + \ldots + 100$$

to avoid listing all 10 terms. We can abbreviate this expression even further by using the summation symbol, Σ.

The series is a sum of squares. It can be rewritten as:

$$1^2 + 2^2 + 3^2 + \ldots + 10^2$$

Each term of the series is of the form k^2, where k takes, in turn, the values 1, 2, 3, … , 10. Therefore, we write:

The sum of … $\longrightarrow \displaystyle\sum_{k=1}^{10} k^2 \longleftarrow$ … all numbers of the form k^2

… for integral values of k from 1 to 10.

The symbol Σ is the capital Greek letter sigma, which corresponds to S, the first letter in the word "sum". For this reason, this method of representing a series is called *sigma notation*.

Sophie Germain (1776–1831)
Born: Paris, France

Germain taught herself while her parents slept because they disapproved of her passion for mathematics. Although there was a mathematical and scientific academy in Paris, women were not allowed to enrol. Germain obtained lecture notes for several of the courses and studied from them. She sent a paper to a professor using a pseudonym. The professor was amazed that the author was a woman and became her mentor.
Germain's major contribution to mathematics was in number theory. She also researched vibrations of elastic surfaces for which she won a contest sponsored by the French Academy of Sciences.

The variable k under the Σ sign, and in the expression after it, is called the *index of summation*. Any letter not used elsewhere can be used for the index of summation. The numbers 1 and 10 are the limits of the summation. They indicate that k is to take every integer value from 1 to 10.

When we write out a series that is expressed using sigma notation, we are writing the series in *expanded form*.

Example 1

Write each summation in expanded form.

a) $\displaystyle\sum_{k=1}^{4} (3k - 2)$

b) $\displaystyle\sum_{j=5}^{10} jx^j$

Solution

a) $\displaystyle\sum_{k=1}^{4}(3k-2)$

Substitute values of k from 1 to 4 in the expression $3k-2$ and add the results.

$$\sum_{k=1}^{4}(3k-2) = [3(1)-2] + [3(2)-2] + [3(3)-2] + [3(4)-2]$$
$$= 1 + 4 + 7 + 10$$

b) $\displaystyle\sum_{j=5}^{10} jx^j$

Substitute values of j from 5 to 10 in the expression jx^j and add the results.

$$\sum_{j=5}^{10} jx^j = 5x^5 + 6x^6 + 7x^7 + 8x^8 + 9x^9 + 10x^{10}$$

The expression following the Σ sign represents the general term of the series. If a series is arithmetic or geometric, we use the formulas for the general term that were developed in grade 11.

Example 2

Write the following series using sigma notation.
a) $3 + 9 + 15 + 21 + 27$
b) $1 + 2 + 4 + 8 + 16 + 32 + 64$

Solution

a) $3 + 9 + 15 + 21 + 27$

This is an arithmetic series with $a = 3$ and $d = 6$.

The general term is $t_n = a + (n-1)d$
$$= 3 + (n-1)(6)$$
$$= 6n - 3$$

Since there are 5 terms, the series can be written as $\displaystyle\sum_{k=1}^{5}(6k-3)$.

b) $1 + 2 + 4 + 8 + 16 + 32 + 64$

This is a geometric series with $a = 1$ and $r = 2$.

The general term is $t_n = ar^{n-1}$
$$= 1 \times 2^{n-1}$$
$$= 2^{n-1}$$

Since there are 7 terms, the series can be written as $\displaystyle\sum_{k=1}^{7} 2^{k-1}$.

A series can be written using sigma notation in more than one way. For example, the series in *Example 2b* is a sum of powers of 2:

$1 + 2 + 4 + 8 + 16 + 32 + 64$. It can be rewritten as:

$2^0 + 2^1 + 2^2 + 2^3 + 2^4 + 2^5 + 2^6$

Each term in the series is of the form 2^k, where k starts at 0 and ends at 6.

Thus, the series can be written as $\sum\limits_{k=0}^{6} 2^k$.

Sometimes, we wish to find the general term of a series that is neither arithmetic nor geometric.

Example 3

Write the following series using sigma notation.

$$\frac{2}{1 \cdot 3} + \frac{4}{3 \cdot 5} + \frac{6}{5 \cdot 7} + \dots + \frac{20}{19 \cdot 21}$$

The dots in the denominator of each term of the series indicate multiplication.

Solution

The numerators form the arithmetic sequence 2, 4, 6, … , 20.
The sequence can be rewritten as 2(1), 2(2), 2(3), … , 2(10).
This is a sequence of 10 terms, each of the form $2k$, where k starts at 1 and ends at 10.

In each denominator, the numbers to the left of the dot are 1 less than the numerator, while the numbers to the right of the dot are 1 greater than the numerator. Thus, the denominators are of the form $(2k - 1)(2k + 1)$.

Thus, the series can be written as $\sum\limits_{k=1}^{10} \frac{2k}{(2k - 1)(2k + 1)}$.

Something to Think About

- How else could we have determined the general term for the series in *Example 3*?

The upper limit of a summation can be the variable n instead of a number.

Example 4

Write the binomial theorem using sigma notation.

Solution

The binomial theorem states:
$$(a + b)^n = C(n, 0)a^n + C(n, 1)a^{n-1}b + C(n, 2)a^{n-2}b^2 + \ldots + C(n, r)\,a^{n-r}b^r + \ldots$$
$$+ C(n, n-1)ab^{n-1} + C(n, n)b^n$$

The general term is $C(n, r)\,a^{n-r}b^r$, where $0 \le r \le n$.

Thus, $(a + b)^n = \displaystyle\sum_{r=0}^{n} C(n, r)\,a^{n-r}b^r$

7.3 Exercises

A

1. Write the series in expanded form.

a) $\displaystyle\sum_{k=1}^{5}(k + 3)$　　　　**b)** $\displaystyle\sum_{j=1}^{5}\frac{1}{j}$　　　　**c)** $\displaystyle\sum_{m=1}^{5}3^{m-1}$

d) $\displaystyle\sum_{j=1}^{5}(9 - 2j)$　　　　**e)** $\displaystyle\sum_{j=1}^{5}(-1)^j$　　　　**f)** $\displaystyle\sum_{j=1}^{5}3(2^j)$

2. Write each series using sigma notation.

a) $1 + 2 + 3 + \ldots + 100$　　　　**b)** $4 + 4 + 4 + 4 + 4 + 4 + 4$

c) $1^3 + 2^3 + 3^3 + 4^3 + 5^3$　　　　**d)** $\frac{1}{2} + \frac{1}{3} + \frac{1}{4} + \frac{1}{5}$

e) $3^3 + 4^4 + 5^5 + \ldots + 12^{12}$　　　　**f)** $a + a^2 + a^3 + \ldots + a^{12}$

3. Which sigma notation is correct for each series?

a) $5 + 7 + 9 + 11 + 13$　　　　**b)** $-1 + 1 + 3 + 5 + 7$

c) $1 + 4 + 7 + 10 + 13$　　　　**d)** $4 + 9 + 14 + 19 + 24$

　　i) $\displaystyle\sum_{k=1}^{5}(3k + 1)$　　**ii)** $\displaystyle\sum_{k=1}^{5}(2k - 3)$　　**iii)** $\displaystyle\sum_{k=1}^{5}(3k - 2)$

　　iv) $\displaystyle\sum_{k=1}^{5}(2k + 3)$　　**v)** $\displaystyle\sum_{k=1}^{5}(3 - 2k)$　　**vi)** $\displaystyle\sum_{k=1}^{5}(5k - 1)$

4. Write each series using sigma notation.

a) $2 + 4 + 6 + 8 + 10 + 12 + 14$　　　　**b)** $2 + 5 + 8 + 11 + 14 + 17$

c) $15 + 11 + 7 + 3 - 1$　　　　**d)** $4 + 20 + 100 + 500 + 2500$

e) $1 - 1 + 1 - 1$　　　　**f)** $3 - 6 + 12 - 24 + 48$

B

5. Knowledge/Understanding Write each series in expanded form.

a) $\displaystyle\sum_{k=1}^{6}(k+4)$

b) $\displaystyle\sum_{k=1}^{5}(-2)^k$

c) $\displaystyle\sum_{s=1}^{6}5(2)^{s-1}$

6. Write each series in expanded form.

a) $\displaystyle\sum_{k=1}^{4}a^k$

b) $\displaystyle\sum_{k=1}^{4}ka^k$

c) $\displaystyle\sum_{k=1}^{4}ak^k$

d) $\displaystyle\sum_{k=1}^{4}(-ak)^k$

7. Write each series using sigma notation.

a) $3+9+15+\ldots+93$

b) $18+13+8+\ldots-32$

c) $-2+2+6+\ldots+46$

d) $1+\dfrac{1}{2}+\dfrac{1}{4}+\ldots+\dfrac{1}{256}$

e) $3+6+12+\ldots+768$

f) $2-6+18-\ldots+1458$

8. Write each series in expanded form and simplify.

a) $\displaystyle\sum_{j=3}^{8}(2j-2)$

b) $\displaystyle\sum_{k=1}^{7}\dfrac{(x-1)^k}{k}$

c) $\displaystyle\sum_{i=0}^{5}C(5,i)$

d) $\displaystyle\sum_{i=2}^{6}C(2i-1,i)$

e) $\displaystyle\sum_{j=3}^{7}(-2)^{2j-3}$

f) $\displaystyle\sum_{k=1}^{5}\dfrac{1}{(2k-1)(2k+1)}$

9. Write each series using sigma notation.

a) $1\cdot2+2\cdot3+3\cdot4+\ldots+99\cdot100$

b) $1^2+3^2+5^2+\ldots+49^2$

c) $\dfrac{1}{1\cdot3}+\dfrac{1}{2\cdot4}+\dfrac{1}{3\cdot5}+\ldots+\dfrac{1}{10\cdot12}$

d) $C(4,0)a^4+C(4,1)a^3b+C(4,2)a^2b^2+C(4,3)ab^3+C(4,4)b^4$

e) $1-3+5-\ldots+29$

f) $1\cdot2+2\cdot2^2+3\cdot2^3+\ldots+8\cdot2^8$

g) $1+2^2+4^3+8^4+16^5+32^6+64^7$

h) $a+(a+d)+(a+2d)+\ldots+[a+(n-1)d]$

i) $a+ar+ar^2+\ldots+ar^{n-1}$

10. Communication Π, the capital Greek letter P, is the first letter in the word "product". Explain what the Π notation could mean. Support your explanation with examples.

11. **Application** Using the diagram at the right, write each set of numbers in combinatorial notation and use sigma notation to express their sum.

   a) the numbers in the 4th row

   b) the first 8 numbers in the 1st diagonal

   c) the first 5 numbers in the 2nd diagonal that runs from left to right.

   d) the first n numbers in the 3rd diagonal

```
                        1
                     1     1
                  1     2     1
               1     3     3     1
            1     4     6     4     1
         1     5    10    10     5     1
      1     6    15    20    15     6     1
   1     7    21    35    35    21     7     1
1     8    28    56    70    56    28     8     1
```

12. **Thinking/Inquiry/Problem Solving**

   a) Use sigma notation to represent the sum of the numbers in any given row of Pascal's triangle.

   b) Use sigma notation to express the sum of all the numbers in rows 0 to 8 of Pascal's triangle.

C

13. Use sigma notation to write the following sum.

$$1^2 + (2 + 3)^2 + (4 + 5 + 6)^2 + (7 + 8 + 9 + 10)^2 +$$
$$(11 + 12 + 13 + 14 + 15)^2 + \ldots + (172 + 173 + \ldots + 190)^2$$

Throughout this book, we have used a variety of methods to prove results. In this section, you will learn a new method of proof that can be used to prove that a result is true for all natural numbers. The nature of this method of proof is illustrated in the following example.

Suppose we want to prove that $1 + 3 + 5 + 7 + \ldots + (2n - 1) = n^2$ for all natural numbers, n.

It is natural to verify the result for a few values of n.

Let S_n represent the sum of the first n terms of the series.
When $n = 1$, $S_1 = 1$, or 1^2

When $n = 2$, $S_2 = 1 + 3$
$$= 4, \text{ or } 2^2$$

When $n = 3$, $S_3 = 1 + 3 + 5$
$$= 9, \text{ or } 3^2$$

We can continue and add the first 4 terms to determine S_4. A more efficient method is to use the fact that we already know the sum of the first 3 terms. To find S_4, add S_3 to the 4th term.

When $n = 4$, $S_4 = S_3 + t_4$
$$= 9 + 7$$
$$= 16, \text{ or } 4^2$$

Since we now know the sum of the first 4 terms, we can determine S_5 in the same way. We can extend these calculations as far as we please to verify the result for any value of n. But we cannot do this for all values of n. A proof for all values of n requires that the above calculations be generalized. We can do this as follows.

Suppose we have already proved that $S_k = k^2$ for some value of k.
The following calculation proves that the result is true for the next value of k; that is, it shows that $S_{k+1} = (k + 1)^2$.

$$S_{k+1} = S_k + t_{k+1}$$
$$= k^2 + (2(k + 1) - 1)$$
$$= k^2 + 2k + 1$$
$$= (k + 1)^2$$

Consider what we have done.

- We verified that the formula $S_n = n^2$ holds up to S_4.

- Then, we showed that *if* the formula holds for S_k, *then* it also holds for S_{k+1}.

The last statement implies that since the formula holds for S_4, it must also hold for S_{4+1}, or S_5. Since it holds for S_5, it must also hold for S_{5+1}, or S_6. Since we can continue this reasoning for all natural numbers, we have proved that $S_n = n^2$ for all natural numbers n.

We write $n \in N$ for "n is a natural number."

This method of proof is called the *Principle of Mathematical Induction*. Notice that the proof is a two-step process.

Take Note

The Principle of Mathematical Induction

A result involving natural numbers is true for all natural numbers if *both* of the following are true:

1. The result is true when $n = 1$.
2. *If* the result is true when $n = k$, *then* it is true for $n = k + 1$.

The following analogy illustrates how mathematical induction works.

Suppose we line up a series of dominoes numbered 1, 2, 3, 4, ... with equal spacing in a straight line as follows.

Suppose the dominoes are lined up in such a way that when one domino falls, the next one also falls, that is, when domino k falls, it knocks down domino $k + 1$ too.

Thus, if domino 1 is pushed down, it will knock down domino 2, which will knock down domino 3, and so on. Eventually, all the dominoes fall over.

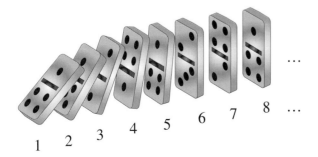

Example 1

Use the Principle of Mathematical Induction to prove that
$1^2 + 2^2 + 3^2 + \ldots + n^2 = \frac{n(n+1)(2n+1)}{6}$ for all $n \in N$.

Solution

Let S_n denote the sum of the first n terms of the above series.
Use the Principle of Mathematical Induction.

Step 1: Verify that S_n is true when $n = 1$.

When $n = 1$, $S_1 = 1^2 = 1$, and $\frac{1(1+1)(2(1)+1)}{6} = 1$

Therefore, the result is true when $n = 1$.

Step 2: Given that S_n is true when $n = k$, prove that it is true when $n = k + 1$.

Given: $S_k = \frac{k(k+1)(2k+1)}{6}$

Required to prove: $S_{k+1} = \frac{(k+1)(k+2)(2(k+1)+1)}{6}$

$\qquad\qquad\qquad\qquad = \frac{(k+1)(k+2)(2k+3)}{6}$

Proof: $S_{k+1} = S_k + t_{k+1}$

$\qquad\qquad = \frac{k(k+1)(2k+1)}{6} + (k+1)^2$

$\qquad\qquad = \frac{k(k+1)(2k+1) + 6(k+1)^2}{6}$

$\qquad\qquad = \frac{(k+1)[k(2k+1) + 6(k+1)]}{6}$

$\qquad\qquad = \frac{(k+1)[2k^2 + k + 6k + 6]}{6}$

$\qquad\qquad = \frac{(k+1)[2k^2 + 7k + 6]}{6}$

$\qquad\qquad = \frac{(k+1)(k+2)(2k+3)}{6}$

Thus, S_{k+1} is true if S_k is true.

Therefore, by the Principle of Mathematical Induction,
$1^2 + 2^2 + 3^2 + \ldots + n^2 = \frac{n(n+1)(2n+1)}{6}$ for all $n \in N$

Example 2

Prove that $3 + 6 + 12 + 24 + \ldots + 3(2^{n-1}) = 3(2^n - 1)$ for all $n \in N$.

Solution

Let S_n denote the sum of the first n terms of the above series.
Use the Principle of Mathematical Induction.

Step 1: When $n = 1$, $S_1 = 3$, and $3(2^1 - 1) = 3$

Therefore, the result is true when $n = 1$.

Step 2: Given: $S_k = 3(2^k - 1)$

Required to prove: $S_{k+1} = 3(2^{k+1} - 1)$

Proof: $S_{k+1} = S_k + t_{k+1}$

$$= 3(2^k - 1) + 3(2^k)$$
$$= 3(2^k) + 3(2^k) - 3$$
$$= 3(2^k + 2^k - 1)$$
$$= 3(2 \times 2^k - 1)$$
$$= 3(2^{k+1} - 1)$$

Thus, S_{k+1} is true if S_k is true.

Therefore, by the Principle of Mathematical Induction,
$3 + 6 + 12 + 24 + \ldots + 3(2^{n-1}) = 3(2^n - 1)$ for all $n \in N$

In the preceding examples, the formula to be proved was given in the statement of the problem. In the next example, the formula is not given.

Example 3

Establish a formula for the sum of the first n terms of this series and prove it using mathematical induction.

$$\frac{1}{1 \cdot 3} + \frac{1}{3 \cdot 5} + \frac{1}{5 \cdot 7} + \ldots + \frac{1}{(2n - 1)(2n + 1)}$$

Solution

Since no formula is given, calculate the first few partial sums and see if a pattern emerges.

Let S_n denote the sum of the first n terms of the above series.

$$S_1 = \frac{1}{3}$$

$$S_2 = \frac{1}{3} + \frac{1}{15}$$
$$= \frac{6}{15}, \text{ or } \frac{2}{5}$$

$$S_3 = S_2 + \frac{1}{35}$$
$$= \frac{2}{5} + \frac{1}{35}$$
$$= \frac{15}{35}, \text{ or } \frac{3}{7}$$

From these examples, it appears that $S_n = \dfrac{n}{2n + 1}$.

Now prove this using the Principle of Mathematical Induction.

Step 1: The result is true when $n = 1$, as shown above.

Step 2: Given: $S_k = \dfrac{k}{2k + 1}$

    Required to prove: $S_{k+1} = \dfrac{k + 1}{2(k + 1) + 1}$

                                      $= \dfrac{k + 1}{2k + 3}$

Proof: $S_{k+1} = S_k + t_{k+1}$

$$= \frac{k}{2k + 1} + \frac{1}{(2k + 1)(2k + 3)}$$

$$= \frac{k(2k + 3) + 1}{(2k + 1)(2k + 3)}$$

$$= \frac{2k^2 + 3k + 1}{(2k + 1)(2k + 3)}$$

$$= \frac{(2k + 1)(k + 1)}{(2k + 1)(2k + 3)}$$

$$= \frac{k + 1}{2k + 3}$$

Thus, S_{k+1} is true if S_k is true.

Therefore, by the Principle of Mathematical Induction,

$$\frac{1}{1 \cdot 3} + \frac{1}{3 \cdot 5} + \frac{1}{5 \cdot 7} + \ldots + \frac{1}{(2n - 1)(2n + 1)} = \frac{n}{2n + 1} \text{ for all } n \in N$$

When we guessed the formula for the solution of *Example 3*, we used inductive reasoning or induction. We then proved the formula using mathematical induction. The following quotation from *How to Solve It* by George Polya explains the difference between induction and mathematical induction.

> **Induction is the process of discovering general laws by the observation and combination of particular instances. It is used in all sciences and in mathematics. Mathematical induction is used in mathematics alone to prove theorems of a certain kind. It is rather unfortunate that their names are similar because there is very little logical connection between the two processes. There is, however, some practical connection; we often use both methods together.**

This was done in *Example 3*. The result to be proved was *discovered* by induction and *proved* by mathematical induction. To use mathematical induction, we must know what assertion is to be proved. It may come from any source, and it does not matter what the source is. In some cases, the source is induction, that is, the assertion is found experimentally.

Mathematical induction is a very powerful method of proof, but it can only be used to solve certain kinds of problems:

- The statement to be proved must involve natural numbers.
- The statement to be proved must be known in advance.

7.4 Exercises

A

1. In each expression below, the variable k represents a natural number. Substitute $k + 1$ for k and simplify the expression.

a) $\dfrac{k}{k + 1}$ **b)** $\dfrac{k}{2k + 1}$ **c)** $\dfrac{k + 1}{k - 1}$

d) $\dfrac{2k - 1}{3k - 1}$ **e)** $\dfrac{1}{3}k(k + 1)(k + 2)$ **f)** $\dfrac{1}{2}k(2k - 1)(2k + 1)$

2. Communication On page 363, we used mathematical induction to prove that $1 + 3 + 5 + 7 + \ldots + (2n - 1) = n^2$ for all $n \in N$. Provide a geometric proof of this result based on the diagram at the right.

B

3. To prove that a result is true using mathematical induction, *both* of the conditions in the *Take Note* box on page 364 must be satisfied.

a) Show that the formula $1 \cdot 2 + 2 \cdot 3 + 3 \cdot 4 + \ldots + n(n + 1) = n^2 + 1$ satisfies condition 1 of the Principle of Mathematical Induction, but does not satisfy condition 2.

b) Show that the formula $2 + 6 + 10 + \ldots + 2(2n - 1) = 2n^2 + 2$ satisfies condition 2 of the Principle of Mathematical Induction, but does not satisfy condition 1.

c) What conclusion must we draw about the formulas in parts a and b? Explain.

4. Knowledge/Understanding Prove using the Principle of Mathematical Induction for all $n \in N$.
$$2 + 4 + 6 + \ldots + 2n = n(n + 1)$$

5. Prove using the Principle of Mathematical Induction for all $n \in N$.

a) $3 + 4 + 5 + \ldots + (n + 2) = \dfrac{n(n + 5)}{2}$

b) $3 + 7 + 11 + \ldots + (4n - 1) = 2n^2 + n$

c) $1 + 2 + 4 + \ldots + 2^{n-1} = 2^n - 1$

d) $1 + 4 + 7 + \ldots + (3n - 2) = \dfrac{n(3n - 1)}{2}$

6. Prove by mathematical induction for all $n \in N$.

a) $1 \cdot 2 + 2 \cdot 3 + 3 \cdot 4 + \ldots + n(n + 1) = \dfrac{1}{3}n(n + 1)(n + 2)$

b) $4 + 14 + 30 + \ldots + (3n^2 + n) = n(n + 1)^2$

c) $1 \cdot 1 + 2 \cdot 2 + 3 \cdot 4 + 4 \cdot 8 + \ldots + n(2^{n-1}) = 1 + (n - 1)2^n$

d) $\dfrac{1}{4 \cdot 7} + \dfrac{1}{7 \cdot 10} + \dfrac{1}{10 \cdot 13} + \ldots + \dfrac{1}{(3n + 1)(3n + 4)} = \dfrac{n}{4(3n + 4)}$

7. The first diagonal of Pascal's triangle consists of the natural numbers. Recall that the partial sums of these numbers are found in the second diagonal. For example, $1 + 2 + 3 + 4 = 10$.

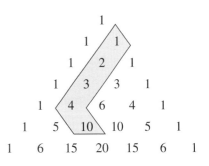

a) Write this partial sum using combinatorial notation.

b) Generalize the result of part a to determine a formula for the sum of the first n natural numbers.

c) Use mathematical induction to prove that your formula is correct.

8. Prove that your formula in exercise 7 is correct in two other ways.

a) Use the formula for the sum of an arithmetic series.

b) Give a geometric proof based on the diagram at the right.

9. **Application** The natural numbers shown below are the *triangular numbers*. They appear in the second diagonal of Pascal's triangle.

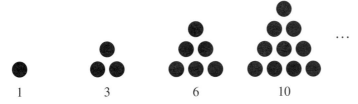

a) Use Pascal's triangle to determine a formula for the sum of the first n triangular numbers.

b) Use mathematical induction to prove that your formula is correct.

10. a) Prove, by mathematical induction, that
$$1^3 + 2^3 + 3^3 + \ldots + n^3 = \left[\frac{1}{2}n(n + 1)\right]^2 \text{ for all } n \in N.$$

b) Use the result of part a.
Determine $2^3 + 4^3 + 6^3 + \ldots + (2n)^3$.

c) Use the result of parts a and b.
Determine $1^3 + 3^3 + 5^3 + \ldots + (2n + 1)^3$.

11. a) Prove, by mathematical induction, that
$$1^2 + 3^2 + 5^2 + \ldots + (2n - 1)^2 = \frac{n(2n - 1)(2n + 1)}{3} \text{ for all } n \in N.$$

b) Suppose you had not been given the sum in part a. Explain how you could have found the sum using the formula from *Example 1* for the sum of the first n squares.

12. Prove, by mathematical induction, that $\sum_{i=1}^{n} x^i = \frac{x^{n+1} - x}{x - 1}$ where $x \neq 1$.

13. Establish a formula for each series and prove it using mathematical induction.

a) $\displaystyle\sum_{k=1}^{n} \frac{1}{(3k-2)(3k+1)}$

b) $\displaystyle\sum_{k=1}^{n} \frac{1}{(4k-3)(4k+1)}$

14. Establish a formula for each product and prove it using mathematical induction.

a) $(1+1)\left(1+\frac{1}{2}\right)\left(1+\frac{1}{3}\right)\cdots\left(1+\frac{1}{n}\right)$

b) $\left(1-\frac{1}{2}\right)\left(1-\frac{1}{3}\right)\left(1-\frac{1}{4}\right)\cdots\left(1-\frac{1}{n+1}\right)$

15. Prove, by mathematical induction, that

$$\frac{1}{1 \cdot 2} + \frac{1}{2 \cdot 3} + \frac{1}{3 \cdot 4} + \ldots + \frac{1}{n(n+1)} = \frac{n}{n+1}$$

for all numbers $n \in N$.

16. **Thinking/Inquiry/Problem Solving** Establish a formula for $1 + 2 \cdot 2! + 3 \cdot 3! + \ldots + n \cdot n!$ and prove it using mathematical induction.

17. a) Use mathematical induction to prove the formula for the sum of n terms of an arithmetic series with initial term a and common difference d.

$$a + (a+d) + (a+2d) + \ldots + [a+(n-1)d] = \frac{n}{2}[2a+(n-1)d]$$

b) Give another proof of the result in part a.

18. a) Use mathematical induction to prove the formula for the sum of n terms of a geometric series with initial term a and common ratio r.

$$a + ar + ar^2 + \ldots + ar^{n-1} = \frac{a(r^n - 1)}{r-1}, r \neq 1$$

b) Give another proof of the result in part a.

C

19. Establish a formula for $\dfrac{1}{2!} + \dfrac{2}{3!} + \dfrac{3}{4!} + \ldots + \dfrac{n}{(n+1)!}$ and prove it using mathematical induction.

20. Prove that $C(n,0) + C(n,2) + C(n,4) + \ldots + C(n,n) = 2^{n-1}$ for all even numbers $n \in N$.

7.5 Applications of Mathematical Induction

In Section 7.4, we used mathematical induction to prove formulas for the sums of series. We can also use mathematical induction in other types of problems. The essential requirement is that the problem involves natural numbers.

Example 1

Prove that $n^3 + 2n$ is divisible by 3 for all $n \in N$.

Solution

Let P_n be the statement $n^3 + 2n$ is divisible by 3.
Use the Principle of Mathematical Induction.

Step 1: When $n = 1$, $n^3 + 2n = 1^3 + 2(1)$ or 3, which is divisible by 3
Therefore, the result is true when $n = 1$.

Step 2: Given: $k^3 + 2k$ is divisible by 3.
Required to prove: $(k + 1)^3 + 2(k + 1)$ is divisible by 3.
Proof: $(k + 1)^3 + 2(k + 1)$
$= k^3 + 3k^2 + 3k + 1 + 2k + 2$
$= k^3 + 3k^2 + (2k + k) + 1 + 2k + 2$
$= (k^3 + 2k) + (3k^2 + 3k + 3)$
$= (k^3 + 2k) + 3(k^2 + k + 1)$ ①

The expression $k^3 + 2k$ is divisible by 3 (given). The expression $3(k^2 + k + 1)$ has a common factor of 3 so it is divisible by 3.
Therefore, expression ① is divisible by 3.

Thus, if P_k is true, then P_{k+1} is true.

Therefore, by the Principle of Mathematical Induction, $n^3 + 2n$ is divisible by 3 for all $n \in N$.

Example 2

Prove that $9^n - 1$ is divisible by 8 for all $n \in N$.

Solution

Let P_n be the statement $9^n - 1$ is divisible by 8.
Use the Principle of Mathematical Induction.

Step 1: When $n = 1$, $9^n - 1 = 9^1 - 1$ or 8, which is divisible by 8
Therefore, the result is true when $n = 1$.

Step 2: *Given*: $9^k - 1$ is divisible by 8.

  Required to prove: $9^{k+1} - 1$ is divisible by 8.

  Proof: $\quad 9^{k+1} - 1$

$$= 9^k \bullet 9 - 1$$
$$= 9^k(1 + 8) - 1$$
$$= 9^k + 8 \bullet 9^k - 1$$
$$= (9^k - 1) + 8 \bullet 9^k \qquad ①$$

The expression $9^k - 1$ is divisible by 8 (given).

The expression $8 \bullet 9^k$ has a factor of 8 so it is divisible by 8.

Therefore, expression ① is divisible by 8.

Thus, if P_k is true, then P_{k+1} is true.

Therefore, by the Principle of Mathematical Induction, $9^n - 1$ is divisible by 8 for all $n \in N$.

Something to Think About

- In *Example 1*, we wrote $3k$ as $2k + k$; and in *Example 2*, we wrote $9^k \bullet 9 - 1$ as $9^k(1 + 8) - 1$. Why did we do this? How did we know to do this? Explain.

In exercise 7 on page 355, you used a combinatorial approach to prove the binomial theorem. Here is an alternate proof that uses mathematical induction. Recall Pascal's formula from Section 7.1 on page 345. You proved this formula in exercise 11 on page 347.

$$C(n, r) = C(n - 1, r - 1) + C(n - 1, r)$$

The Binomial Theorem

For all $n \in N$, $(a + b)^n = \displaystyle\sum_{r=0}^{n} C(n, r)\, a^{n-r} b^r$.

Proof using mathematical induction

Let P_n be the above statement.

Use the Principle of Mathematical Induction.

Step 1: When $n = 1$, $(a + b)^1 = a + b$, and $\displaystyle\sum_{r=0}^{1} C(1, r) a^{1-r} b^r$

$$= C(1, 0)a^{1-0}b^0 + C(1, 1)a^{1-1}b^1$$
$$= a + b$$

Therefore, the result is true when $n = 1$.

Step 2: Given: $(a + b)^k = \displaystyle\sum_{r=0}^{k} C(k, r)a^{k-r}b^r$

Required to prove: $(a + b)^{k+1} = \displaystyle\sum_{r=0}^{k+1} C(k + 1, r)a^{k+1-r}b^r$

Proof: $(a + b)^{k+1}$

$= (a + b)(a + b)^k$

$= a(a + b)^k + b(a + b)^k$

$= a\Big[C(k, 0)a^k + C(k, 1)a^{k-1}b + C(k, 2)a^{k-2}b^2 + \ldots$

$\qquad + C(k, r)a^{k-r}b^r + \ldots + C(k, k)b^k\Big]$

$\qquad + b\Big[C(k, 0)a^k + C(k, 1)a^{k-1}b + C(k, 2)a^{k-2}b^2 + \ldots$

$\qquad + C(k, r)a^{k-r}b^r + \ldots + C(k, k)b^k\Big]$

$= \Big[C(k, 0)a^{k+1} + C(k, 1)a^kb + C(k, 2)a^{k-1}b^2 + \ldots$

$\qquad + C(k, r)a^{k-r+1}b^r + \ldots + C(k, k)ab^k\Big]$

$\qquad + \Big[C(k, 0)a^kb + C(k, 1)a^{k-1}b^2 + C(k, 2)a^{k-2}b^3 + \ldots$

$\qquad + C(k, r)a^{k-r}b^{r+1} + \ldots + C(k, k)b^{k+1}\Big]$

$= C(k, 0)a^{k+1} + [C(k, 0) + C(k, 1)]a^kb + [C(k, 1) + C(k, 2)]a^{k-1}b^2 + \ldots$

$\qquad + [C(k, r - 1) + C(k, r)]a^{k-r+1}b^r + \ldots + C(k, k)b^{k+1}$

By Pascal's formula, $C(n, r) = C(n - 1, r - 1) + C(n - 1, r)$.

Therefore,

$C(k, 0) + C(k, 1) = C(k + 1, 1), C(k, 1) + C(k, 2) = C(k + 1, 2),$
$\qquad\qquad C(k, r - 1) + C(k, r) = C(k + 1, r)$ and so on

Also, $C(k, 0) = C(k + 1, 0)$ and $C(k, k) = C(k + 1, k + 1)$

Therefore,

$(a + b)^{k+1} = C(k + 1, 0)a^{k+1} + C(k + 1, 1)a^kb + C(k + 1, 2)a^{k-1}b^2 + \ldots$

$\qquad\qquad + C(k + 1, r)a^{k-r+1}b^r + \ldots + C(k + 1, k + 1)b^{k+1}$

$\qquad = \displaystyle\sum_{r=0}^{k+1} C(k + 1, r)\, a^{k+1-r}b^r$

Thus, if P_k is true, then P_{k+1} is true.

Therefore, by the Principle of Mathematical Induction,

$(a + b)^n = \displaystyle\sum_{r=0}^{n} C(n, r)\, a^{n-r}b^r$ for all $n \in N$

Something to Think About

- Explain each step of the proof.
- How do we know that $C(k, 0) = C(k + 1, 0)$ and $C(k, k) = C(k + 1, k + 1)$?

Use mathematical induction.

B

1. Knowledge/Understanding Prove that $4^n - 1$ is divisible by 3 for all $n \in N$.

2. Prove that $n(n + 1)(n + 2)$ is divisible by 3 for all $n \in N$.

3. Prove that $3^{2n} - 2^{2n}$ is divisible by 5 for all $n \in N$.

4. Prove that $6^{2n-1} + 1$ is divisible by 7 for all $n \in N$.

5. a) Prove that $n(n + 1)$ is divisible by 2 for all $n \in N$.

   b) Use the result of part a to prove that $n^3 + 5n$ is divisible by 6.

6. Prove that $x - y$ is a factor of $x^n - y^n$ for all $n \in N$.

7. Prove that $\dfrac{n^3 + 6n^2 + 2n}{3}$ is a natural number for all $n \in N$.

8. Prove that 4 is a factor of $3^n + 2n - 1$ for all $n \in N$.

9. Prove that $C(n + 2, 3) - C(n, 3) = n^2$ for all natural numbers $n \geq 3$.

10. Communication As each group of business people arrives at a meeting, each person shakes hands with all the other people present.

   a) Explain why if n people come to the meeting, then $\dfrac{n(n - 1)}{2}$ handshakes occur.

   b) Prove the result in part a using mathematical induction.

11. Application Prove that $5^n - 4^n$ is divisible by 9 for all even positive integers n.

12. Prove that $a^n + b^n$ is divisible by $a + b$ for all positive odd integers n.

13. Thinking/Inquiry/Problem Solving Prove that n distinct lines passing through a point on a plane divide the plane into $2n$ regions.

C

14. Prove that the maximum number of points of intersection of n distinct lines in a plane is $\dfrac{n(n - 1)}{2}$.

Pascal's Triangle

- Pascal's triangle is the following triangular number pattern.

$$
\begin{array}{ccccccccccccc}
 & & & & & & 1 & & & & & & \\
 & & & & & 1 & & 1 & & & & & \\
 & & & & 1 & & 2 & & 1 & & & & \\
 & & & 1 & & 3 & & 3 & & 1 & & & \\
 & & 1 & & 4 & & 6 & & 4 & & 1 & & \\
 & 1 & & 5 & & 10 & & 10 & & 5 & & 1 & \\
1 & & 6 & & 15 & & 20 & & 15 & & 6 & & 1 \\
 & & & & & & \vdots & & & & & &
\end{array}
$$

- The rth number in the nth row of Pascal's triangle is $C(n, r) = \dfrac{n!}{r!(n-r)!}$ where $n = 0, 1, 2, \ldots$ and $0 \le r \le n$.
- $C(n, r) = C(n, n - r)$
- $C(n, r) = C(n - 1, r - 1) + C(n - 1, r)$ (Pascal's formula)

The Binomial Theorem

- For any natural number n,

$$
\begin{aligned}
(a + b)^n &= \sum_{r=0}^{n} C(n, r)\, a^{n-r} b^r \\
&= C(n, 0)a^n + C(n, 1)a^{n-1}b + C(n, 2)a^{n-2}b^2 + \ldots \\
&\quad + C(n, r)\, a^{n-r}b^r + \ldots + C(n, n)b^n
\end{aligned}
$$

- The general term in the expansion of $(a + b)^n$ is $t_{r+1} = C(n, r)a^{n-r}b^r$

Sigma Notation

- Sigma notation is a concise way to write a series.
- The sum $a_1 + a_2 + a_3 + \ldots + a_n$ can be written in sigma notation as $\displaystyle\sum_{k=1}^{n} a_k$.

The Principle of Mathematical Induction

- A result involving natural numbers is true for all natural numbers if *both* of the following are true:
   1. The result is true when $n = 1$.
   2. *If* the result is true when $n = k$, *then* it is true for $n = k + 1$.

1. State another expression in the form $C(n, r)$ that is equal to each of the following.

   a) $C(7, 3)$
   b) $C(9, 5) + C(9, 6)$
   c) $C(n, r)$
   d) $C(n - 1, r) + C(n - 1, r - 1)$

2. Use the properties of Pascal's triangle to evaluate each sum.

   a) $C(5, 0) + C(5, 1) + C(5, 2) + C(5, 3) + C(5, 4) + C(5, 5)$
   b) $C(3, 3) + C(4, 3) + C(5, 3) + C(6, 3) + C(7, 3)$
   c) $C(2, 2) + C(3, 2) + C(4, 2) + C(5, 2) + C(6, 2)$

3. Visualize joining different numbers of points with line segments in all possible ways. These diagrams show the line segments for 2, 3, 4, 5, and 6 points.

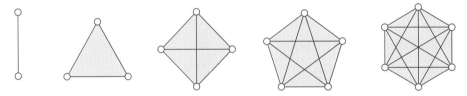

   a) Count the line segments on each diagram and record the results.

   b) Compare the results of part a with Pascal's triangle. Where are these numbers found on Pascal's triangle? Use combinations to explain why these numbers in the triangle represent the numbers of line segments on these diagrams.

   c) What is the general formula for the number of line segments when there are n points? Prove that your formula is correct.

4. a) Use Pascal's triangle to expand $(a + b)^5$.

   b) Use Pascal's triangle to find the coefficient of x^5 in the expansion of $(x + y)^8$.

5. Expand each expression using the binomial theorem.

   a) $(x + 2)^5$
   b) $(2x - 3)^4$
   c) $(x^2 - 4)^3$

6. Find the specified terms in each expansion.

   a) $(2 - x)^7$; the first 3 terms
   b) $(1 - 3x)^9$; the 5th term
   c) $\left(x^3 - \dfrac{1}{x^2}\right)^{10}$; the constant term
   d) $(1 + \sqrt{x})^5$; the two middle terms

7. Find the coefficient of x^7 in the expansion of $(x + 2)^9$.

8. Find the coefficient of x^3y^4 in the expansion of $(x - y)^7$.

9. Write each summation in expanded form.

a) $\displaystyle\sum_{k=1}^{5}(k^2 + 2)$

b) $\displaystyle\sum_{k=1}^{5}(k + 2)^2$

c) $\displaystyle\sum_{k=1}^{4}(-2)^{2k+1}$

d) $\displaystyle\sum_{k=5}^{n}\frac{1}{(k + 1)(k - 1)}$

10. Write each series using sigma notation.

a) $7 + 10 + 13 + \ldots + 28$

b) $2 + 1 + \dfrac{1}{2} + \dfrac{1}{4} + \ldots + \dfrac{1}{32}$

c) $1 + 2 \cdot 2! + 3 \cdot 3! + 4 \cdot 4! + \ldots + 10 \cdot 10!$

d) $1 \cdot 2 + 2 \cdot 3 + 3 \cdot 4 + \ldots + 15 \cdot 16$

e) $\dfrac{1}{4 \cdot 7} + \dfrac{1}{7 \cdot 10} + \dfrac{1}{10 \cdot 13} + \ldots + \dfrac{1}{31 \cdot 34}$

11. Prove by mathematical induction for all $n \in N$.

a) $2 + 6 + 10 + \ldots + (4n - 2) = 2n^2$

b) $1 \cdot 3 + 2 \cdot 5 + 3 \cdot 7 + \ldots + n(2n + 1) = \dfrac{1}{6}n(n + 1)(4n + 5)$

c) $\dfrac{1}{2} + \dfrac{3}{2^2} + \dfrac{5}{2^3} + \ldots + \dfrac{2n - 1}{2^n} = 3 - \dfrac{2n + 3}{2^n}$

12. Prove by mathematical induction for all $n \in N$.

a) $10^n - 3^n$ is divisible by 7.

b) 64 is a factor of $9^n - 8n - 1$.

c) $3^{2n+1} + 5^{2n-1}$ is divisible by 16.

13. a) Establish a formula for the sum of the first n terms of the series $\displaystyle\sum_{k=1}^{n}\frac{1}{k(k + 1)}$ and prove it using mathematical induction.

b) Use the result of part a to evaluate $\displaystyle\sum_{k=50}^{100}\frac{1}{k(k + 1)}$.

14. Prove that $x^{2n+1} + y^{2n+1}$ is divisible by $x + y$ for all integers $n \geq 0$.

Self-Test

1. **Knowledge/Understanding**

   a) The entries in the 8th row of Pascal's triangle are:

   1   8   28   56   70   56   28   8   1

   What are the entries in the 9th row of Pascal's triangle?

   b) Write the terms in the expansion of $(a + b)^8$.

   c) State another expression in the form $C(n, r)$ that is equal to $C(11, 6)$.

2. **Communication** Use the meaning of combinations to prove Pascal's formula: $C(n, r) = C(n - 1, r - 1) + C(n - 1, r)$.

3. **Application** Using the diagram at the right, determine the number of ways in which the word BINOMIAL can be spelled out starting at the letter B and moving to an adjacent letter in any direction.

   <pre>
           B
        I   I
      N   N   N
    O   O   O   O
       M   M   M
         I   I
           A
        L   L
   </pre>

4. Write $\dfrac{2}{\sqrt{1}} + \dfrac{3}{\sqrt{2}} + \dfrac{4}{\sqrt{3}} + \ldots + \dfrac{11}{\sqrt{10}}$ using sigma notation.

5. Write $\displaystyle\sum_{j=1}^{5}(2j - 1)2^{-j}$ in expanded form.

6. Expand and simplify $(2x^3 - 5)^3$.

7. Determine the coefficient of $a^{16}b^4$ in the expansion of $(a^2 - b^2)^{10}$.

8. Determine the middle terms in the expansion of $(1 + 4x)^7$.

9. **Thinking/Inquiry/Problem Solving** Conjecture a formula for the product $\left(1 + \dfrac{3}{1}\right)\left(1 + \dfrac{5}{4}\right)\left(1 + \dfrac{7}{9}\right) \ldots \left(1 + \dfrac{2n + 1}{n^2}\right)$ and prove it using mathematical induction.

10. Prove that $7^n + 4^n$ is divisible by 11 for all odd positive integers n.

Performance Problems for Discrete Mathematics

The problems in this section offer you the opportunity to solve some complex problems related to the topics you have studied. Some of these problems are challenging. You may find it helpful to work with others, to share ideas and strategies. You may be unable to complete a solution to some of the problems at the first attempt. Be prepared to research, to return to a problem again and again.

Curriculum Expectations

By the end of this section you will:

- Solve complex problems and present the solutions with clarity and justification.
- Solve problems of significance, working independently, as individuals and in small groups.
- Solve problems requiring effort over extended periods of time.

- Demonstrate significant learning and the effective use of skills in tasks such as solving challenging problems, researching problems, applying mathematics, creating proofs, using technology effectively, and presenting course topics or extensions of course topics.

Focus on ... The Divider

Suppose we wish to determine the number of ways that 10 loonies can be distributed among 6 people: A, B, C, D, E, and F. Any distribution is possible; for example, the first four people could receive 2 loonies each, while the last two people receive 1 loonie each. Alternatively, one person could receive all 6 loonies.

We can represent the problem graphically by writing 10 Ls in a row. We can then divide the Ls into 6 groups by inserting 5 dividing lines. Assume the first group of Ls goes to A, the second group to B, the third group to C, and so on. For example, in the representation:

LL|LLLL|||LLL

A gets 2 loonies, B gets 1, C gets 4, D gets 0, E gets 0, and F gets 3 loonies.

We can represent other distributions by changing the position of the dividers. Thus, the total number of possible distributions corresponds to number of ways of arranging 10 Ls and 5 dividers. From Section 6.3, we know that the number of ways to arrange 15 symbols, 10 of which are of one kind and 5 of which are of another kind, is:

$$\frac{15!}{10!5!} = 3003$$

There are 3003 ways to allocate the loonies.

If we could distinguish between the loonies—for example, if all had different dates—then the problem would be straightforward. Each loonie could be distributed in 6 ways, so there would be 6^{10} ways to distribute 10 loonies. Since we cannot distinguish between the loonies, it does not matter which person is given a particular loonie, only how many loonies each person is given.

Problem 1

We solved the preceding problem by modelling it as a permutations problem. It could also have been solved using a combinatorial approach. Provide a combinatorial solution to the problem.

Problem 2

How many numbers between 1 and 9999 have 8 as the sum of their digits?

Problem 3

How many ways can 10 loonies be distributed among 6 people if each person must receive at least 1 loonie?

Problem 4

Suppose 10 coins are to be chosen from an unlimited supply of pennies, nickels, dimes, and quarters. In how many ways can this be done? Assume that two coins of the same kind are indistinguishable.

Focus on ... Probability

In an earlier grade, you learned the following definition of probability. If an event A can occur in r ways out of a total of n equally likely ways, then the probability of event A, P(A), is:

$$P(A) = \frac{r}{n}$$

For example, suppose four cards are dealt from a well-shuffled deck. What is the probability that they all are red?

There are 52 cards, of which 26 are red. The total number of 4-card deals is $C(52, 4)$. The event A is being dealt 4 red cards, which can occur in $C(26, 4)$ ways.

$$\begin{aligned}
P(\text{red deal}) &= \frac{C(26, 4)}{C(52, 4)} \\
&= \frac{\frac{26 \times 25 \times 24 \times 23}{4 \times 3 \times 2 \times 1}}{\frac{52 \times 51 \times 50 \times 49}{4 \times 3 \times 2 \times 1}} \\
&= \frac{26 \times 25 \times 24 \times 23}{52 \times 51 \times 50 \times 49} \\
&\doteq 0.055
\end{aligned}$$

There is approximately a 5.5% chance of being dealt 4 red cards.

We could also have argued as follows. The probability that the first card is red is $\frac{26}{52}$. Since there are 51 remaining cards, of which 25 are red, the probability that the second card is red is $\frac{25}{31}$. Similarly, the probability that the third and fourth cards are red is $\frac{24}{50}$ and $\frac{23}{49}$, respectively. Thus, the probability that all 4 cards are red is $\frac{26}{52} \times \frac{25}{51} \times \frac{24}{50} \times \frac{23}{49}$.

Problem 5

Suppose 4 cards are dealt from a well-shuffled deck. What is the probability of getting at least one spade?

Problem 6

Suppose 4 letters are selected at random from the alphabet with repetitions allowed. What is the probability that all the letters are different?

Problem 7

There are 4 aces in a standard 52-card deck. A bridge hand consists of 13 cards from the 52-card deck. Determine the probability that a bridge hand contains:

 a) all four aces

 b) no aces

Problem 8

A drawer contains 6 white socks and 6 black socks. Six children each take 2 socks at random. Determine the probability that each child gets one white sock and one black sock.

Focus on ... Fibonacci Numbers

The Fibonacci sequence $\{u_n\}$ is generated by the recursive equations:

$$u_1 = u_2 = 1$$
$$u_n = u_{n-1} + u_{n-2} \qquad n = 3, 4, 5, \ldots$$

Thus, each term is the sum of the two previous terms. The first 20 terms of the sequence are listed at the right.

The Fibonacci sequence is rich in arithmetic patterns. In these problems, you will explore and prove some of these patterns.

This is the most famous sequence in mathematics, and is an object of continued study by mathematicians. In fact, there is a professional journal devoted to the study of the Fibonacci numbers, *The Fibonacci Quarterly.*

u_1	1
u_2	1
u_3	2
u_4	3
u_5	5
u_6	8
u_7	13
u_8	21
u_9	34
u_{10}	55
u_{11}	89
u_{12}	144
u_{13}	233
u_{14}	377
u_{15}	610
u_{16}	987
u_{17}	1597
u_{18}	2584
u_{19}	4181
u_{20}	6765

Problem 9

Observe the following pattern.

$$1^2 + 1^2 + 2^2 = 2 \times 3$$
$$1^2 + 1^2 + 2^2 + 3^2 = 3 \times 5$$
$$1^2 + 1^2 + 2^2 + 3^2 + 5^2 = 5 \times 8$$

In u_n notation, it appears that:

$$1^2 + 1^2 + 2^2 + 3^2 + 5^2 + \ldots + u_n^2 = u_n u_{n+1}$$

Prove this result using mathematical induction.

Problem 10

Observe that $13^2 - 8^2 = 5 \times 21$. Find the general form of this pattern and prove it directly.

Problem 11

What is the sum of the first n Fibonacci numbers? Use the Fibonacci numbers on this page to make a conjecture, and prove it using mathematical induction.

Problem 12

Observe that $8^2 = 5 \times 13 - 1$. Is this part of a pattern? If so, find the general form using u_n notation, and prove it using mathematical induction.

Problem 13

The formula $1^2 + 1^2 + 2^2 + 3^2 + 5^2 + 8^2 = 8 \times 13$ has a nice geometric proof. Use the diagram at the right to find it. Does this proof generalize to other formulas in the same family?

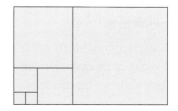

Problem 14

In the array below, Pascal's triangle is written with the numbers left-justified.

```
1
1   1
1   2   1
1   3   3   1
1   4   6   4   1
1   5   10  10  5   1
1   6   15  20  15  6   1
1   7   21  35  35  21  7   1
1   8   28  56  70  56  28  8   1
```

Srinivasa
Ramanujan
(1887–1920)
Born: Erode,
India

Ramanujan was one of India's greatest mathematicians. Despite his lack of formal training, his publications in mathematical journals gained him fame in India. Ramanujan started corresponding with a Cambridge professor, G.H. Hardy, who was impressed with Ramanujan's work and brought him to England.
Ramanujan was admitted to the university and graduated in 1916. He is most noted for his work in the analytical theory of numbers, elliptic functions, and infinite series. Ramanujan was the first Indian to be elected a Fellow of the Royal Society.

Starting at the top, look at the diagonals that point towards the right and sum the numbers in the diagonal. For example, for the first 5 diagonals we have:

1
1
$1 + 1 = 2$
$1 + 2 = 3$
$1 + 3 + 1 = 5$

Formulate the general pattern and prove it.

Other Problems

Problem 15

An urn contains 3 white balls and 5 black balls. Three balls are selected at random. Determine the probability that:

a) all the balls are white   **b)** there is exactly one white ball

Problem 16

A drawer contains 6 white socks and 6 black socks. Three girls and three boys each take 2 socks at random. Find the probability that:

a) all the girls get the white socks and all the boys get the black socks

b) each child gets socks of the same colour

Problem 17

Suppose 4 committees, A, B, C and D, are to be filled by 12 students. At the beginning, each student is asked to name the committee they would most like to be on. Let a, b, c, and d represent the numbers of students who choose committees A, B, C, and D, respectively. In how many ways can this be done?

Problem 18

Suppose 10 cards are chosen from a standard deck of 52 cards and the number of spades, hearts, diamonds, and clubs selected are recorded. How many different outcomes are possible?

Problem 19

Suppose 10 indistinguishable dimes and 6 indistinguishable quarters are to be distributed among 6 people: A, B, C, D, E, and F. How many ways can this be done if it is possible for any person to receive no coins?

Problem 20

Find how many ways a group of 12 students can be divided into 3 groups of 4 students each if:

a) one group is to focus on permutations, another on combinations, and the third on mathematical induction

b) all groups have the same task

Problem 21

The student council consists of two grade 9 students, three grade 10 students, four grade 11 students, and five grade 12 students. A committee of 4 is formed by placing all 14 names in a hat and drawing 4 names. What is the probability that the members of the committee are:

a) all in the same grade?

b) all from different grades?

Problem 22

Calculate the probability that a bridge hand contains:

Explain why the answer to part a is reasonable.

a) the ace of spades   **b)** exactly one ace

c) exactly two aces   **d)** only black cards

e) at least one black card   **f)** more black cards than red cards

g) a 3-3-3-4 distribution (that is, at least 3 cards of each suit)

Problem 23

Consider 5 cards with both sides blank. On the 10 sides are written 5 English letters (A, B, C, D, and E) and 5 Greek letters ($\alpha, \beta, \gamma, \delta$, and ε), one letter per side. If the letters were assigned to a side randomly, what is the probability that each card has an English letter on one side and a Greek letter on the other?

Problem 24

Suppose four people sit down to dinner at a table, and each place is set with 3 pieces of cutlery. In total, there are 4 knives, 4 forks, and 4 spoons on the table, but a mischievous butler has allocated these 12 utensils at random. Determine the probability that:

a) each person gets one of each utensil

b) one person gets all knives, one person gets all forks, and one person gets all spoons

**G.H. Hardy
(1877–1947)**
Born: Cranleigh,
England

In his youth, Hardy did not have a passion for mathematics even though he excelled in the subject. At the start of his studies at Cambridge, he considered switching to history. However, he switched mentors instead and became engaged in mathematics. Hardy's other life-long interest was cricket.
Hardy collaborated with Ramanujan and other colleagues, contributing to many topics of pure mathematics, including summation of divergent series, Fourier series, and the distribution of primes.

Problem 25

A standard deck of 52 cards is divided at random into two equal piles of 26 cards each. What is the probability that each pile has the same number of red and black cards?

Problem 26

Multiples of 11 are easy to recognize when they are small. Observe the following pattern in the Fibonacci numbers.

$34 = 11 \times 3 + 1$
$55 = 11 \times 5 + 0$
$89 = 11 \times 8 + 1$

Is this pattern part of a general relationship? If so, formulate the general pattern and prove it using mathematical induction.

Problem 27

Consider this variation of the Fibonacci sequence.

$$t_1 = t_2 = 1$$
$$t_n = t_{n-1} + 2t_{n-2} \qquad n = 3, 4, 5, \ldots$$

a) Generate the first few terms of the sequence.

b) Since the original Fibonacci sequence has many simple arithmetic properties, it is likely that this sequence will too. Find an equation that corresponds to the Fibonacci formula: $8^2 = 5 \times 13 - 1$.

Formulate your equation in general using t_n notation.

c) The sequence $\{t_n\}$ is simple enough that it is possible to guess a formula for t_n that is not a recursive formula in terms of other t-values, but a formula in terms of n. Find such a formula, and prove it using mathematical induction.

Problem 28

Consider this statement:

Every number less than or equal to n can be written as a sum of distinct Fibonacci numbers.

Use mathematical induction to prove this statement.

Problem 29

The identities of problem 12 give rise to a famous geometrical paradox illustrated by the diagram at the right for the case $8^2 = 5 \times 13 - 1$. The rectangle and the square are composed of the same 4 pieces, yet the rectangle has an area of 65 and the square has an area of 64. Explain.

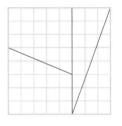

Challenge Problem 30

For each series, conjecture a formula for the sum of n terms, then prove it using mathematical induction.

a) $1 \bullet 1 + 1 \bullet 2 + 2 \bullet 3 + 3 \bullet 5 + 5 \bullet 8 + 8 \bullet 13 + \ldots$

b) $\dfrac{1}{1 \times 2} + \dfrac{1}{1 \times 3} + \dfrac{1}{2 \times 5} + \dfrac{1}{3 \times 8} + \dfrac{1}{5 \times 13} + \dfrac{1}{8 \times 21} + \ldots$

Challenge Problem 31

Consider any row of Pascal's triangle. Multiply the entries of the row by successive Fibonacci numbers and add the results. For example, for the fifth row 1, 5, 10, 10, 5, 1 the associated sum is

$1 \times 1 + 5 \times 1 + 10 \times 2 + 10 \times 3 + 5 \times 5 + 1 \times 8 = 89$

Find the general case of this formula and prove it using mathematical induction.

Cumulative Performance Problems

The problems in this section offer you the opportunity to solve some significant problems related to the topics you have studied throughout the course. Several problems can be solved in more than one way. Some of the problems are challenging. Considerable ingenuity may be needed to solve them. You may be unable to complete a solution at the first attempt. You may find it helpful to work with others, to share ideas and strategies. Be persistent—try a problem, set it aside, try it again later, or try another strategy. It may take several days, or even longer, to solve some of these problems.

Curriculum Expectations

By the end of this section you will:

- Solve complex problems and present the solutions with clarity and justification.

- Solve problems of significance, working independently, as individuals and in small groups.

- Solve problems requiring effort over extended periods of time.

- Demonstrate significant learning and the effective use of skills in tasks such as solving challenging problems, researching problems, applying mathematics, creating proofs, using technology effectively, and presenting course topics or extensions of course topics.

Focus on ... Vector Proofs Using Linear Combinations

We can use linear combinations in vector proofs.

Example

In $\triangle ABC$, medians AM and BN intersect at R.
Prove that $MR = \frac{1}{3} MA$.

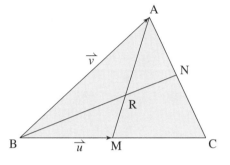

Proof

Let $\overrightarrow{u} = \overrightarrow{BM}$ and $\overrightarrow{v} = \overrightarrow{BA}$. Express $\overrightarrow{MA}$ and $\overrightarrow{MR}$ as linear combinations of $\overrightarrow{u}$ and $\overrightarrow{v}$.

$$\overrightarrow{MA} = -\overrightarrow{u} + \overrightarrow{v} \qquad ①$$

$$\overrightarrow{MR} = -\overrightarrow{u} + \overrightarrow{BR} \qquad ②$$

$$\begin{aligned}
\overrightarrow{BR} &= k\overrightarrow{BN} \\
&= k(0.5\overrightarrow{BC} + 0.5\overrightarrow{BA}) \\
&= k(\overrightarrow{u} + 0.5\overrightarrow{v}) \\
&= k\overrightarrow{u} + 0.5k\overrightarrow{v}
\end{aligned}$$

Substitute this expression for $\overrightarrow{BR}$ into ②:
$$\begin{aligned}
\overrightarrow{MR} &= -\overrightarrow{u} + k\overrightarrow{u} + 0.5k\overrightarrow{v} \\
&= (k-1)\overrightarrow{u} + 0.5k\overrightarrow{v} \qquad ③
\end{aligned}$$

Equation ③ applies for any position of R along BN. However, $\overrightarrow{MR}$ and $\overrightarrow{MA}$ are collinear. Therefore, in equations ③ and ①, the coefficients of $\overrightarrow{u}$ and $\overrightarrow{v}$ are proportional.
$$\frac{k-1}{-1} = \frac{0.5k}{1}$$
Solve for k to obtain $k = \frac{2}{3}$.

Substitute this value of k into ③ to obtain:
$$\overrightarrow{MR} = -\frac{1}{3}\overrightarrow{u} + \frac{1}{3}\overrightarrow{v}$$
$$\overrightarrow{MR} = \frac{1}{3}(-\overrightarrow{u} + \overrightarrow{v})$$
$$\overrightarrow{MR} = \frac{1}{3}\overrightarrow{MA}$$

Therefore, $MR = \frac{1}{3}MA$.

Something to Think About

- This step uses a property of linear combinations that was developed in exercise 22 on page 33.
- Explain why NR $= \frac{1}{3}$NB.

Notice the strategy that was used in the example.

- Represent two segments with vectors $\vec{u}$ and $\vec{v}$.
- Express segments MA and MR in terms of $\vec{u}$ and $\vec{v}$.
- Impose the condition that M, R, and A are collinear.

Give vector proofs for the next three problems.

Problem 1

Points M and N are the midpoints of opposite sides of parallelogram ABCD. Prove that:

a) R and S trisect diagonal BD.

b) R is a point of trisection of AN and S is a point of trisection of MC.

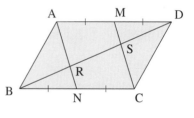

Problem 2

In the diagram, D and E are the midpoints of AB and AC respectively, and F is the midpoint of EC. Segment DF is extended to meet BC extended at P.

a) Prove that CP is half as long as BC.

b) Prove that F is the midpoint of DP.

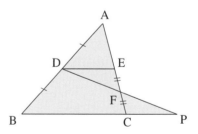

Problem 3

In problem 2, let G be the midpoint of AD. Prove that G, E, and P are collinear.

Focus on ... Sweeping a Circle with Lines

P is a point outside a circle. Visualize a line through P that rotates and sweeps across the circle. The turning line touches the circle at Q and leaves it at R. As it moves from Q to R, the points of intersection A and B move around the two arcs of the circle, approaching R. In the next problem, you will investigate how the lengths of the segments PQ, PA, PB, and PR are related.

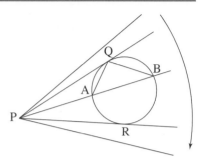

Problem 4

a) Prove that $\triangle PAQ \sim \triangle PQB$.

b) Use the result of part a to establish a relationship between the lengths of PQ, PA, and PB.

c) Visualize what happens for other positions of PB. Describe how the lengths of segments PQ, PA, PB, and PR are related as the line sweeps from Q to R.

Problem 5

Find out what happens if P is inside the circle. Prove any relationships that you think exist.

Other Problems

Problem 6

Two sides of a triangle have lengths 6 and 8 units respectively. The length of the third side is an integer.

a) How many triangles are there satisfying these conditions?

b) How many of the triangles are isosceles? acute? obtuse?

Problem 7

A triangle has sides of length 6 cm, 8 cm, and 10 cm. If a circle is drawn through its vertices, what is the diameter of the circle?

Problem 8

When one side of a quadrilateral is extended, an exterior angle is formed. Prove that the exterior angle of a cyclic quadrilateral is equal to its interior opposite angle. That is, for the diagram at the right, prove that $\angle CBE = \angle ADC$.

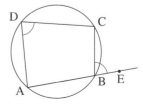

Problem 9

To construct a regular octagon, construct a square, and locate its centre, O. Then construct two arcs through O with centres at opposite vertices. Using the other vertices, draw similar arcs through O. Join the points located on the square to form an octagon. Prove that the octagon is a regular octagon (that is, all its sides have the same length, and all its angles are equal).

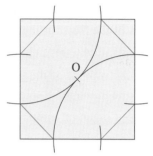

Problem 10

A parallelogram is defined as a quadrilateral with both pairs of opposite sides parallel. We can define a "perpendicularogram" as a quadrilateral with both pairs of opposite sides perpendicular.

a) Sketch an example of a perpendicularogram.

b) State a property of one of the angles of a perpendicularogram.

c) The parallel sides of a parallelogram are equal in length. Are the perpendicular sides of a perpendicularogram equal in length? Explain.

Problem 11

In a unit cube, there are two kinds of diagonals: face diagonals (such as AH), and body diagonals (such as AG). These diagonals form various angles when one endpoint is joined to another vertex of the cube. For example, visualize ∠AHC.

a) Find as many different angle measures as you can that are formed by a face diagonal and another vertex.

b) Repeat part a for a body diagonal.

Problem 12

The angle sum theorem can be illustrated with a graphing calculator.

| Graph three lines to form a triangle | Zoom out by a factor of 10 | Zoom out again by a factor of 10 |

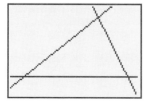  

The triangle seems to have disappeared. Zooming out does not change the slopes of the lines, or the angles formed by the lines.

a) Explain why this demonstrates that the sum of the angles in a triangle is 180°.

b) Is this a proof of the theorem? If your answer is no, does it suggest a proof of the theorem? Explain.

c) What other geometric properties can be illustrated by zooming out? Explain.

Problem 13

In △PQR, M is the midpoint of QR, and PM bisects ∠P. Prove that △PQR is isosceles.

Problem 14

In the diagram at the right, D is the midpoint of AB, and T is a point of trisection of AC. Segment DT is extended to meet BC produced at U.

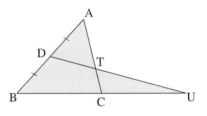

a) Prove that CU has the same length as BC.

b) Prove that TU is twice as long as DT.

Problem 15

In problem 14, let E be the midpoint of AT. Segment ED is extended to meet UB produced at V. Prove that VB has the same length as BC.

Problem 16

a) Prove that the medians of any △ABC are concurrent. The point of intersection of the medians is called the *centroid*.

b) Prove that the centroid divides each median in the ratio 2:1.

Problem 17

M and N are midpoints of two adjacent sides of rectangle ABCD. Segments AN and CM intersect at E.

a) Prove that ∠AEM = ∠MBN.

b) Determine how the angles in part a are related to the length:width ratio of the rectangle.

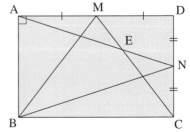

Problem 18

In pentagon ABCDE, all five sides have the same length. O is the midpoint of AB, and ∠EOC = 90°.

a) Determine ∠BCD.

b) Explain why there are two possible answers in part a.

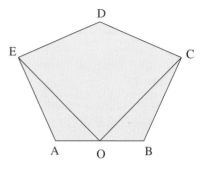

Problem 19

In the diagram (below left), ABCD is a square and H is any point on AD. Prove that DG ⊥ BE.

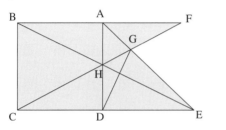

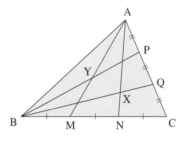

Problem 20

In the diagram (above right), M and N trisect side BC, and P and Q trisect side AC of △ABC. Prove that C, X, and Y are collinear.

Problem 21

In isosceles triangle ABC, inscribed in a unit circle with centre O, AB = AC (first two diagrams below). The triangle is oriented so that side BC is horizontal. The perpendicular distance from O to BC is represented by d. Visualize how ∠BAC changes as side BC moves up and down through all possible positions inside the circle.

a) Express ∠BAC as a function of d.

b) Graph the function.

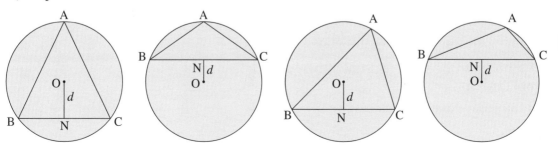

Problem 22

Repeat problem 21, but without assuming that the triangle is isosceles (last two diagrams).

Problem 23

a) Find the point B on the line with parametric equations $x = 2 + t$, $y = -1 - t$, $z = 4 - 2t$ that is closest to the point A(8, −2, 3).

b) Find the length of the segment AB.

Problem 24

In the diagram, $\angle AOC = \angle COB = 60°$. The lengths of OA, OB, and OC are a, b, and c respectively. Show that $\frac{1}{a} + \frac{1}{b} = \frac{1}{c}$.

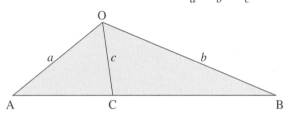

Problem 25

Two consecutive odd numbers that are powers of natural numbers are $25 = 5^2$ and $27 = 3^3$. Prove that two consecutive even numbers cannot be powers of natural numbers.

Problem 26

Prove that the sum of the squares of five consecutive integers can never be a perfect square.

Problem 27

The double factorial symbol !! is defined as follows.

$n!! = n(n - 2)(n - 4) \ldots 5 \times 3 \times 1$ if n is odd
$\quad = n(n - 2)(n - 4) \ldots 6 \times 4 \times 2$ if n is even

a) Simplify $n!!(n - 1)!!$

b) Prove that $(2n)!! = 2^n \times n!$

c) Find a similar expression for $(2n - 1)!!$

Problem 28

Find a formula for the greatest number in the nth row of Pascal's triangle.

Problem 29

Prove that the numbers in any row of Pascal's triangle can always be divided into two sets with the same sum.

Problem 30

Some natural numbers can be expressed as a difference of two squares, but others cannot. For example, $12 = 4^2 - 2^2$, but 10 cannot be written as a difference of two squares. Find a way to determine whether or not a given natural number can be expressed as the difference of two perfect squares.

Problem 31

Any point P is chosen inside an equilateral triangle. Prove that the sum of the perpendicular distances from P to the sides of the triangle is constant. How is the constant related to the triangle?

Problem 32

In the diagram at the right, $EC \perp BD$, $\angle ACD = 60°$ and $AE = BC = 1$. Determine the lengths of BE and CA.

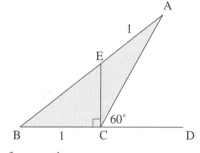

Problem 33

P is a point inside a square. The distances from P to three of the four vertices are 3 units, 4 units, and 5 units. Find the possible side lengths of the square.

Problem 34

A survey consists of 10 questions. Each question has 5 possible responses: SA, A, N, D and SD. (SA stands for "strongly agree", and so on). Suppose each respondent is to be classified according to the number of responses of each type. If all respondents answer all 10 questions, how many categories are possible?

Problem 35

The number 100! shown on the screen at the top of the following page was determined using *TI-Interactive!*.

a) Explain why there are 24 zeros at the end of 100!.

b) Suppose we use *TI-Interactive!* to calculate 200!. How many zeros would there be at the end of this number? Explain.

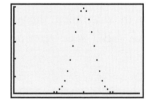

```
Factorial.tii - TI InterActive!                                    _□×
File  Edit  View  Insert  Format  Tools  Help

     100!
         933262154439441526816992388562667004907159682643816 2...
         468592963895217599993229915608941463976156518286253 6...
         792082722375825118521091686400000000000000000000000000

Ready                                        Ln 2, Col 0    NUM
```

Problem 36

Prove that there is no infinite arithmetic sequence of natural numbers whose terms are all prime numbers, except for the trivial case when the common difference is 0.

Problem 37

A deck of 52 cards is shuffled, and a hand containing *x* cards is dealt. The graphing calculator screen shows the number of possible hands, *y*, as a function of *x*.

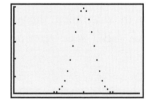

a) For what value of *x* does the maximum value of *y* occur? Explain.

b) Determine the coordinates of the maximum point. What does the *y*-coordinate of this point represent?

c) Explain why the graph is symmetric about the line $x = 26$.

d) Write the equation of the function, and state its domain.

Problem 38

Visualize rolling a die several times. These graphing calculator screens show the probabilities of rolling no 6s and of rolling at least one 6 as the number of rolls increases.

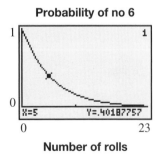

Probability of no 6

X=5   Y=.40187757
Number of rolls

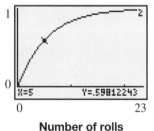

Probability of at least one 6

X=5   Y=.59812243
Number of rolls

a) Carry out calculations to check the results shown at the bottom of each screen. That is, for 5 rolls, P(no 6s) $\doteq$ 0.402 and P(at least one 6) $\doteq$ 0.598.

b) The graphs shown on the screens are functions. Write the equation of each function, where n is the number of rolls.

c) Determine the least number of rolls so the probability of at least one 6 is greater than 0.99.

Problem 39

A hand of 13 cards is dealt from a shuffled deck of 52 cards. The graphing calculator screen shows the probability that the hand contains different numbers of spades.

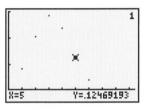

a) Calculate to confirm the result shown; that is, P(5 spades) $\doteq$ 0.125.

b) The graph shown on the screen is the graph of a function. Write the equation of the function, where n is the number of spades dealt.

c) Determine the probability that the hand contains each number of spades.
  i) 3 spades   **ii)** 8 spades   **iii)** 13 spades

Problem 40

a) Suppose 10 distinguishable books are to be put into 4 distinguishable boxes, numbered 1 to 4. In how many ways can this be done if any box can remain empty?

b) Suppose 10 distinguishable books are to be arranged on 4 shelves, numbered 1 to 4. In how many ways can this be done if any shelf can be empty? This is different from part a in that you will have to account for the order in which the books are displayed on each shelf.

c) Consider 10 books: 2 copies of Macbeth (M), 2 copies of Hamlet (H), 3 copies of King Lear (L), and 3 other books that are different from each other. Assume copies of the same book are indistinguishable. The books are to be arranged on 4 shelves, numbered 1 to 4. In how many ways can this be done if any shelf can be empty?

Problem 41

Use mathematical induction to prove that $(1 + x)^n \geq 1 + nx$ for all natural numbers n, where x is a real number that is greater than or equal to -1.

Problem 42

Prove that a regular polygon with n sides has $\frac{1}{2}n(n - 3)$ diagonals.

Problem 43

The outer rectangle in the diagram has height 1 unit and length x units. Visualize how the inner shaded rectangle changes as x varies. Express the area of the inner shaded rectangle as a function of x. Graph the function.

Problem 44

In certain rural areas of Russia, an unmarried girl who wants to know her fortune would get a friend to hold six long blades of grass in her fist with the ends protruding above and below. The girl would tie the six top ends in pairs and then tie the six bottom ends in pairs. If she had succeeded in tying all six blades into a single ring, she would be married within a year. What is the probability of forming the ring?

Problem 45

The natural numbers are written in a triangle as shown at the right.

Prove that the sum of the numbers in the nth row is $\dfrac{n(n^2 + 1)}{2}$.

```
          1
        2   3
      4   5   6
    7   8   9   10
 11  12  13  14  15
```

Problem 46

A sequence is defined recursively as follows: $t_1 = 1$, $t_{n+1} = \sqrt{2t_n + 1}$

 a) Prove that every term of the sequence is less than 3.

 b) Prove that every term of the sequence is greater than the preceding term.

Problem 47

In $\triangle ABC$, $AB = AC$, and $\angle A = 20°$. M is a point on AB such that $\angle MCB = 50°$, and N is a point on AC such that $\angle NBC = 60°$. Calculate $\angle BNM$.

Problem 48

In the diagram below, A, B, and C are the midpoints of segments FC, HA, and DB respectively. Prove that $\triangle ABC$ and $\triangle FHD$ have the same centroid.

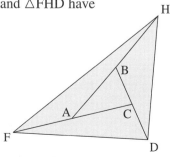

Problem 49

In the diagram at the right, segments AB, BC and CD are equal in length. Segments AE, EF and FG are also equal in length. Prove that A, P and Q are collinear.

Challenge Problem 50

A triangle is inscribed in a circle, and P is any point on the circle. Prove that the distance from P to the farthest vertex of the triangle is equal to the sum of its distances to the other two vertices if and only if the triangle is equilateral.

Challenge Problem 51

Prove that a triangle with sides of length a, b, and c is equilateral if and only if $(a + b + c)^2 = 3(ab + bc + ac)$.

Challenge Problem 52

In $\triangle ABC$ at the right, the incircle with centre I is tangent to BC at P. If M is the midpoint of BC and N is the midpoint of AP, prove that M, I, and N are collinear.

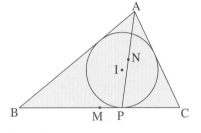

Challenge Problem 53

We say that a product is calculated "by pairs" when the product of two factors is used as a factor in the next calculation. For example, here is one way to calculate $2 \times 3 \times 4 \times 5 \times 6 \times 7$ by pairs.

$$2 \times 3 \times 4 \times 5 \times 6 \times 7 = 2 \times 3 \times 4 \times 30 \times 7$$
$$= 6 \times 4 \times 30 \times 7$$
$$= 6 \times 120 \times 7$$
$$= 6 \times 840$$
$$= 5040$$

a) In how many different ways can the above product be calculated by pairs? Assume that the order of the factors is not changed; that is, only numbers that are beside each other are multiplied in each step.

b) Obtain a recursion formula for calculating the number of ways a product of n factors can be evaluated by pairs.

Challenge Problem 54

You have 12 balls: 6 black and 6 white.

a) Suppose these balls are randomly distributed among 6 people, with each person getting 2 balls. What is the probability that each person gets 1 ball of each colour?

b) Suppose the balls are randomly distributed among 2 people so that each person gets 6 balls. What is the probability that each receives 3 of each colour?

c) The problems in parts a and b appear to be similar. In fact, they belong to a family of problems with a common solution pattern. Formulate another problem in the family and solve it.

d) Find a general pattern in your solutions to parts a, b, and c. Show that the solutions and answers to the three problems in parts a, b, and c are really particular versions of a general solution.

Challenge Problem 55

In the diagram at the right, points A, B and C lie on the circle with centre O. $\overrightarrow{CB'} = \overrightarrow{OB}$ and $\overrightarrow{B'H} = \overrightarrow{OA}$.

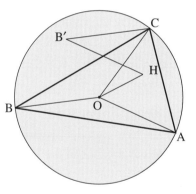

a) Build a dynamic model of this situation using *The Geometer's Sketchpad*.

b) As each of the points A, B and C move about the circle, describe the locus of point H.

c) Prove that H is the orthocentre of triangle ABC.

Student Reference

absolute value: the non-negative distance between any real number and zero on the number line

$|-5| = 5$, and also $|5| = 5$

actual velocity: the resultant velocity of two or more velocities

acute angle: an angle whose measure is less than 90°

Addition Principle: if two actions are mutually exclusive, and one can be done in m ways and the other in n ways, then there are $m + n$ ways in which the first or second action can be performed; see *Section 6.4*

alternate angles: a pair of angles that are between two lines on opposite sides of a transversal that cuts the two lines; see *parallel lines*

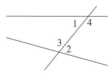

Angles 1 and 2 are alternate angles.
Angles 3 and 4 are alternate angles.

Alternate-Angles Theorem: suppose a transversal intersects two lines l_1 and l_2; the lines are parallel if and only if the alternate angles are equal

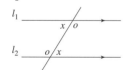

altitude: a perpendicular line segment drawn from a vertex or side of a figure to the opposite side (or an extension of the opposite side); also called height

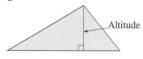

angle between two vectors: the angle θ between two vectors $\vec{a}$ and $\vec{b}$ is the acute angle between the two vectors when they are arranged tail-to-tail; to find θ, use the formula

$$\cos \theta = \frac{\vec{a} \cdot \vec{b}}{|\vec{a}||\vec{b}|}$$

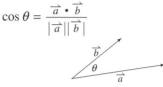

angle bisector: the line that divides an angle into two equal angles

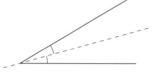

Angle Sum Theorem: in any triangle, the sum of the angles is 180°

Angles in a Circle Theorem: the inscribed angles on the same side of a chord of a circle are equal

arc: a segment of the circumference of a circle

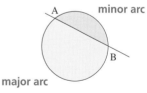

arithmetic sequence: a sequence in which the same number, the *common difference*, is added to each term to get the next term; the general arithmetic sequence is $a, a + d, a + 2d + \ldots + a + (n - 1)d$, where a is the first term, d is the common difference, and n is the number of terms; the nth term is $t_n = a + (n - 1)d$

In the arithmetic sequence 4, 1, –2, –5, –8 …, $a = 4$, $d = -3$, and $t_n = 4 + (n - 1)(-3)$, or $7 - 3n$.

STUDENT REFERENCE **401**

arithmetic series: the indicated sum of the terms of an arithmetic sequence; the general arithmetic series is $a + (a + d) + (a + 2d) + \ldots + [a + (n - 1)d]$, where a is the first term, d is the common difference, and n is the number of terms; the sum of the first n terms of an arithmetic series is $S_n = \frac{n}{2}[2a + (n - 1)d]$

Associative Law of Addition: the result of adding three items does not depend on the grouping
- for all real numbers a, b, and c:
  $(a + b) + c = a + (b + c)$
- for all vectors $\vec{a}$, $\vec{b}$, and $\vec{c}$:
  $(\vec{a} + \vec{b}) + \vec{c} = \vec{a} + (\vec{b} + \vec{c})$

axiom: a statement generally accepted without proof; also called a postulate or assumption

axis of symmetry: see *line symmetry*

base: the side of a polygon or the face of a solid from which the height is measured; also, the factor repeated in a power

bearing: in navigation, the clockwise angle between due north and the line of travel of an object

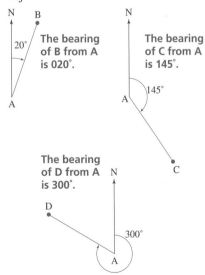

Binomial Theorem: for any natural number n,

$$(a + b)^n = \sum_{r=0}^{n} C(n, r)a^{n-r}b^r \text{; see Section 7.2}$$

bisector: a line that divides a line segment into two equal parts

The broken line is a bisector of AB.

Cartesian coordinates: in $\mathbf{R}^2$, an ordered pair that locates a point by its distance from two intersecting lines (the axes), the distance from one line being measured parallel to the other line

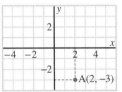

The coordinates of point A are (2, –3).

Cartesian vector: a vector that is described in terms of its components and is plotted on a grid
- in $\mathbf{R}^2$, a vector $\vec{v} = [x, y]$ or $\vec{v} = x\vec{i} + y\vec{j}$, where $\vec{i} = [1, 0]$ is the unit vector along the x-axis and $\vec{j} = [0, 1]$ is the unit vector along the y-axis; see *Section 1.5*
- in $\mathbf{R}^3$, a vector $\vec{v} = [x, y, z]$ or $\vec{v} = x\vec{i} + y\vec{j} + z\vec{k}$, where $\vec{i} = [1, 0, 0]$ is the unit vector along the x-axis, $\vec{j} = [0, 1, 0]$ is the unit vector along the y-axis, and $\vec{k} = [0, 0, 1]$ is the unit vector along the z-axis; see *Section 2.1*

Cartesian vector operations:
- in $\mathbf{R}^2$, for any vectors $\vec{a} = [x_1, y_1]$ and $\vec{b} = [x_2, y_2]$ and any real number k,
  $\vec{a} + \vec{b} = [x_1 + x_2, y_1 + y_2]$,
  $\vec{a} - \vec{b} = [x_1 - x_2, y_1 - y_2]$,
  and $k\vec{a} = [kx_1, ky_2]$; see *Section 1.5*
- in $\mathbf{R}^3$, for any vectors $\vec{a} = [x_1, y_1, z_1]$ and $\vec{b} = [x_2, y_2, z_2]$ and any real number k,
  $\vec{a} + \vec{b} = [x_1 + x_2, y_1 + y_2, z_1 + z_2]$,
  $\vec{a} - \vec{b} = [x_1 - x_2, y_1 - y_2, z_1 - z_2]$,
  and $k\vec{a} = [kx_1, ky_1, kz_1]$; see *Section 2.1*

cell reference: the name of a cell in a spreadsheet, given by indicating the column and row to which it belongs

> Cell B3 is the cell in column B and row 3 of the spreadsheet document.

centroid: the point where the three medians of a triangle intersect

chord: a line segment whose endpoints lie on a circle

AB is a chord.

circumcentre: the point of intersection of the perpendicular bisectors of the sides of a triangle

circumcircle: a circle drawn through each of the vertices of a triangle with its centre at the circumcentre of the triangle

coefficient: the numerical factor of a term

> The coefficient in the term $10xy^2$ is 10.

coincident: to occupy the same position

collinear points: points that lie on the same line

4 collinear points   4 non-collinear points

collinear vectors: vectors that are scalar multiples of each other

combination: a selection from a group of objects without regard to order; a combination of n different objects taken r at a time is denoted $C(n, r)$, where $C(n, r) = \dfrac{n!}{r!(n - r)!}$; see *Section 6.5*

combined statement: a single statement that combines a statement and its converse, when they are both true, using the words "…if and only if…"

common difference: the number obtained by subtracting any term from the next term in an arithmetic sequence

> For the arithmetic sequence 3, 7, 11, 15, …, the common difference is $7 - 3 = 4$.

Commutative Law of Addition: the order of addition of two quantities does not affect the sum

- for all real numbers a and b: $a + b = b + a$
- for all vectors $\vec{a}$ and $\vec{b}$:
  $$\vec{a} + \vec{b} = \vec{b} + \vec{a}$$

complementary angles: two angles whose measures add to 90°

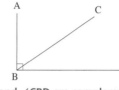

∠ABC and ∠CBD are complementary angles.

components: the values of the ordered pair $[x, y]$ or ordered triple $[x, y, z]$ used to describe Cartesian vectors

concentric circles: circles with the same centre

concurrent: having a point in common

concyclic points: points that lie on the circumference of the same circle

congruence axioms for triangles:

- *SSS Congruence Axiom:* if three sides of one triangle are equal to three sides of another triangle, then the triangles are congruent
- *SAS Congruence Axiom:* if two sides and the contained angle of one triangle are equal to two sides and the contained angle of another triangle, then the triangles are congruent
- *ASA Congruence Axiom:* if two angles and the contained side of one triangle are equal to two angles and the contained side of another triangle, then the triangles are congruent

congruent: figures that have the same size and shape, but not necessarily the same orientation

conjecture: a conclusion based on examples

consecutive integers: integers that come one after the other without any integers missing

23, 24, 25 are consecutive integers; so are –5, –4, –3, –2, –1, and 0.

consistent system of equations: a system of equations with at least one solution

converse: the statement formed by interchanging the hypothesis and conclusion of an "if … then" statement

The converse of "If a triangle has three equal sides then it has three equal angles" is "If a triangle has three equal angles then it has three equal sides."

coordinate axes: in two dimensions, two perpendicular or oblique lines on a grid that represent the plane; in three dimensions, three intersecting lines that are usually mutually perpendicular

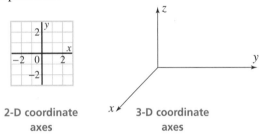

2-D coordinate axes   3-D coordinate axes

coordinate plane: a two-dimensional surface on which a coordinate system has been set up

- in R^3, the coordinate planes are the xy-plane, the xz-plane, and the yz-plane; points on each plane have ordered pairs as follows: $(x, y, 0)$ on the xy-plane, $(x, 0, z)$ on the xz-plane, and $(0, y, z)$ on the yz-plane

coplanar vectors: vectors that lie on the same plane; see *Sections 2.2 and 2.5*

corollary: a theorem that follows directly from another theorem

corresponding angles: angles on the same side of a transversal that cuts through two lines and that are on the same side of each line

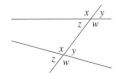

Corresponding-Angles Theorem: a transversal intersects two lines l_1 and l_2; the lines are parallel if and only if the corresponding angles are equal

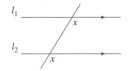

Cosine Law: a trigonometric law used to solve triangles that are not right triangles; to use the Cosine Law, we need to know:

- the measure of two sides and their included angle, or
- the measure of three sides

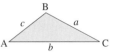

In any triangle ABC, the following relationships exist:
$a^2 = b^2 + c^2 - 2bc \cos A$
$b^2 = a^2 + c^2 - 2ac \cos B$
$c^2 = a^2 + b^2 - 2ab \cos C$

In $\triangle ABC$, $\angle B = 48°$, AB = 7.3 cm, and BC = 5.2 cm; calculate the length of AC.

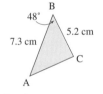

Use the Cosine Law.
$b^2 = a^2 + c^2 - 2ac \cos B$
Substitute the known measures.
$b^2 = 5.2^2 + 7.3^2 - 2(5.2)(7.3) \cos 48°$
$\quad = 29.529\,604$
$b \doteq 5.4$

AC is approximately 5.4 cm.

In $\triangle PQR$, PQ = 7.8 cm, QR = 6.2 cm, and PR = 9.7 cm; calculate the measure of $\angle Q$ to 1 decimal place.

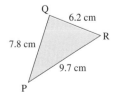

Use the Cosine Law.

$q^2 = p^2 + r^2 - 2pr \cos Q$

Substitute the known measures, then solve for Q.

$9.7^2 = 6.2^2 + 7.8^2 - 2(6.2)(7.8) \cos Q$

$\cos Q = 0.053\,950$

$\angle Q \doteq 86.907°$

$\angle Q$ is approximately 86.9°.

counterexample: an example that shows a conjecture to be false

cross product of Cartesian vectors: if $\vec{a} = [a_1, a_2, a_3]$ and $\vec{b} = [b_1, b_2, b_3]$, then $\vec{a} \times \vec{b} = [a_2b_3 - b_2a_3, a_3b_1 - b_3a_1, a_1b_2 - b_1a_2]$

cross product of geometric vectors: in R^3, the vector $\vec{a} \times \vec{b}$ that is perpendicular to the plane of two non-collinear vectors $\vec{a}$ and $\vec{b}$ arranged tail-to-tail and forming an angle θ, such that $0° \leq \theta \leq 180°$; the vectors $\vec{a}$, $\vec{b}$, and $\vec{a} \times \vec{b}$ satisfy the *right-hand rule*, and $|\vec{a} \times \vec{b}| = |\vec{a}||\vec{b}| \sin \theta$

cross product properties:

- $\vec{a} \times \vec{b} = -(\vec{b} \times \vec{a})$
- $\vec{a} \times (\vec{b} + \vec{c}) = \vec{a} \times \vec{b} + \vec{a} \times \vec{c}$
- $\vec{a} \times \vec{a} = 0$

cyclic quadrilateral: a quadrilateral whose vertices lie on a circle

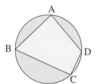

deductive proof: the derivation of a result by logical process from axioms accepted as true

diagonal: a line segment that joins two vertices of a polygon but is not a side

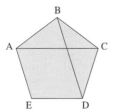

AC is a diagonal and BD is also a diagonal.

direct proof: the method of beginning with a statement that is accepted as true and using deduction to arrive at the desired conclusion

direction angles: the angles that a vector makes with the positive coordinate axes; see *Section 2.1*

direction cosines: the cosines of the direction angles of a vector; see *Section 2.1*

direction vector: one or more non-zero vectors used to specify the direction of a line or plane; the direction vector of a line is any vector $\vec{m}$ parallel to the line; the direction vectors of a plane are any two non-collinear vectors $\vec{u}$ and $\vec{v}$ contained in the plane

directrix of a parabola: the fixed line such that the distance from any point P on the parabola to the fixed line is equal to the distance from P to the focus F; see *focus of a parabola*

distance formula: a formula used to determine the distance between two points whose coordinates are known; the distance between the points $P_1(x_1, y_1)$ and $P_2(x_2, y_2)$ is

$P_1P_2 = \sqrt{(x_2 - x_1)^2 + (y_2 - y_1)^2}$

Determine the distance between the points A(3, 4) and B(-5, 1).

$AB = \sqrt{(3 + 5)^2 + (4 - 1)^2}$

$= \sqrt{64 + 9}$

$= \sqrt{73}$

distance from a point to a line: the distance from a point $P(x_1, y_1)$ to the line $Ax + By + C = 0$ is $d = \dfrac{|Ax_1 + By_1 + C|}{\sqrt{A^2 + B^2}}$

distance from a point to a plane: the distance from a point $P(x_1, y_1, z_1)$ to the plane $Ax + By + Cz + D = 0$ is

$d = \dfrac{|Ax_1 + By_1 + Cz_1 + D|}{\sqrt{A^2 + B^2 + C^2}}$

Distributive Property: a product can be written as a sum or difference of two products

- for all real numbers a, b, and c: $a(b \pm c) = ab \pm ac$

dot product of geometric vectors: $\vec{a} \cdot \vec{b} = |\vec{a}||\vec{b}| \cos \theta$, where $\vec{a}$ and $\vec{b}$ are arranged tail-to-tail forming an angle θ, such that $0° \leq \theta \leq 180°$; also known as the scalar product or inner product

dot product of Cartesian vectors:
- in R^2, if $\vec{a} = [a_1, a_2]$ and $\vec{b} = [b_1, b_2]$, then $\vec{a} \cdot \vec{b} = a_1b_1 + a_2b_2$
- in R^3, if $\vec{a} = [a_1, a_2, a_3]$ and $\vec{b} = [b_1, b_2, b_3]$, then $\vec{a} \cdot \vec{b} = a_1b_1 + a_2b_2 + a_3b_3$

dot product properties: for any three vectors $\vec{a}$, $\vec{b}$, and $\vec{c}$:
- $\vec{a} \cdot \vec{b} = \vec{b} \cdot \vec{a}$
- $\vec{a} \cdot (\vec{b} + \vec{c}) = \vec{a} \cdot \vec{b} + \vec{a} \cdot \vec{c}$
- $\vec{a} \cdot \vec{a} = |\vec{a}|^2$
- $k(\vec{a} \cdot \vec{b}) = (k\vec{a}) \cdot \vec{b} = \vec{a} \cdot (k\vec{b})$, for any scalar k

elementary row operations: are used to solve a system of equations using matrices; an equivalent system is obtained by performing any of the following operations:
- multiply the numbers in any row by any constant
- replace any row by adding the numbers in any other row to the numbers in that row
- replace any row with a linear combination of that row and another row

ellipse: the closed curve that results when a plane intersects a cone; or the locus of a point P that moves so the sum of its distances from two fixed points (the foci) is constant

equal vectors: vectors that have the same magnitude and direction

equation of a line: an equation that gives the relationship between the coordinates of every point on the line
- the *slope-point* form: $y - y_1 = m(x - x_1)$, where m is the slope of the line and (x_1, y_1) is a point on the line
- the *slope-intercept* form: $y = mx + b$, where m is the slope of the line and b is the y-intercept of the line
- the *general form*: $Ax + By + C = 0$, where A,

B, and C are constants such that $-\frac{A}{B}$ is the slope of the line, and $-\frac{C}{B}$ is the y-intercept of the line

equidistant: the same distance apart

Points A and B are equidistant from the y-axis since they are both 3 units from the y-axis.

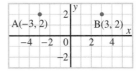

equilibrant: a force equal in magnitude but opposite in direction to the resultant force

equilibrium: when an object is acted upon by forces but does not move, the object is said to be in equilibrium

equivalent systems: systems of equations with the same solution(s)

exterior angle: an angle formed outside a polygon by extending a side of the polygon

45-45-90 triangle: a triangle with angles $45°$, $45°$, and $90°$; the ratio of the sides corresponding to these angles is $1:1:\sqrt{2}$

factorial: the product of the first n natural numbers is called n factorial, denoted $n! = n(n - 1)(n - 2)(n - 3) \times \ldots \times 3 \times 2 \times 1$; also, $0! = 1$; see *Section 6.2*

foci of a hyperbola: the two points F_1 and F_2 on the transverse axis of a hyperbola such that $|PF_1 - PF_2|$ is constant for all points P on the hyperbola

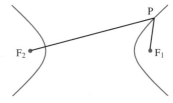

foci of an ellipse: the two points F_1 and F_2 on the major axis of an ellipse such that $PF_1 + PF_2$ is constant for all points P on the ellipse

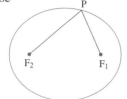

focus of a parabola: the point F on the axis of symmetry of a parabola such that the distance of any point P on the parabola from F is equal to the distance of P from the directrix

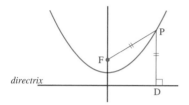

When the focus is on the *x*-axis, the equation of the parabola is $y^2 = 4px$. The coordinates of the focus are F(*p*, 0) and the equation of the directrix is $x = -p$.

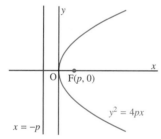

When the focus is on the *y*-axis, the equation of the parabola is $x^2 = 4py$. The coordinates of the focus are F(0, *p*) and the equation of the directrix is $y = -p$.

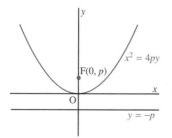

force: a push or a pull on an object in a certain direction; a quantity that can be represented by a vector

Fundamental Counting Principle: if an action can be done in *m* ways, and for each way a second action can be done in *n* ways, then the two actions can be performed, in that order, in *mn* ways; see *Section 6.1*

geometric sequence: a sequence in which each term is multiplied by the same number, the *common ratio*, to get the next term; the general geometric sequence is a, ar, ar^2, ar^{n-1}, where a is the first term, r is the common ratio, and n is the number of terms; the general term is $t_n = ar^{n-1}$

In the geometric sequence 16, 4, 1, $\frac{1}{4}$, $\frac{1}{16}$... , each term after the first is calculated by multiplying the previous term by $\frac{1}{4}$.

geometric series: the indicated sum of the terms of a geometric sequence; the general geometric series with *n* terms is $a + ar + ar^2 + \ldots + ar^{n-1}$, where a is the first term, r is the common ratio, and n is the number of terms; the sum of the first *n* terms of a geometric series is $S_n = \dfrac{a(r^n - 1)}{r - 1}$

geometric vector: an arrow or a directed line segment; the arrowhead points in the direction of the vector

The vector $\vec{v}$ below may also be written as $\overrightarrow{AB}$, where the point A is the initial point or tail, and the point B is the terminal point or head.

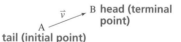

head: the head of vector $\overrightarrow{AB}$ is the point B, also called the terminal point of the vector $\overrightarrow{AB}$

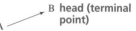

heading: the direction in which an object is being steered

- a wind or current can add another velocity component to the object, so the actual bearing relative to the ground is usually not the same as the heading

head-to-tail: a method of joining vectors so that the head of one vector connects with the tail of the other

hexagon: a six-sided polygon

identity: an equation that is true for all values of the variable for which both sides of the equation are defined; identities occur in algebra as well as in trigonometry

> The equation $3(x - y) = 3x - 3y$ is an algebraic identity. It is true for all values of x and y.

incentre: the point of intersection of the three angle bisectors of a triangle

incircle: a circle drawn inside a triangle, with its centre at the incentre and with the radius the shortest distance from the incentre to one of the sides of the triangle

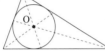

inconsistent system of equations: a system of equations with no solution

index of summation: the variable under the $\sum$ sign and in the expression after it

> The variable k is the index of summation for the sum $\sum_{k=1}^{100}(2k - 1)$.

indirect proof: a method of proof that involves assuming that the statement to be proved is false and working towards a contradiction

inductive reasoning: a method of making a conjecture on the basis of observing and generalizing a series of examples

inequality: a statement that one quantity is greater than or less than another quantity

inscribed angle: the angle between two chords of a circle that have a common endpoint

∠ABC is an inscribed angle.

irrational number: a number that cannot be written in the form $\frac{a}{b}$, where a and b are integers $(b \neq 0)$

> Numbers such as $\sqrt{2}$, $\sqrt{3}$, π, and non-terminating, non-repeating decimals are irrational.

isosceles right triangle: a triangle containing two equal sides and a 90° angle

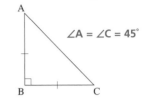

∠A = ∠C = 45°

Isosceles Triangle Theorem: in an isosceles triangle, the angles opposite the equal sides are equal

joule: a unit of measure for the work done by an object; also called a newton metre

legs: the sides of a right triangle that form the right angle

line symmetry: a figure that maps onto itself when it is reflected in a line is said to have line symmetry

> Line l is the axis of symmetry for figure ABCD.

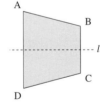

linear combinations of vectors: a linear combination of two vectors $\vec{a}$ and $\vec{b}$ has the form $s\vec{a} + t\vec{b}$, where s and t are any scalars; see *Section 1.4*

locus: the path traced by a point that moves according to a given condition

> Determine the locus of a point P that moves so it is equidistant from A(4, 0) and B(1, 2).
>
> Let P(x, y) be any point on the locus such that PA = PB. Use the distance formula to determine the lengths of PA and PB.
>
> $$\sqrt{(x - 4)^2 + (y - 0)^2} = \sqrt{(x - 1)^2 + (y - 2)^2}$$
>
> Square each side.
> $$(x - 4)^2 + y^2 = (x - 1)^2 + (y - 2)^2$$
> $$x^2 - 8x + 16 + y^2 = x^2 - 2x + 1 + y^2 - 4y + 4$$

Collect like terms.
$-6x + 4y + 11 = 0$
The equation of the locus is $6x - 4y - 11 = 0$.
The locus is a straight line.

magnitude: the length of a vector, often written using absolute value bars
- in $\mathbf{R}^2$, $\overrightarrow{a} = [a_1, a_2]$ has magnitude
  $$|\overrightarrow{a}| = \sqrt{a_1^2 + a_2^2}$$
- in $\mathbf{R}^3$, $\overrightarrow{a} = [a_1, a_2, a_3]$ has magnitude
  $$|\overrightarrow{a}| = \sqrt{a_1^2 + a_2^2 + a_3^2}$$

major axis of an ellipse: the longer axis of symmetry of an ellipse

matrix: a rectangular array of numbers

median of a triangle: a line from one vertex to the midpoint of the opposite side

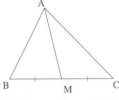

AM is a median of △ABC.

midpoint: the point that divides a line segment into two equal parts; if the coordinates of the endpoints of the line segment are $A(x_1, y_1)$ and $B(x_2, y_2)$, the coordinates of $M(x, y)$ are
$x = \frac{x_1 + x_2}{2}$ and $y = \frac{y_1 + y_2}{2}$

The ratio of AM : MB is 1 : 2.
It is also true that AM = $\frac{1}{2}$AB.

natural numbers: the set of counting numbers 1, 2, 3, 4, …

normal vector of a plane: a vector that is perpendicular to a plane

obtuse angle: an angle greater that 90° but less that 180°

octant: one of the eight regions into which the three coordinate planes divide 3-space

opposite vectors: vectors that have the same magnitude but act in opposite directions

orthocentre: the point at which the altitudes of a triangle intersect

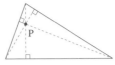

parallel lines: lines in the same plane that do not intersect; see *Alternate-Angles Theorem* and *Corresponding Angles Theorem*

parallelogram: a quadrilateral with opposite sides parallel

A parallelogram has the following properties:
The opposite sides have equal lengths.
AB = CD and AD = BC
The opposite angles have equal measures (congruent).
∠A = ∠C and ∠B = ∠D
The diagonals bisect each other (cut each other into equal lengths).
AE = EC and DE = EB

Parallelogram Law of Vector Addition: a method for adding vectors that are arranged tail-to-tail; to add $\overrightarrow{a}$ and $\overrightarrow{b}$, complete the parallelogram determined by $\overrightarrow{a}$ and $\overrightarrow{b}$; the sum, $\overrightarrow{a} + \overrightarrow{b}$, is the vector with the same tail as $\overrightarrow{a}$ and $\overrightarrow{b}$ and with its head at the opposite vertex of the parallelogram

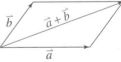

parameter: a constant in an expression that may have many values but does not change the form of the expression
In $y = mx + b$, m and b are parameters which specify the particular line represented by the equation.

parametric equations of a line: a set of equations that describe each coordinate of any point on a line in R^2 or R^3 in terms of the coordinates of a fixed point on the line and the components of a direction vector parallel to the line; see *vector equation of a line*

- in R^2, the parametric equations of the line through A(a_1, a_2) with direction vector $\vec{m} = [m_1, m_2]$ are $x = a_1 + tm_1$ and $y = a_2 + tm_2$, where t is any real number
- in R^3, the parametric equations of the line through A(a_1, a_2, a_3) with direction vector $\vec{m} = [m_1, m_2, m_3]$ are $x = a_1 + tm_1$, $y = a_2 + tm_2$, and $z = a_3 + tm_3$, where t is any real number

parametric equations of a plane: a set of equations that describe each coordinate of any point on a plane in terms of the coordinates of a fixed point on the plane and the components of two non-collinear direction vectors contained in the plane

- the parametric equations of the plane through A(a_1, a_2, a_3) with direction vectors $\vec{u} = [u_1, u_2, u_3]$ and $\vec{v} = [v_1, v_2, v_3]$ are $x = a_1 + su_1 + tv_1$, $y = a_2 + su_2 + tv_2$, and $z = a_3 + su_3 + tv_3$, where s and t represent any real numbers

Pascal's Triangle: the following triangular number pattern; see *Section 7.1*

```
              1
            1   1
          1   2   1
        1   3   3   1
      1   4   6   4   1
    1   5   10  10  5   1
  1   6   15  20  15  6   1
              ⋮
```

permutations: an ordered arrangement of objects

- the number of permutations of n different objects taken all at a time is denoted by $P(n, n)$ where $P(n, n) = n!$
- the number of permutations of n different objects taken r at a time is denoted by $P(n, r) = \dfrac{n!}{(n - r)!}, 0 \geq r \geq n$

- the number of permutations of n objects, of which a objects are alike, another b objects are alike, another c objects are alike, and so on, is $\dfrac{n!}{a!b!c!\ldots}$

perpendicular bisector: a line that bisects at right angles

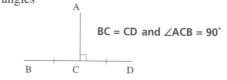

BC = CD and ∠ACB = 90°

plane: a flat, two-dimensional surface that extends indefinitely in all directions

plane figures: a geometric figure that can be drawn or visualized on a two-dimensional plane; for example, circles, ellipses, and polygons

point symmetry: a figure that maps onto itself after a rotation of 180° about a point is said to have point symmetry

polygon: a closed figure that consists of three or more line segments that only intersect at their endpoints

The above figures are polygons.

These figures are not polygons.

The table below gives the names of some common polygons.

Number of sides	Polygon
3	Triangle
4	Quadrilateral
5	Pentagon
6	Hexagon
8	Octagon
10	Decagon
n	n-gon

PolySmlt: a program for solving matrices using the ⌈APPS⌋ menu of the TI-83 Plus calculator

position vector: a vector whose tail is at the origin and whose components are the coordinates of its head

prime number: a whole number with exactly two factors, itself and 1

> 3, 5, 7, 11, 13, 17, 19, 23, and 29 are prime numbers.

Principle of Mathematical Induction: a result involving natural numbers is true for all natural numbers if *both* of the following are true:

- the result is true when $n = 1$
- if the result is true when $n = k$, then it is true for $n = k + 1$

prism: a solid with two congruent and parallel faces (bases); all other faces are parallelograms

projection of a vector: the projection of $\vec{a}$ on $\vec{b}$, written $\vec{a} \downarrow \vec{b}$, is a new vector $\vec{c}$ such that $\vec{c} = \left(\dfrac{\vec{a} \cdot \vec{b}}{\vec{b} \cdot \vec{b}} \right) \vec{b}$, where $\vec{b} \neq \vec{0}$

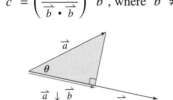

proportion: a statement that two ratios are equal

pyramid: a solid with one face that is a polygon (base) and other faces that are triangles with a common vertex

Pythagorean identity: for any angle θ, $\sin^2 \theta + \cos^2 \theta = 1$

Pythagorean Theorem: for any right triangle, the area of the square on the hypotenuse is equal to the sum of the areas of the squares on the other two sides

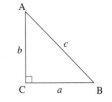

If $\triangle ABC$ is a right triangle, then $c^2 = a^2 + b^2$. The converse is also true. If $c^2 = a^2 + b^2$ in $\triangle ABC$, then $\angle C = 90°$.

quadrant: one of four regions into which the coordinate axes divide the plane, usually numbered as shown in the diagram

quadrilateral: a four-sided polygon

radical: the root of a number

$$\sqrt{a} \times \sqrt{b} = \sqrt{a \times b}, \ a \geq 0, \ b \geq 0$$

$$\frac{\sqrt{a}}{\sqrt{b}} = \sqrt{\frac{a}{b}}, \ a \geq 0, \ b > 0$$

rational numbers: a number that can be written in the form $\frac{a}{b}$, where a and b are integers $(b \neq 0)$; all integers, terminating decimals, and repeating decimals are rational numbers

recursion formula: a rule by which each term of a sequence is generated from the preceding term or terms

> State the recursion formula for the sequence 1, 3, 4, 7, 11, ...
>
> In the given sequence, the third term is the sum of the first and second terms, the fourth term is the sum of the second and third terms, and each term after that is the sum of the previous two terms.
>
> Thus, the terms of the sequence are $t_1 = 1$, $t_2 = 3$, $t_3 = 1 + 3$, $t_4 = 3 + 4$, $t_5 = 7 + 11$, and so on.
>
> The recursion formula for the sequence is $t_{n+1} = t_n + t_{n-1}$, where $n \geq 2$.

reduced matrix: the matrix that results from the use of elementary row operations and has the

$$\text{form} \begin{bmatrix} 1 & 0 & 0 & | & * \\ 0 & 1 & 0 & | & * \\ 0 & 0 & 1 & | & * \end{bmatrix}$$

regular polygon: a polygon with all sides and all angles equal

The polygons above are regular polygons.

relative velocity: see *actual velocity*

resolving a vector: the procedure for determining the components of a vector
- if $\overrightarrow{r}$ be a non-zero vector that makes an angle θ with the positive *x*-axis then, $\overrightarrow{r} = [a, b]$, where $a = |\overrightarrow{r}| \cos \theta$ and $b = |\overrightarrow{r}| \sin \theta$

resultant vector: a single vector which represents the combined effect of two or more individual vectors

rhombus: a parallelogram with four equal sides

right-hand rule: the direction of $\overrightarrow{a} \times \overrightarrow{b}$ is perpendicular to the plane containing $\overrightarrow{a}$ and $\overrightarrow{b}$ so that $\overrightarrow{a}$, $\overrightarrow{b}$, and $\overrightarrow{a} \times \overrightarrow{b}$ satisfy the *right-hand rule*: when the fingers of the right hand point in the direction of $\overrightarrow{a}$ and curl towards $\overrightarrow{b}$, the thumb points in the direction of $\overrightarrow{a} \times \overrightarrow{b}$

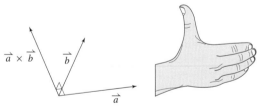

row reduction: the method of using elementary row operations to obtain a reduced matrix when solving a system of equations

scalar: a quantity that can be described by a single number

scalar equation of a line: has the form $Ax + By + C = 0$, where *A* and *B* are the components of its normal vector $\overrightarrow{n} = [A, B]$; also called a *Cartesian equation*

scalar equation of a plane: has the form $Ax + By + Cz + D = 0$ where *A*, *B*, and *C* are the components of its normal vector $\overrightarrow{n} = [A, B, C]$; also called a *Cartesian equation*

scalar multiplication—Distributive Property: let *m* be a scalar and $\overrightarrow{a}$ and $\overrightarrow{b}$ any vectors, then $m(\overrightarrow{a} + \overrightarrow{b}) = m\overrightarrow{a} + m\overrightarrow{b}$

scalar multiplication of vectors: the operation of multiplying a vector $\overrightarrow{v}$ by a scalar *k* to produce a new vector $k\overrightarrow{v}$
- if $k > 0$, $k\overrightarrow{v}$ has the same direction as $\overrightarrow{v}$
- if $k < 0$, $k\overrightarrow{v}$ is opposite in direction to $\overrightarrow{v}$
- if $k = 0$, $k\overrightarrow{v}$ is the zero vector

scalar triple product: an expression of the form $\overrightarrow{a} \bullet \overrightarrow{b} \times \overrightarrow{c}$, where $\overrightarrow{a}$, $\overrightarrow{b}$, and $\overrightarrow{c}$ are vectors in 3-space
- when the value of the scalar triple product is 0, the three vectors are coplanar

Semicircle Theorem: if P is any point on a semicircle with diameter AB, then $\angle APB = 90°$

Side-Splitting Theorem: the line that joins the midpoint of two sides of a triangle is parallel to and one-half as long as the third side

sigma notation: a concise way to express the sum of a series using the capital Greek letter sigma, $\sum$, which corresponds to S, the first letter of the word "sum"

The sum $a_1 + a_2 + a_3 + a_4 + \ldots + a_n$ can be written in sigma notation as $\sum_{k=1}^{n} a_k$.

similar figures: figures that have the same shape but not necessarily the same size

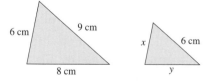

When two figures are similar, their corresponding angles have equal measures, and their corresponding sides are in proportion (all have the same scale factor). The symbol $\sim$ is used to indicate similarity.

To find an unknown side of one similar figure, use a proportion.

$\frac{9}{6} = \frac{8}{y} = \frac{6}{x}$

Scale factor $= \frac{9}{6}$

$\qquad = 3 : 2$

To find x, solve the following proportion.

$\frac{3}{2} = \frac{6}{x}$

$3x = 12$

$x = 4$

To find y, solve the following proportion.

$\frac{3}{2} = \frac{8}{y}$

$3y = 16$

$y \doteq 5.33$

similar triangles: triangles with corresponding angles having equal measures, and corresponding sides being proportional

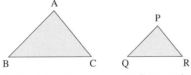

In similar triangles, corresponding angles are equal; given $\triangle ABC$ is similar to $\triangle PQR$, then:

$\angle ABC = \angle PQR$

$\angle BAC = \angle QPR$

$\angle ACB = \angle PQR$

In similar triangles, the ratios of corresponding sides are equal; given $\triangle ABC$ is similar to $\triangle PQR$, then: $\frac{AB}{PQ} = \frac{BC}{QR} = \frac{AC}{PR}$

In similar triangles, the ratio of the areas are equal to the squares of the ratios of the corresponding sides; given $\triangle ABC$ is similar to $\triangle PQR$, then:

$\frac{\text{area } \triangle ABC}{\text{area } \triangle PQR} = \left(\frac{AB}{PQ} \right)^2 = \left(\frac{BC}{QR} \right)^2 = \left(\frac{AC}{PR} \right)^2$

Determine the length AD.

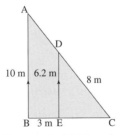

From the diagram, in $\triangle ABC$ and $\triangle DEC$:

$\angle B = \angle E$

$\angle C$ is a common angle

Therefore, $\triangle ABC \sim \triangle DEC$, since two pairs of corresponding angles are equal.

The ratios of the corresponding sides are equal:

$\frac{AB}{DE} = \frac{BC}{EC} = \frac{AC}{DC}$

Let y represent the length AD. To solve for y, use the first and the third ratios above.

$\frac{10}{6.2} = \frac{y + 8}{8}$

$80 = 6.2(y + 8)$

$80 = 6.2y + 49.6$

$30.4 = 6.2y$

$y \doteq 4.9$

AC $= y + 8$; so, AD $= 12.9$

AD is approximately 12.9 m.

Sine Law: a trigonometric law used to solve triangles

Use the Sine law in an oblique triangle where two angles and one side are known.

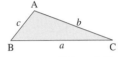

In any triangle ABC: $\frac{\sin A}{a} = \frac{\sin B}{b} = \frac{\sin C}{c}$ and

$\frac{a}{\sin A} = \frac{b}{\sin B} = \frac{c}{\sin C}$

In $\triangle DEF$, $\angle D = 72°$, DE $= 8.5$ cm, and EF $= 11.3$ cm; calculate the measures of $\angle F$ and DF.

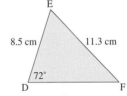

Use the Sine Law to calculate $\angle F$.

$\frac{\sin F}{f} = \frac{\sin D}{d}$

Substitute the known measures.

$\frac{\sin F}{8.5} = \frac{\sin 72°}{11.3}$

Multiply each side by 8.5.

$\sin F = \frac{8.5 \sin 72°}{11.3}$

$\qquad \doteq 0.715396$

$\angle F \doteq 46°$

Calculate the measure of $\angle E$.

Use the sum of the angles in a triangle.

$\angle E = 180° - 72° - 46°$

$\qquad = 62°$

Use the Sine Law.

$\frac{e}{\sin E} = \frac{d}{\sin D}$

$\frac{e}{\sin 62°} = \frac{11.3}{\sin 72°}$

Multiply each side by $\sin 62°$.

$e = \frac{11.3 \sin 62°}{\sin 72°}$

$\quad \doteq 10.49$

DF is approximately 10.5 cm.

skew lines: non-intersecting, non-parallel lines in 3-space

slope: a measure of the steepness of a line
- the slope of a line segment joining $P_1(x_1, y_1)$ and $P_2(x_2, y_2)$ is

$$\text{slope} = \frac{\text{rise}}{\text{run}}$$
$$= \frac{\Delta y}{\Delta x}$$
$$= \frac{y_2 - y_1}{x_2 - x_1}$$

solving a linear system in 2 variables: determining the values of the unknowns that, when substituted for the unknowns in each equation, result in a true statement

Solve this linear system:
$x - 2y = 3$ ①
$4x + 3y = 1$ ②

i) Using the Method of Substitution
Isolate x in ① to get $x = 3 + 2y$. ③
Substitute ③ in ② and solve for y.
$4(3 + 2y) + 3y = 1$
$\quad 12 + 8y + 3y = 1$
$\qquad\qquad 11y = -11$
$\qquad\qquad\quad y = -1$
Substitute $y = -1$ in ③.
$x = 3 + 2(-1)$
$\ = 1$
The solution is $(1, -1)$.

ii) Using the Method of Elimination
Multiply ① by 4 to get $4x - 8y = 12$.
Subtract ② from this new equation.
$4x - 8y = 12$
$\underline{4x + 3y = \ \ 1}$
$\ -11y = 11$
$\qquad y = -1$
Solve for x. Substitute $y = -1$ into ①.
$x - 2(-1) = 3$
$\qquad\quad x = 1$
The solution is $(1, -1)$.

spreadsheet: a computer-generated arrangement of data in rows and columns, where a change in one value can result in appropriate calculated changes in other values

square-based right pyramid: a solid with one square face (base) and four lateral faces that are congruent isosceles triangles with a common vertex

sum of a geometric series: the total value of all the terms in a geometric series;

$$S_n = \frac{a(r^n - 1)}{r - 1}, \ r \neq 1$$

sum of an arithmetic series: the total value of all the terms in an arithmetic series;

$$S_n = \left(\frac{a + t_n}{2}\right)n \text{ or } S_n = \frac{n}{2}[2a + (n - 1)d]$$

supplementary angles: two angles whose sum is 180°

$x + y = 180°$, thus x and y are supplementary angles.

symmetric equation of a line: an equation that describes a line in R^2 or R^3 in terms of a point on a line and a direction vector parallel to the line without using a parameter
- in R^2, the symmetric equation of the line through $A(a_1, a_2)$ with direction vector $\vec{m} = [m_1, m_2]$ is $\frac{x - a_1}{m_1} = \frac{y - a_2}{m_2}, m_1 \neq 0, m_2 \neq 0$
- in R^3, the symmetric equations of the line through $A(a_1, a_2, a_3)$ with direction vector $\vec{m} = [m_1, m_2, m_3]$ are $\frac{x - a_1}{m_1} = \frac{y - a_2}{m_2} = \frac{z - a_3}{m_3}, m_1 \neq 0, m_2 \neq 0, m_3 \neq 0$

symmetrical: possessing symmetry; see *line symmetry* and *point symmetry*

30-60-90 triangle: a triangle with angles 30°, 60°, and 90°; the ratio of sides corresponding to the angles is $1 : \sqrt{3} : 2$

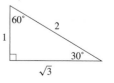

tail: the tail of vector $\overrightarrow{AB}$ is the point A, also called the initial point of the vector $\overrightarrow{AB}$

A   tail (initial point)

tail-to-tail: a method of joining vectors so that the tail of one vector meets the tail of the other

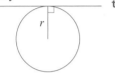

Tangent-Radius Theorem: a tangent to a circle is perpendicular to the radius at the point of tangency

tangent to a circle: a line that intersects a circle in exactly one point

tetrahedron: a solid with four triangular faces

theorem: a statement that has been proved

torque: a measure of the rotational effect caused by a force; measured in newton metres
- torque is a vector quantity; it is calculated using the formula $\overrightarrow{T} = \overrightarrow{r} \times \overrightarrow{F}$ where $\overrightarrow{r}$ is the radius vector from the centre of rotation to the point where the force $\overrightarrow{F}$ is applied

translation: a transformation that moves all points in the plane in a given direction through a given distance; also called a *slide*

Determine the image of the point P(–3, 5) after applying the translation (7, –1).

Let P'(x, y) represent the image of P. To apply the translation, add 7 to the x-coordinate of P and subtract 1 from the y-coordinate of P. The image point is P'(4, 4).

transversal: a line that intersects two or more lines

Line *t* is a transversal.

trapezoid: a quadrilateral with only one pair of opposite parallel sides

tree diagram: a branching diagram used to show all possible outcomes of an event

Triangle Law of Vector Addition: a method for adding vectors that are arranged head-to-tail; to add $\overrightarrow{a}$ and $\overrightarrow{b}$, draw $\overrightarrow{b}$ with its tail at the head of $\overrightarrow{a}$; the sum, $\overrightarrow{a} + \overrightarrow{b}$, is the vector from the tail of $\overrightarrow{a}$ to the head of $\overrightarrow{b}$, as shown in the diagram

undefined terms: words that express notions so fundamental that they cannot be defined using other terms

Point, line, angle, and figure are undefined terms.

unit vector: a vector with magnitude 1; for any non-zero vector $\overrightarrow{u}$, $\frac{1}{|\overrightarrow{u}|}\overrightarrow{u}$ is a unit vector in the same direction as $\overrightarrow{u}$

vector: a quantity that has both magnitude and direction

vector addition and scalar multiplication properties:
- commutative law: $\overrightarrow{a} + \overrightarrow{b} = \overrightarrow{b} + \overrightarrow{a}$
- associative law:
  $\overrightarrow{a} + (\overrightarrow{b} + \overrightarrow{c}) = (\overrightarrow{a} + \overrightarrow{b}) + \overrightarrow{c}$
- $\overrightarrow{a} + \overrightarrow{0} = \overrightarrow{a}$
- $\overrightarrow{a} + (-\overrightarrow{a}) = \overrightarrow{0}$
- distributive law:
  $k(\overrightarrow{a} + \overrightarrow{b}) = k\overrightarrow{a} + k\overrightarrow{b}$, where k is any scalar

- distributive law: $(s + t)\vec{a} = s\vec{a} + t\vec{a}$, where s, t are any scalars
- associative law: $s(t\vec{a}) = (st)\vec{a}$, where s, t are any scalars

vector equation of a line: an equation that describes a line in R^2 or R^3 in terms of a point on the line and a direction vector parallel to the line

- in R^2, the vector equation of the line through $A(a_1, a_2)$ with direction vector $\vec{m} = [m_1, m_2]$ is $[x, y] = [a_1, a_2] + t[m_1, m_2]$, where t is any real number
- in R^3, the vector equation of the line through $A(a_1, a_2, a_3)$ with direction vector $\vec{m} = [m_1, m_2, m_3]$ is
$[x, y, z] = [a_1, a_2, a_3] + t[m_1, m_2, m_3]$,

  where t is any real number

vector equation of a plane: an equation that describes a plane in terms of a point on the plane and two non-collinear direction vectors lying in the plane

- the vector equation of the plane through $A(a_1, a_2, a_3)$ with direction vectors $\vec{u} = [u_1, u_2, u_3]$ and $\vec{v} = [v_1, v_2, v_3]$ is $[x, y, z] = [a_1, a_2, a_3] + s[u_1, u_2, u_3] + t[v_1, v_2, v_3]$, where s and t represent any real numbers

vector operations: see *geometric vectors* and *Cartesian vectors*

vertex: the corner of a figure or solid

whole numbers: the set of numbers 0, 1, 2, 3, ...

work: when a constant force, $\vec{F}$, moves an object from point A to point B, the *work* done is the product of the magnitude of the displacement vector $\vec{d} = AB$ and the magnitude of the force in the direction of the displacement; measured in newton metres

- work is a scalar quantity calculated by the formula $\vec{F} \cdot \vec{d}$

zero vector: a vector that has zero length and no specified direction; represented by $\vec{0}$

Answers

Chapter 1 Geometric and Cartesian Vectors

1.1 Exercises, page 8

1. Parts c, e, and h are vectors and the rest are scalars.

2. Parts a, e, f, and h can be described by a vector.

3. a) 23 m/s, E   **b)** 20 m, S
   c) 34 km/h, SE   **d)** 50 m/s^2, NE   **e)** 225 m, NW

4. $\overrightarrow{CD} = \overrightarrow{LM}$, $\overrightarrow{EF} = \overrightarrow{RS}$, $\overrightarrow{AB} = \overrightarrow{JK}$, $\overrightarrow{NO} = \overrightarrow{VW}$,
   $\overrightarrow{AB} = \overrightarrow{PQ}$, $\overrightarrow{JK} = \overrightarrow{PQ}$

5. a) $\overrightarrow{AD} = \overrightarrow{BC}$, $\overrightarrow{DC} = \overrightarrow{AB}$
   b) $\overrightarrow{QT} = \overrightarrow{TS}$, $\overrightarrow{PT} = \overrightarrow{TR}$, $\overrightarrow{SR} = \overrightarrow{PQ}$, $\overrightarrow{SP} = \overrightarrow{RQ}$
   c) $\overrightarrow{KJ} = \overrightarrow{CL}$, $\overrightarrow{KJ} = \overrightarrow{LA}$, $\overrightarrow{CL} = \overrightarrow{LA}$, $\overrightarrow{JL} = \overrightarrow{BK}$, $\overrightarrow{JL} = \overrightarrow{KC}$,
     $\overrightarrow{BK} = \overrightarrow{KC}$, $\overrightarrow{LK} = \overrightarrow{AJ}$, $\overrightarrow{LK} = \overrightarrow{JB}$, $\overrightarrow{AJ} = \overrightarrow{JB}$
   d) $\overrightarrow{ED} = \overrightarrow{AB}$, $\overrightarrow{CD} = \overrightarrow{AF}$, $\overrightarrow{CB} = \overrightarrow{EF}$, $\overrightarrow{DG} = \overrightarrow{GA}$,
     $\overrightarrow{BG} = \overrightarrow{GE}$, $\overrightarrow{FG} = \overrightarrow{GC}$, $\overrightarrow{AF} = \overrightarrow{GE}$, $\overrightarrow{BG} = \overrightarrow{CD}$,
     $\overrightarrow{ED} = \overrightarrow{GC}$, $\overrightarrow{FG} = \overrightarrow{AB}$, $\overrightarrow{EF} = \overrightarrow{GA}$, $\overrightarrow{DG} = \overrightarrow{CB}$,
     $\overrightarrow{AF} = \overrightarrow{BG}$, $\overrightarrow{GE} = \overrightarrow{CD}$, $\overrightarrow{ED} = \overrightarrow{FG}$, $\overrightarrow{GC} = \overrightarrow{AB}$,
     $\overrightarrow{EF} = \overrightarrow{DG}$, $\overrightarrow{GA} = \overrightarrow{CB}$

6. $\overrightarrow{DE} = \overrightarrow{EF}$, $\overrightarrow{AB} = \overrightarrow{BC}$, $\overrightarrow{AB} = -\overrightarrow{EF}$, $\overrightarrow{AB} = -\overrightarrow{DE}$

10. a) i) F   **ii)** T   **iii)** F
   b) $3\sqrt{2}$ cm

11. a) Yes   **b)** No

1.2 Exercises, page 15

1. a) $\overrightarrow{AC}$ **b)** $\overrightarrow{AD}$ **c)** $\overrightarrow{BA}$ **d)** $\overrightarrow{BA}$ **e)** $\overrightarrow{CB}$ **f)** $\overrightarrow{0}$
2. a) $\overrightarrow{PQ}$ **b)** $\overrightarrow{QU}$ **c)** $\overrightarrow{RS}$ **d)** $\overrightarrow{PS}$ **e)** $\overrightarrow{UV}$ **f)** $\overrightarrow{SR}$
3. a) $\overrightarrow{HC}$ **b)** $\overrightarrow{HB}$ **c)** $\overrightarrow{FC}$ **d)** $\overrightarrow{0}$
4. a) $\overrightarrow{AE}$ **b)** $\overrightarrow{AE}$ **c)** $\overrightarrow{CD}$ **d)** $\overrightarrow{BF}$ **e)** $\overrightarrow{AC}$ **f)** $\overrightarrow{0}$
6. a) $\overrightarrow{KR}$ **b)** $\overrightarrow{KS}$ **c)** $\overrightarrow{MR}$ **d)** $\overrightarrow{NM}$ **e)** $\overrightarrow{KM}$ **f)** $\overrightarrow{0}$
7. a) $\overrightarrow{DB} + \overrightarrow{BA}$ **b)** $\overrightarrow{CB} + \overrightarrow{BD}$ **c)** $\overrightarrow{CD} + \overrightarrow{DB}$
   d) $\overrightarrow{AD} + \overrightarrow{DB}$ **e)** $\overrightarrow{DC} + \overrightarrow{CB}$ **f)** $\overrightarrow{BD} + \overrightarrow{DC}$

8. a) $\overrightarrow{x} + \overrightarrow{0} = \overrightarrow{x}$

12. $\overrightarrow{0}$

13. a) $\overrightarrow{0}$ **b)** Vertices of a regular pentagon

14. a) 11.7 km/h   **b)** 59°   **c)** 72 m

15. a) 53.1°   **b)** 0.9 min

16. a) $\overrightarrow{NR}$ **b)** $\overrightarrow{RM}$

17. b) 18.4 N

18. a) Yes   **c)** No

1.3 Exercises, page 22

1. a) $\overrightarrow{CA}$ **b)** $\overrightarrow{DA}$ **c)** $\overrightarrow{CA}$ **d)** $\overrightarrow{CE}$
2. a) $\overrightarrow{TQ}$ **b)** $\overrightarrow{PT}$ **c)** $\overrightarrow{UQ}$ **d)** $\overrightarrow{PU}$
5. a) i) $\overrightarrow{AC}$ **ii)** $\overrightarrow{DB}$ **iii)** $\overrightarrow{CA}$ **iv)** $\overrightarrow{BD}$
   b) $\overrightarrow{v} + \overrightarrow{u}$, $\overrightarrow{u} + \overrightarrow{v}$, Commutative

6. a) $\overrightarrow{TR} - \overrightarrow{QR}$ **b)** $\overrightarrow{RS} - \overrightarrow{TS}$ **c)** $\overrightarrow{TS} - \overrightarrow{TP}$ **d)** $\overrightarrow{TR} - \overrightarrow{TP}$
7. $\overrightarrow{0}$
8. a) $\overrightarrow{AG}$ **b)** $\overrightarrow{EC}$ **c)** $\overrightarrow{DF}$ **d)** $\overrightarrow{HB}$
9. a) F   **b)** F
11. b) Yes to all

1.4 Exercises, page 29

2. a) $1\overrightarrow{u}$ **b)** $2\overrightarrow{u}$ **c)** $3\overrightarrow{u}$ **d)** $1\overrightarrow{u}$
   e) $2\overrightarrow{u}$ **f)** $-1\overrightarrow{u}$ **g)** $-2\overrightarrow{u}$ **h)** $-3\overrightarrow{u}$

3. a) collinear   **b)** Y is between X and Z.

4. BD = 2XY

5. a) $2\overrightarrow{u}$ **b)** $2\overrightarrow{u} + \overrightarrow{v}$ **c)** $-\overrightarrow{v} - \overrightarrow{u}$

6. a) $0.5\overrightarrow{OQ} + \overrightarrow{OP}$ **b)** $\overrightarrow{OP} + 2\overrightarrow{OQ}$
   c) $2\overrightarrow{OP} + 1.5\overrightarrow{OQ}$ **d)** $\overrightarrow{OQ} + \overrightarrow{OP}$
   e) $2\overrightarrow{OP} + 0.5\overrightarrow{OQ}$ **f)** $\overrightarrow{OQ} + 3\overrightarrow{OP}$

7. a) No
   b) i) $-0.5\overrightarrow{a} - 6\overrightarrow{b}$ **ii)** $6.5\overrightarrow{a} - \overrightarrow{b}$ **iii)** $6\overrightarrow{a} - 7\overrightarrow{b}$
8. a) i) $2\overrightarrow{a} + 4\overrightarrow{b}$ **ii)** $3\overrightarrow{b} - 3\overrightarrow{a}$
    iii) $-2\overrightarrow{a} - 2\overrightarrow{b}$ **iv)** $4\overrightarrow{a} - 2\overrightarrow{b}$
   b) i) $-5\overrightarrow{a} - \overrightarrow{b}$ **ii)** $\overrightarrow{a} - 5\overrightarrow{b}$ **iii)** $6\overrightarrow{a}$
    iv) $-2\overrightarrow{a} + 6\overrightarrow{b}$ **v)** $7\overrightarrow{a} - 5\overrightarrow{b}$ **vi)** $4\overrightarrow{a} + 6\overrightarrow{b}$

11. b) The heads lie on a straight line.

12. a) $\overrightarrow{AB} + 0.5\overrightarrow{AD}$, $\overrightarrow{AD} + 0.5\overrightarrow{AB}$
   b) $\frac{4}{3}\overrightarrow{AM} - \frac{2}{3}\overrightarrow{AN}$, $\frac{4}{3}\overrightarrow{AN} - \frac{2}{3}\overrightarrow{AM}$

13. a) $\overrightarrow{v} + \overrightarrow{u}$ **b)** $2\overrightarrow{u} + \overrightarrow{v}$ **c)** $\overrightarrow{u} + \overrightarrow{v}$ **d)** $2\overrightarrow{u} - \overrightarrow{v}$
14. a) $\overrightarrow{u} + \overrightarrow{v}$ **b)** $\overrightarrow{v} + 2\overrightarrow{u}$ **c)** $3\overrightarrow{u} + \overrightarrow{v}$ **d)** $\overrightarrow{v}$
15. a) $\overrightarrow{u}$, $\overrightarrow{v} + \overrightarrow{u}$, $\overrightarrow{v}$, $-\overrightarrow{u}$, $-\overrightarrow{v} - \overrightarrow{u}$, $-\overrightarrow{v}$
   b) $2\overrightarrow{u} + \overrightarrow{v}$, $\overrightarrow{u} + 2\overrightarrow{v}$, $\overrightarrow{v} - \overrightarrow{u}$, $-2\overrightarrow{u} - \overrightarrow{v}$, $-\overrightarrow{u} - 2\overrightarrow{v}$,
    $\overrightarrow{v} + \overrightarrow{u}$

17. a) $\overrightarrow{AR} = -\overrightarrow{u} + 7\overrightarrow{v}$, $\overrightarrow{BQ} = -2\overrightarrow{u} + 6\overrightarrow{v}$, $\overrightarrow{CP} = -3\overrightarrow{u} + 5\overrightarrow{v}$,
   $\overrightarrow{DO} = -4\overrightarrow{u} + 4\overrightarrow{v}$, $\overrightarrow{EN} = -5\overrightarrow{u} + 3\overrightarrow{v}$, $\overrightarrow{FM} = -6\overrightarrow{u} + 2\overrightarrow{v}$,
   $\overrightarrow{GL} = -7\overrightarrow{u} + \overrightarrow{v}$

18. a) $0 \cdot \overrightarrow{x} = 0$, $1\overrightarrow{x} = \overrightarrow{x}$

21. a) 3   **b)** $\frac{1}{4}$ **c)** $\sqrt{19}$ **d)** $\sqrt{19}$ **e)** $\frac{\sqrt{7}}{2}$ **f)** $\sqrt{7}$

1.5 Exercises, page 40

1. $\overrightarrow{AB} = [3, -1]$, $\overrightarrow{CD} = [2, -5]$, $\overrightarrow{EF} = [-5, 1]$, $\overrightarrow{GH} = [4, 4]$,
   $\overrightarrow{IJ} = [-2, -2]$, $\overrightarrow{KL} = [-3, 0]$, $\overrightarrow{MN} = [-1, 4]$, $\overrightarrow{PQ} = [2, 3]$

2. a) [1, 3]   **b)** [3, 3]   **c)** [-5, -4]   **d)** [4, -5]

3. a) B(2, 3)   **b)** B(-8, -3)   **c)** B(-10, 1)

4. a) (-3, 2)   **b)** (7, 1)   **c)** (-6, -10)

5. a) i) [6, 4]   **ii)** [9, 6]
    iii) [15, 10]   **iv)** [-12, -8]
   c) i) $2\sqrt{13}$ **ii)** $3\sqrt{13}$ **iii)** $5\sqrt{13}$ **iv)** $4\sqrt{13}$
6. a) [12, 9]   **b)** [2, 1.5]
   c) [8, 6]   **d)** [0.8, 0.6]

7. a) [6, 2], [−4, 2], [−6, −2], [4, −2]
b) $2\sqrt{10}, 2\sqrt{5}, 2\sqrt{10}, 2\sqrt{5}$ **c)** Parallelogram

8. a) [1, 8], [7, −4], [−1, −8], [−7, 4]
b) $\sqrt{65}, \sqrt{65}, \sqrt{65}, \sqrt{65}$ **c)** Rhombus

9. b) i) Not collinear   **ii)** Collinear

10. a) i) [1, −2]   **ii)** [12, −4]   **iii)** [1, 3]
iv) [−5, 5]   **v)** [8, −6]   **vi)** [−13, 11]

12. a) [11, −9]   **b)** [2, 22]   **c)** [−5, −29]

14. a) $6\vec{i} - 4\vec{j}$ **b)** $-6\vec{i} - 3\vec{j}$ **c)** $5\vec{i} - \vec{j}$
d) $\vec{i} - 3\vec{j}$ **e)** $8\vec{i} - 10\vec{j}$ **f)** $7\vec{j}$

15. a) [6, 4], [2, −2]   **c)** $2\sqrt{13}, 2\sqrt{2}$ **e)** No

16. a) $2\vec{u} + 4\vec{v}$

17. a) $-2\vec{v} + 0.5\vec{w}$ **b)** $-0.5\vec{u} + 0.25\vec{w}$

18. a) $5\vec{u} - 2\vec{v}$

19. a) $0.4\vec{v} + 0.2\vec{w}$ **b)** $2.5\vec{u} - 0.5\vec{w}$

20. a) [6, 2], [4, 3], [2, 4], [0, 5], [−2, 6], [−4, 7], [−6, 8]
d) i) Adds [2, 4] to each answer.
ii) Adds [−1, 2] to each answer.

21. a) [−3, 8], [−1, 5], [1, 2], [3, −1], [5, −4], [7, −7]   **d)** Yes

23. $\left[\frac{8}{\sqrt{5}}, \frac{4}{\sqrt{5}}\right]$ and $\left[\frac{-8}{\sqrt{5}}, \frac{-4}{\sqrt{5}}\right]$

24. $-2 \pm \sqrt{21}$

25. No

1.6 Exercises, page 50

1. a) [0, 150]   **b)** [−56.6, −56.6]   **c)** [200.8, 286.7]
d) [70, −121.2]   **e)** [−28.2, 10.3]

2. 61 N

3. a) 556 N   **b)** 36°

4. 26.5 N, 139°

5. 72.6 N, 56.8°

6. 28.3 N at 131°

8. 115.5 N, 57.8 N

9. 5.8 N

10. 832.3 km/h at a bearing of 130.1°

11. 614.9 km/h at a bearing of 037.4°

12. a) 68.6°   **b)** 598 km/h   **c)** 51 min

13. 42.3 km/h

1.7 Exercises, page 55

1. a) 45°   **b)** 135°   **c)** 60°

2. a) 5.1   **b)** −5.2   **c)** 0

3. a) 26   **b)** −1   **c)** 0   **d)** 19

4. a) 1   **b)** 1   **c)** 0

6. a) 78.7°   **b)** 150.3°   **c)** 97.8°   **d)** 90°

8. a) ∠ABC = 90°   ∠BAC = 71.6°   ∠ACB = 18.4°

10. a) i) 40   **ii)** 0   **iii)** 40
c) The 3 dot products would be equal.

11. a) i) 11   **ii)** 11   **iii)** −11   **iv)** −11
d) All dot products equal zero.

12. b) i) No   **ii)** Yes

13. b) i) Yes   **ii)** No

14. [5, 2], [−2, 5], [−2, 5], or [5, 2], [2, −5], [2, −5]

15. [4, 2], [−4, 8], [−4, 8], or [4, 2], [4, −8], [4, −8] or [4, 2],
[−1, 2], [−1, 2], or [4, 2], [1, −2], [1, −2]

17. b) i) [4, 8]   **ii)** [8, 0]   **iii)** [4, 2]

18. a) −4   **b)** $\frac{15}{4}$

19. a) −10   **b)** 7   **c)** 6   **d)** −126

20. a) $|F| \cos \theta$

21. Approximately 2600 J

1.8 Exercises, page 64

1. a) $\vec{a} \cdot \vec{b} + \vec{a} \cdot \vec{c}$ **b)** $|\vec{a}|^2 + \vec{a} \cdot \vec{b}$
c) $|\vec{u}|^2 + 2\vec{u} \cdot \vec{v}$ **d)** $6|\vec{u}|^2 - 9\vec{u} \cdot \vec{v}$

2. a) $|\vec{a}|^2 - |\vec{b}|^2$ **b)** $|\vec{a}|^2 - \vec{a} \cdot \vec{b} - 2|\vec{b}|^2$
c) $4|\vec{a}|^2 + 9\vec{a} \cdot \vec{b} + 2|\vec{b}|^2$
d) $6|\vec{a}|^2 + 5\vec{a} \cdot \vec{b} - 6|\vec{b}|^2$

3. a) No   **b)** No

5. a) No

6. a) $\vec{a} + \vec{c}, -\vec{a} + \vec{c}$ **b)** Rhombus

7. These are properties of dot products: $\vec{a} \cdot \vec{b} = \vec{b} \cdot \vec{a}$,
$\vec{a} \cdot (\vec{b} + \vec{c}) = \vec{a} \cdot \vec{b} + \vec{a} \cdot \vec{c}$, $\vec{a} \cdot \vec{a} = |\vec{a}|^2$,
$(k\vec{a}) \cdot \vec{b} = \vec{a} \cdot (kb) = k(\vec{a} \cdot \vec{b})$, $\vec{a} \cdot \vec{0} = 0$
These do not correspond to dot products: $(xy)z = x(yz)$,
$a \times 1 = a$

8. c) $|\vec{a} + \vec{b}|^2 = |\vec{a}|^2 + |\vec{b}|^2$

10. a) [3.20, −1.60]   **b)** $\left[\frac{48}{13}, \frac{32}{13}\right]$ **d)** No

11. a) $\left[\frac{12}{13}, \frac{18}{13}\right]$ **b)** $\vec{0}$
c) [−4.20, −1.40]   **d)** $0.9\vec{i} + 0.30\vec{j}$

12. b) i) [3, 6]   **ii)** [−4, 2]
iii) [4.83, 2.76]   **iv)** [2.15, 1.23]

13. a) $\frac{2}{7}\vec{b}$

14. a) $-\frac{4\sqrt{2}}{11}\vec{v}$

15. a) Yes   **b)** Yes

16. a) $\vec{a} \downarrow \vec{b}$ **b)** $\vec{b}$
c) $k\vec{a}$ **d)** $\vec{a} \downarrow \vec{b}$

17. a) Yes

18. $\left[\frac{22}{5}, -\frac{4}{5}\right], \left[\frac{8}{5}, \frac{44}{5}\right]$ or [−2, 4], [8, 4]

19. b) $xy = \frac{1}{4}(x + y)^2 - \frac{1}{4}(x - y)^2$

Chapter 1 Review Exercises, page 69

1. Distance, speed, mass, displacement, velocity, weight

3. a) $\overrightarrow{AO} = \overrightarrow{OC}, \overrightarrow{DC} = \overrightarrow{AB}, \overrightarrow{BO} = \overrightarrow{OD}, \overrightarrow{AD} = \overrightarrow{BC}$
b) $\overrightarrow{AD} = -\overrightarrow{CB}, \overrightarrow{OD} = -\overrightarrow{OB}, \overrightarrow{AO} = -\overrightarrow{CO}, \overrightarrow{DC} = -\overrightarrow{BA}$

4. a) $\overrightarrow{HA} + \overrightarrow{AE}$ **b)** $\overrightarrow{GC} + \overrightarrow{CF}$
c) $\overrightarrow{DH} + \overrightarrow{HG}$ **d)** $\overrightarrow{DG} + \overrightarrow{GC}$

5. a) $\overrightarrow{PQ}$ **b)** $\overrightarrow{RB}$ **c)** $\overrightarrow{GE}$ **d)** $4\overrightarrow{DR}$

6. $\vec{0}$

8. a) $\overrightarrow{AD} - \overrightarrow{AF}$ **b)** $\overrightarrow{DB} - \overrightarrow{DE}$
c) $\overrightarrow{AB} - \overrightarrow{AC}$ **d)** $\overrightarrow{BE} - \overrightarrow{BA}$

10. a) $2\vec{u}$ **b)** $2\vec{u} + \vec{v}$ **c)** $-\vec{v} - \vec{u}$

11. $\overrightarrow{CD} + 0.5\overrightarrow{CB}$; $\overrightarrow{CB} + 0.5\overrightarrow{CD}$

12. a) i) $[-3, 6]$ **ii)** $[-2, 4]$ **iii)** $[1, -2]$ **iv)** $[4, -8]$
b) i) $3\sqrt{5}$ **ii)** $2\sqrt{5}$ **iii)** $\sqrt{5}$ **iv)** $4\sqrt{5}$

13. a) $[4, 2], [-8, 6], [4, -8]$ **b)** Scalene, right triangle

14. a) $10\vec{u} + 4\vec{v}$

15. a) 164.4 N at 24° to the 90 N force, 164.4 N at 180° to the resultant force

16. 543.5 N at a bearing of 125.2°

17. 15.3 m/s, 66.4° to shore

18. a) 36.9° **b)** 94.4° **c)** 81.9° **d)** 135°

19. 60.6°, 31.3°, 88.1°

20. a) 1 **b)** 9 **c)** 37

22. a) $2|\vec{u}|^2 + 7\vec{u} \cdot \vec{v} + 3|\vec{v}|^2$
b) $9|\vec{a}|^2 - 16|\vec{b}|^2$

23. b) $-\dfrac{5\sqrt{3}}{6}\vec{b}$, $-\dfrac{3\sqrt{3}}{10}\vec{b}$

Chapter 1 Self-Test, page 72

1. a) $\overrightarrow{BD}$ **b)** $\overrightarrow{AB}$ **c)** $\overrightarrow{AC}$

2. $\vec{0}$

3. 414.9 km/h, 134.5°

4. a) $\left[-\dfrac{\sqrt{5}}{5}, -\dfrac{2\sqrt{5}}{5}\right]$ **b)** $\left[\sqrt{13}, \sqrt{39}\right]$ **c)** $[3.2, 6.4]$

5. 10 or 4

6. $\vec{a} + \vec{b}$, $-k\vec{a} - \ell\vec{b}$, $k = \ell$

Chapter 2 Vectors in Three Dimensions

2.1 Exercises, page 80

1. a) $(4, 0, -3)$ **b)** $\vec{v} = [4, 0, -3]$ **c)** 5
d) $\cos \alpha = \dfrac{4}{5}$, $\cos \beta = 0$; $\cos \gamma = \dfrac{-3}{5}$
e) $\alpha \doteq 36.87°$; $\beta = 90°$; $\gamma \doteq 126.87°$

2. a) R **b)** R and S **c)** Q **d)** Q **e)** 7 units

3. a) $5\sqrt{2}$ **b)** $\dfrac{3}{5\sqrt{2}}, \dfrac{1}{\sqrt{2}}, \dfrac{4}{5\sqrt{2}}$
c) $\alpha \doteq 64.90°$; $\beta = 45°$; $\gamma \doteq 55.55°$

d)

N	$|\overrightarrow{ON}|$	Direction cosine	Direction angle
$(3, 0, 0)$	3	$\cos \alpha = 1$	$\alpha = 0°$
		$\cos \beta = 0$	$\beta = 90°$
		$\cos \gamma = 0$	$\gamma = 90°$
$(0, 5, 0)$	5	$\cos \alpha = 0$	$\alpha = 90°$
		$\cos \beta = 1$	$\beta = 0°$
		$\cos \gamma = 0$	$\gamma = 90°$
$(0, 0, 4)$	4	$\cos \alpha = 0$	$\alpha = 90°$
		$\cos \beta = 0$	$\beta = 90°$
		$\cos \gamma = 1$	$\gamma = 0°$
$(3, 0, 4)$	5	$\cos \alpha = \dfrac{3}{5}$	$\alpha \doteq 53°$
		$\cos \beta = 0$	$\beta = 90°$
		$\cos \gamma = \dfrac{4}{5}$	$\gamma \doteq 37°$
$(3, 5, 0)$	$\sqrt{34}$	$\cos \alpha = \dfrac{3}{\sqrt{34}}$	$\alpha \doteq 59°$
		$\cos \beta = \dfrac{5}{\sqrt{34}}$	$\beta \doteq 31°$
		$\cos \gamma = 1$	$\gamma = 90°$
$(0, 5, 4)$	$\sqrt{41}$	$\cos \alpha = 0$	$\alpha = 90°$
		$\cos \beta = \dfrac{5}{\sqrt{41}}$	$\beta \doteq 39°$
		$\cos \gamma = \dfrac{4}{\sqrt{41}}$	$\gamma \doteq 51°$

4. a) $\sqrt{29}$ **b)** $\dfrac{-4}{\sqrt{29}}, \dfrac{2}{\sqrt{29}}, \dfrac{-3}{\sqrt{29}}$
c) $\alpha \doteq 137.97°$; $\beta \doteq 68.20°$; $\gamma \doteq 123.85°$

d)

N	$|\overrightarrow{ON}|$	Direction cosine	Direction angle
$(-4, 0, 0)$	4	$\cos \alpha = -1$	$\alpha = 180°$
		$\cos \beta = 0$	$\beta = 90°$
		$\cos \gamma = 0$	$\gamma = 90°$
$(0, 2, 0)$	2	$\cos \alpha = 0$	$\alpha = 90°$
		$\cos \beta = 1$	$\beta = 0°$
		$\cos \gamma = 0$	$\gamma = 90°$
$(0, 0, -3)$	3	$\cos \alpha = 0$	$\alpha = 90°$
		$\cos \beta = 0$	$\beta = 90°$
		$\cos \gamma = -1$	$\gamma = 180$
$(-4, 2, 0)$	$2\sqrt{5}$	$\cos \alpha = \dfrac{-2\sqrt{5}}{5}$	$\alpha \doteq 153°$
		$\cos \beta = \dfrac{\sqrt{5}}{5}$	$\beta \doteq 63°$
		$\cos \gamma = 0$	$\gamma = 90°$
$(-4, 0, -3)$	5	$\cos \alpha = \dfrac{-4}{5}$	$\alpha \doteq 143°$
		$\cos \beta = 0$	$\beta = 90°$
		$\cos \gamma = \dfrac{-3}{5}$	$\gamma \doteq 127°$
$(0, 2, -3)$	$\sqrt{13}$	$\cos \alpha = 0$	$\alpha = 90°$
		$\cos \beta = \dfrac{2}{\sqrt{13}}$	$\beta \doteq 56°$
		$\cos \gamma = \dfrac{-3}{\sqrt{13}}$	$\gamma \doteq 146°$

5. Not if the point is on one of the coordinate planes

6. a) Magnitude: $\sqrt{14}$; Direction cosines: $\cos\alpha = \frac{1}{\sqrt{14}}$, $\cos\beta = \frac{2}{\sqrt{14}}$, $\cos\gamma = \frac{3}{\sqrt{14}}$
Direction angles: $\alpha \doteq 74°$, $\beta \doteq 58°$, $\gamma \doteq 37°$

b) Magnitude: $\sqrt{5}$; Direction cosines: $\cos\alpha = 0$, $\cos\beta = \frac{1}{\sqrt{5}}$, $\cos\gamma = -\frac{2}{\sqrt{5}}$
Direction angles: $\alpha = 90°$, $\beta \doteq 63°$, $\gamma \doteq 153°$

c) Magnitude: $2\sqrt{2}$; Direction cosines: $\cos\alpha = \frac{1}{\sqrt{2}}$, $\cos\beta = \frac{-1}{\sqrt{2}}$, $\cos\gamma = 0$
Direction angles: $\alpha = 45°$, $\beta = 135°$, $\gamma = 90°$

d) Magnitude: 4; Direction cosines: $\cos\alpha = -1$, $\cos\beta = 0$, $\cos\gamma = 0$;
Direction angles: $\alpha = 180°$, $\beta = 90°$, $\gamma = 90°$

e) Magnitude: $\sqrt{26}$; Direction cosines: $\cos\alpha = \frac{3}{\sqrt{26}}$, $\cos\beta = \frac{-4}{\sqrt{26}}$, $\cos\gamma = \frac{-1}{\sqrt{26}}$
Direction angles: $\alpha \doteq 54°$, $\beta \doteq 142°$, $\gamma \doteq 101°$

f) Magnitude: $2\sqrt{3}$; Direction cosines: $\cos\alpha = -\frac{1}{\sqrt{3}}$, $\cos\beta = \frac{1}{\sqrt{3}}$, $\cos\gamma = -\frac{1}{\sqrt{3}}$
Direction angles: $\alpha \doteq 125°$, $\beta \doteq 55°$, $\gamma \doteq 125°$

7. a) $\overrightarrow{PQ} = [-1, 0, -2]$; $|\overrightarrow{PQ}| = \sqrt{5}$
b) $\overrightarrow{PQ} = [-2, 6, -4]$; $|\overrightarrow{PQ}| = 2\sqrt{14}$
c) $\overrightarrow{PQ} = [2, -3, 3]$; $|\overrightarrow{PQ}| = \sqrt{22}$
d) $\overrightarrow{PQ} = [-2, 1, 5]$; $|\overrightarrow{PQ}| = \sqrt{30}$

8. $[9, 11, -3]$

9. $[9, -5, 6]$

10. a) $|\overrightarrow{AB}| = \sqrt{17}$; $|\overrightarrow{AC}| = \sqrt{21}$; $|\overrightarrow{BC}| = \sqrt{38}$
b) $(\sqrt{17})^2 + (\sqrt{21})^2 = (\sqrt{38})^2$

12. $D = (2, -1, 5)$
b) $(-2, -3, 10)$; $(6, -7, -8)$; $(2, 9, 4)$
c) The order of the vertices is given in part a but not in part b.

13. $\alpha = 0°$ or $180°$, $\beta = 90°$, $\gamma = 90°$

14. $\alpha = \cos^{-1}\left(\frac{x}{\sqrt{x^2+y^2}}\right)$, $\beta = \cos^{-1}\left(\frac{y}{\sqrt{x^2+y^2}}\right)$, $\gamma = 90°$

17. a) $54.7°$ or $125.3°$

19. $\left[\frac{-9}{\sqrt{17}}, \frac{-6}{\sqrt{17}}, \frac{6}{\sqrt{17}}\right]$

20. $\left[\sqrt{42}, \sqrt{42}, 4\right]$

21. $P = (0, -7, 0)$

23. a) 2

2.2 Exercises, page 88

1. a) $[4, 1, -1]$ **b)** $[6, -3, 7]$
c) $[-5, 1, -3]$ **d)** $[10, -2, 6]$
e) $[3, 3, -5]$ **f)** $[17, -7, 17]$
2. a) $[8, 7, -3]$ **b)** $[-4, -1, -1]$
c) $[-4, -6, 4]$ **d)** $[3, 2, -0.5]$
e) $[-8, -7, 3]$ **f)** $[-10, 0, -5]$
3. a) $2\vec{i} + 3\vec{j} + \vec{k}$ **b)** $4\vec{i} - \vec{j} - 5\vec{k}$
c) $5\vec{i} + 4\vec{j} - \vec{k}$ **d)** $5\vec{i} - 3\vec{j} - 8\vec{k}$
e) $11\vec{i} + 13\vec{j} + 2\vec{k}$ **f)** $-9\vec{i} + 4\vec{j} + 13\vec{k}$

5. a) $\vec{b} = -\frac{2}{3}\vec{a} + \frac{1}{3}\vec{c}$ **b)** $\vec{a} = -\frac{2}{3}\vec{a} + \frac{1}{2}\vec{c}$

7. c) $[8, -8, 4]$ **d)** $\left[1, -1, \frac{1}{2}\right]$
c) $[4, -4, 2]$ **d)** $\left[\frac{2}{3}, -\frac{2}{3}, \frac{1}{3}\right]$

8. a) $\alpha \doteq 48.2°$; $\beta \doteq 131.8°$; $\gamma \doteq 70.5°$
b) $\alpha \doteq 48.2°$; $\beta \doteq 131.8°$; $\gamma \doteq 70.5°$
c) $\alpha \doteq 48.2°$; $\beta \doteq 131.8°$; $\gamma \doteq 70.5°$
d) $\alpha \doteq 48.2°$; $\beta \doteq 131.8°$; $\gamma \doteq 70.5°$

9. a) $\vec{v_1} = [6, 4, -2]$, $\vec{v_2} = [-6, -4, 2]$
b) $\vec{v_1} = \left[\frac{3}{\sqrt{14}}, \frac{2}{\sqrt{14}}, \frac{-1}{\sqrt{14}}\right]$, $\vec{v_2} = \left[\frac{-3}{\sqrt{14}}, \frac{-2}{\sqrt{14}}, \frac{1}{\sqrt{14}}\right]$

10. a) $\left[\frac{4}{5}, \frac{3}{5}, 0\right]$ and $\left[\frac{-4}{5}, \frac{-3}{5}, 0\right]$
b) $\left[\frac{-2}{3}, \frac{1}{3}, \frac{2}{3}\right]$ and $\left[\frac{2}{3}, \frac{-1}{3}, \frac{-2}{3}\right]$
c) $\left[\frac{-1}{3\sqrt{2}}, \frac{4}{3\sqrt{2}}, \frac{1}{3\sqrt{2}}\right]$ and $\left[\frac{1}{3\sqrt{2}}, \frac{-4}{3\sqrt{2}}, \frac{-1}{3\sqrt{2}}\right]$
d) $\left[\frac{2}{\sqrt{38}}, \frac{-3}{\sqrt{38}}, \frac{5}{\sqrt{38}}\right]$ and $\left[\frac{-2}{\sqrt{38}}, \frac{3}{\sqrt{38}}, \frac{-5}{\sqrt{38}}\right]$

11. a) No   **b)** Yes   **c)** Yes

12. b) $\alpha \doteq 109°$; $\beta \doteq 119°$; $\gamma \doteq 36°$
c) $\alpha \doteq 59°$; $\beta \doteq 40°$; $\gamma \doteq 113°$,
$\alpha \doteq 121°$, $\beta \doteq 140°$, $\gamma \doteq 67°$

13. b) i) Yes   **ii)** No   **iii)** Yes

14. a) $\vec{w} = 2\vec{u} - 3\vec{v}$ **b)** $\vec{u} = \frac{3}{2}\vec{v} + \frac{1}{2}\vec{w}$
c) $\vec{v} = \frac{2}{3}\vec{u} - \frac{1}{3}\vec{w}$

15. a) Yes   **b)** Yes   **c)** No

17. a) Yes   **b)** No   **c)** Yes

18. b) i) Yes   **ii)** Yes   **iii)** No

2.3 Exercises, page 95

1. a) 3   **b)** 0   **c)** 7   **d)** -9
2. a) 1   **b)** 1   **c)** 1   **d)** 0   **e)** 0   **f)** 0
3. a) $90°$ **b)** $57.5°$ **c)** $70.5°$ **d)** $135.7°$
4. a) $B = 60°$, $C = 90°$, $A = 30°$
b) $P \doteq 68.33°$, $R \doteq 89.05°$, $Q \doteq 22.62°$
c) $R \doteq 71.07°$, $S \doteq 37.86°$, $T \doteq 71.07°$
5. $[-1, 6, 5]$
9. b) $A \doteq 72°$, $B \doteq 108°$
$C \doteq 72°$, $D \doteq 108°$
10. a) $90°, 90°, 90°, 90°$
b) Rectangle
11. a) $k = -4$ **b)** $k = \frac{-5}{2}$ **c)** $k = 5$ or -2
12. $x = \frac{-1}{5}, y = \frac{-7}{5}$
13. a) i) $z = -3, y = -5$ **ii)** $x = \frac{-1}{5}, z = \frac{3}{5}$
iii) $x = -1, y = 5$ **iv)** $x = -2, y = 10$
14. a) 8   **b)** 22   **c)** -7 **d)** 208
15. a) -3 **b)** -34 **c)** -14 **d)** -2
16. a) $\angle CAB \doteq 35.26°$ **b)** $|\overrightarrow{AB} \downarrow \overrightarrow{AC}| = \frac{2\sqrt{6}}{3}$
17. c) $\frac{5}{\sqrt{30}}$
18. a) $\vec{u} \downarrow \vec{v} = \left[\frac{-11}{7}, \frac{11}{14}, \frac{-33}{14}\right]$; $|\vec{u} \downarrow \vec{v}| = \frac{11\sqrt{14}}{14}$

420   ANSWERS

b) $\vec{u} \downarrow \vec{v} = \vec{0}$; $|\vec{u} \downarrow \vec{v}| = 0$

c) $\vec{u} \downarrow \vec{v} = \left[\frac{-9}{14}, \frac{27}{14}, \frac{9}{7}\right]$; $|\vec{u} \downarrow \vec{v}| = \frac{9\sqrt{14}}{14}$

d) $\vec{u} \downarrow \vec{v} = \left[\frac{-2}{3}, \frac{1}{3}, \frac{-1}{3}\right]$; $|\vec{u} \downarrow \vec{v}| = \frac{\sqrt{6}}{3}$

19. $\overrightarrow{PQ} \downarrow \overrightarrow{RS} = \left[\frac{205}{33}, \frac{-82}{33}, \frac{-82}{33}\right]$

22. b) 77.4°

2.4 Exercises, page 106

1. Because $\vec{a}$ and $\vec{b}$ define a plane which $\vec{a} \times \vec{b}$ is perpendicular to.
Because $\sin 0 = 0$

2. a) 86.04, ceiling   **b)** 98.30, floor

6. a) [1, 1, 1]   **b)** [−9, −3, 5]
   c) [5, 17, 35]   **d)** [−13, −12, 16]

7. Yes

8. a) 3 units^2 **b)** $\sqrt{29}$ units^2
   c) $\sqrt{129}$ units^2 **d)** $\sqrt{90}$ units^2

9. a) [13, −3, −2]   **c)** $\sqrt{182}$

10. a) [−4, 8, −4]   **b)** [16, 22, −7]
   c) [−4, −2, −4]   **d)** [5, −15, 0]

11. a) [0, 0, 0]   **b)** [0, 0, 0]   **c)** [0, 0, 0]
   d) [0, 0, 1]   **e)** [0, 0, −1]   **f)** [1, 0, 0]
   g) [−1, 0, 0]   **h)** [0, 1, 0]   **i)** [0, −1, 0]

13. a) $\sqrt{42}$ units^2 **b)** $\sqrt{75}$ units^2

14. a) 3 units^2 **b)** $\frac{\sqrt{70}}{2}$ units^2

15. a) $\overrightarrow{AB} = [2, 3, 4]$, $\overrightarrow{BC} = [−4, −1, −1]$, $\overrightarrow{CA} = [2, −2, −3]$
   b) i) [1, −14, 10]   **ii)** [1, −14, 10]   **iii)** [1, −14, 10]

16. a) 30° or 150°

18. a) $\tau \doteq 30.3$ N•m   **c)** Upward

2.5 Exercises, page 114

1. a) 0   **b)** 0

3. a) $\vec{0}$ **b)** $\vec{0}$

4. a) Not coplanar   **b)** Coplanar
   c) Not coplanar

5. a) Not coplanar   **b)** Coplanar
   c) Not coplanar

7. a) (−26, 26, −26)   **b)** (−26, 26, −26)
   c) (−26, 26, −26)

10. a) (−18, −18, −18)   **b)** (−27, −27, −27)
   c) (−45, −45, −45)

Chapter 2 Review Exercises, page 119

1. a) $\sqrt{21}$
   b) $\cos \alpha = \frac{4\sqrt{21}}{21}$, $\cos \beta = \frac{\sqrt{21}}{21}$, $\cos \gamma = \frac{2\sqrt{21}}{21}$
   c) $\alpha = 29.2°$, $\beta = 77.4°$, $\gamma = 64.1°$

2. a) $\alpha \doteq 56.3°$, $\beta \doteq 33.7°$, $\gamma = 90°$
   b) $\alpha \doteq 125.3°$, $\beta \doteq 54.7°$, $\gamma = 54.7°$

3. a) [1, 9, 2]   **b)** [10, −1, −8]
   c) [15, −8, −14]

4. Yes

5. Yes

6. Yes

7. Yes

8. a) −3   **b)** 39

9. a) A $\doteq$ 66°, B = 90°, C $\doteq$ 24°
   b) [0, 2, 0]

10. a) Yes   **b)** No   **c)** Yes   **d)** Yes   **e)** Yes

11. a) $\left[-\frac{7}{10}, 0, \frac{21}{10}\right]$ **b)** $\frac{7\sqrt{10}}{10}$
   c) $\left[\frac{7}{11}, \frac{21}{22}, \frac{21}{22}\right]$ **d)** $\frac{7\sqrt{22}}{22}$

12. Answers may vary. [1, 0, −1]

15. $\left[\frac{\sqrt{3}}{3}, \frac{-\sqrt{3}}{3}, \frac{-\sqrt{3}}{3}\right]$, $\left[\frac{-\sqrt{3}}{3}, \frac{\sqrt{3}}{3}, \frac{\sqrt{3}}{3}\right]$

16. a) [1, 2, 0]   **b)** [−1, −2, 0]   **c)** $\sqrt{5}$

17. $\sqrt{3}$

18. $y = 3$, $x = 2$

19. a) False   **b)** True   **c)** True
   d) False   **e)** True   **f)** True   **g)** True

20. a) i) Magnitude: increased by a factor of 2, direction: unchanged
     ii) Magnitude: unchanged, direction: opposite
   b) 90° because $\sin \theta$ has a maximum of 1 at $\theta = 90°$

Chapter 2 Self-Test, page 122

2. a) 20   **b)** [9, −14, −11]
   c) 44.9°   **d)** $\left[\frac{30}{19}, \frac{-20}{19}, \frac{50}{19}\right]$ **e)** $\frac{10\sqrt{38}}{19}$

5. a) 10   **b)** $\theta \doteq 72°$ **c)** $t = 3$
   d) $\left[\frac{1}{3}, \frac{-2}{3}, \frac{5}{3}\right]$ **e)** [26, −12, −10]

6. Yes

7. $5\sqrt{2}$

8. a) 0   **b)** $\left[\frac{2}{\sqrt{5}}, \frac{1}{\sqrt{5}}, 0\right]$ and $\left[\frac{-2}{\sqrt{5}}, \frac{-1}{\sqrt{5}}, 0\right]$

Chapter 3 Equations of Lines and Planes

3.1 Exercises, page 131

Answers may vary for exercises 2–5.

2. a) (2, −3)   **b)** (7, −2), (12, −1), (19, 0)
   c) $[x, y] = [7, −2] + s[10, 2]$

3. a) (−1, 5)   **b)** (1, 6), (3, 7), (5, 8)
   c) $x = 1 − 2s$, $y = 6 − s$

4. a) (−4, 1)   **b)** (1, −1), (6, −3), (11, −5)
   c) $\frac{x-1}{5} = \frac{y+1}{-2}$

5. a) $[x, y] = [7, −3] + t[−1, 2]$
   b) $x = 7 − t$, $y = 2t − 3$ **c)** $\frac{x-1}{-1} = \frac{y+2}{2}$

6. a) $x = t$, $y = 0$ **b)** $x = 0$, $y = t$

Answers may vary for exercises 7–11.

7. a) $x = 3 + 3t$, $y = -2 + 3t$
b) $(9, 4)$, $(0, -5)$, $(-3, -8)$

8. a) $(2, -1)$, $(-2, -4)$, $(6, 2)$
b) $(-5, 8)$, $(-3, 3)$, $(-1, -2)$

9. a) $[x, y] = [4, 1] + t[-3, 1]$; $x = 4 - 3t$, $y = 1 + t$;
$\frac{x-4}{-3} = \frac{y-1}{1}$
b) $[x, y] = [-6, 2] + t[5, -2]$; $x = -6 + 5t$, $y = 2 - 2t$;
$\frac{x+6}{5} = \frac{y-2}{-2}$
c) $[x, y] = [2, -3] + t[0, 1]$; $x = 2$, $y = -3 + t$;
no symmetric equations

10. a) $y = \frac{2}{3}x + 4$ **b)** $x = 3t$, $y = 2t + 4$
c) $\frac{x}{3} = \frac{y-4}{2}$

11. a) i) $x = 2 + t$, $y = -4 + 2t$ **ii)** $\frac{x-2}{1} = \frac{y+2}{2}$
iii) $y = 2x - 8$ **iv)** $2x - y - 8 = 0$

13. A, B, D

14. The equations all represent the same line.

15. a) $(3, 2)$; $45°$ **b)** $\left(\frac{3}{2}, 5\right)$; $86.8°$

16. a) The lines do not intersect. **b)** $(12, -4)$

17. a) $(7, 0)$; $(0, 7)$ **b)** $(-7, 0)$; $\left(0, \frac{14}{3}\right)$

Answers may vary for exercises 18 and 19.

18. a) $[x, y] = [4, 0] + t[0, 1]$; $x = 4$, $y = t$
b) $[x, y] = [0, 3] + t[1, 0]$; $x = t$, $y = 3$
c) $[x, y] = [0, -2] + t[1, 3]$; $x = t$, $y = -2 + 3t$
d) $[x, y] = [-4, 0] + t[-2, 1]$; $x = -4 - 2t$, $y = t$

19. a) $x = -4t + 5$, $y = 2 - 3t$ **b)** $x = 2t$, $y = 1 - t$

20. $59°$

21. $y = -2x + 7$

22. a) $45°$, $45°$ **b)** $53.1°$, $36.9°$

23. $(6, 6)$ or $(8, 5)$

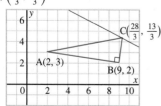

24. a) $\left(\frac{28}{3}, \frac{13}{3}\right)$

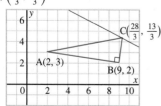

b) $\left(\frac{8}{3}, \frac{23}{3}\right)$

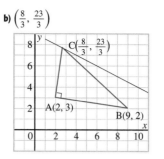

25. a) $30°$ or $150°$
b) $x = t$, $y = 4 + \sqrt{3}t$; $x = t$, $y = 4 - \sqrt{3}t$
c)

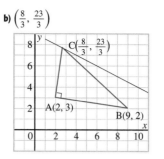

3.2 Exercises, page 141

Answers may vary in exercises 1–3.

1. a) $(5, -4, 1)$ **b)** $(8, -2, 0)$, $(11, 0, -1)$, $(14, 2, -2)$
c) $[x, y, z] = [8, -2, 0] + s[-3, -2, 1]$

2. a) $(2, -3, 4)$ **b)** $(3, -1, 1)$, $(4, 1, -2)$, $(5, 3, -5)$
c) $x = 3 - s$, $y = -1 - 2s$, $z = 1 + 3s$

3. a) $(4, 3, -2)$ **b)** $(6, 2, 1)$, $(8, 1, 4)$, $(10, 0, 7)$
c) $\frac{x-6}{-2} = \frac{y-2}{1} = \frac{z-1}{-3}$

4. No; substituting D into the symmetric equations does not
give three equal ratios.

Answers may vary in exercises 5–9.

5. a) $[x, y, z] = [3, -2, 5] + t[-1, 4, -3]$
b) $x = 3 - t$, $y = 4t - 2$, $z = 5 - 3t$
c) $\frac{x-3}{-1} = \frac{y+2}{4} = \frac{z-5}{-3}$

6. a) $x = t$, $y = 0$, $z = 0$ **b)** $x = 0$, $y = t$, $z = 0$
c) $x = 0$, $y = 0$, $z = t$

8. a) $x = 5 - t$, $y = 1 + 4t$, $z = -3 + 2t$
b) $(3, 9, 1)$, $(2, 13, 3)$, $(1, 17, 5)$

9. a) $(2, 3, -1)$, $(3, 1, -2)$, $(4, -1, -3)$
b) $(1, 0, 1)$, $(4, 1, -1)$, $(7, 2, -3)$
c) $(-3, 5, 2)$, $(-5, 6, 2)$, $(-7, 7, 2)$
d) $(-4, -2, 3)$, $(-4, 1, 7)$, $(-4, 4, 11)$

10. a) The line is parallel to the xy-plane, 2 units above it.
b) The line is parallel to the yz-plane, 4 units behind it.

11. a) $[x, y, z] = [2, -1, 3] + t[-1, 3, 5]$; $x = 2 - t$,
$y = -1 + 3t$, $z = 3 + 5t$; $\frac{x-2}{-1} = \frac{y+1}{3} = \frac{z-3}{5}$
b) $[x, y, z] = [4, -2, 1] + t[-5, 2, 2]$; $x = 4 - 5t$,
$y = -2 + 2t$, $z = 1 + 2t$; $\frac{x-4}{-5} = \frac{y+2}{2} = \frac{z-1}{2}$
c) $[x, y, z] = [5, -1, 0] + t[0, 4, -4]$; $x = 5$,
$y = -1 + 4t$, $z = -4t$; no symmetric equations
d) $[x, y, z] = [3, -1, -1] + t[1, 0, 0]$; $x = 3 + t$,
$y = -1$, $z = -1$; no symmetric equations

e) $[x, y, z] = [-2, 0, 5] + t[0, 1, 0]$; $x = -2$, $y = t$, $z = 5$; no symmetric equations

12. c

13. They all represent the same line.

14. a) $(-4, 3, -4)$ **b)** $(-7, -7, -3)$

15. a) The lines do not intersect.   **b)** $(1, 5, -1)$
c) $(-3, -3, -3)$

17. a) Answers may vary. $x = 2 - t$, $y = 2$, $z = 2 + t$;
$x = 2$, $y = 2 - t$, $z = 2 - t$; $x = 2 - t$, $y = 2 - t$, $z = 2$;
$x = -2$, $y = -2 + t$, $z = 2 - t$; $x = -2 + t$, $y = -2$, $z = 2 - t$;
$x = 2 - t$, $y = -2 + t$, $z = -2$
b) $60°$ or $120°$

19. a) i) $\left(\frac{11}{2}, \frac{-1}{2}, 0\right)$; $\left(\frac{17}{3}, 0, \frac{-1}{3}\right)$; $(0, -17, 11)$
ii) The line does not intersect the xy-plane;
$\left(\frac{-22}{3}, 0, -2\right)$; $(0, 11, -2)$

20. a) One of the parametric equations has only a constant term.
b) There are no symmetric equations.

21. a) Two of the parametric equations have only a constant term.
b) There are no symmetric equations.

22. Answers may vary.
b) $x = \frac{8}{5} + t$, $y = \frac{22}{5} + 2t$, $z = \frac{19}{5} + 2t$

23. Answers may vary.
$x = 2 + t$, $y = 5 + 2t$, $z = 3 + 2t$

24. Answers may vary. $\frac{x+2}{\sqrt{2}} = \frac{y-1}{2} = \frac{z-3}{\sqrt{2}}$

25. a) $45°$ or $135°$
b) Answers may vary. $x = \sqrt{2}t$, $y = \sqrt{2}t$, $z = 4 + 2t$;
$x = \sqrt{2}t$, $y = \sqrt{2}t$, $z = 4 - 2t$
c)

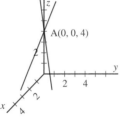

A(0, 0, 4)

26. b) $\overrightarrow{m}$, $\overrightarrow{p}$ and $\overrightarrow{a}$ are coplanar.

28. b) $\frac{x+8}{2} = \frac{y+7}{4} = \frac{z}{1}$

29. t is the distance from A to P(x, y, z).

3.3 Exercises, page 152

Answers may vary in exercises 1–3.
1. a) $(2, 6, -5)$ **b)** $(6, 8, -6)$, $(1, 9, -4)$, $(5, 11, -5)$
c) $\overrightarrow{p} = (6, 8, -6) + s(1, -3, -1) + t(-4, -2, 1)$

2. a) $(3, 1, 5)$ **b)** $(5, 2, 3)$, $(1, 4, 4)$, $(3, 5, 2)$
c) $x = 5 + 2s - 2t$, $y = 2 - 3s - t$, $z = 3 + s + 2t$

3. a) $(3, 0, 0)$, $(0, -6, 0)$, $(0, 0, 2)$
b) $x = 3 + s - 3t$, $y = 2s$, $z = 2t$

4. A, D

5. No

6. Yes

7. Answers may vary.
a) $[x, y, z] = [2, 1, 3] + s[-1, 3, 4] + t[2, 0, -1]$;
$x = 2 - s + 2t$, $y = 1 + 3s$, $z = 3 + 4s - t$
b) $[x, y, z] = [-2, 5, 1] + s[-5, 5, 5] + t[4, 5, 2]$;
$x = -2 - 5s + 4t$, $y = 5 + 5s + 5t$, $z = 1 + 5s + 2t$
c) $[x, y, z] = [-3, 1, 1] + s[1, 1, -2] + t[1, 2, 3]$;
$x = -3 + s + t$, $y = 1 + s + 2t$, $z = 1 - 2s + 3t$

8. a) $[4, -1, 2]$
b) Answers may vary. A$(-2, 0, 0)$, B$(0, 0, -4)$
c) $\overrightarrow{AB} = [2, 0, -4]$

10. Answers may vary.
a) $[x, y, z] = [1, 2, -3] + s[4, -1, 3] + t[2, 0, -3]$
b) $[x, y, z] = [-2, 6, 2] + s[4, -1, 1] + t[10, -10, 0]$

11. Answers may vary.
a) $x = 7 + 7t + 6s$, $y = -3 + t - 2s$, $z = 1 - 2t + s$
b) $x = -2 - 5t - 4s$, $y = 6 + 9t + s$, $z = 1 + 6s$

12. a) $4x - 2y + z + 12 = 0$ **b)** $x - y + 4z + 7 = 0$

13. a) $3x - y + 2z = 0$ **b)** $3x - y + 2z - 7 = 0$
c) $3x - y + 2z + 1 = 0$

14. a) $(3, 2, 0)$
b) The plane is parallel to the z-axis.
c) The line in R^2 lies on the plane in R^3.

15. a) $2x - 4y + 3z - 1 = 0$ **b)** $2x - y + z - 1 = 0$
c) $y - 5 = 0$

17. Answers may vary.
a) $[x, y, z] = [1, 0, 1] + s[2, -2, -1] + t[1, 1, 4]$;
$[x, y, z] = [3, -2, 0] + s[1, 1, 4] + t[1, -3, -5]$
b) $x = 1 + 2s + t$, $y = -2s + t$, $z = 1 - s + 4t$;
$x = 3 + s + t$, $y = -2 + s - 3t$, $z = 4s - 5t$
c) $7x + 9y - 4z - 3 = 0$

18. a) The angle of intersection between two planes is the acute angle between their normal vectors.
b) i) $63°$ **ii)** $82°$

19. $2x + y - z - 9 = 0$
20. a) $x + y + z = 0$ **b)** $x + y + z + 4 = 0$
c) $x + y + z - 4 = 0$ **d)** The planes are parallel.

22. $5x - 13y - 2z + 27 = 0$

23. $4x - 3y + 4z + 11 = 0$

24. $4x + 2z - 15 = 0$

25. a) $4x - y + 3z - 26 = 0$
b) The locus is a plane perpendicular to $\overrightarrow{OA}$ containing the point A and the vector $\overrightarrow{AP}$.

28. a) Answers may vary. $-x + y + z = 0$
b) 4; $x + y + z = 0$, $-x + y + z = 0$, $x - y + z = 0$,
$x + y - z = 0$

3.4 Exercises, page 160

3. a) L_2; t can only take on one value.
b) L_3; t can take on any value. **c)** L_1 is parallel to the plane.

4. a) $x + 3y - z - 6 = 0$ **b)** $3x - y - 5 = 0$

5. $x - 2y - z - 5 = 0$

6. a) $\left(4, \frac{-7}{4}, \frac{7}{2}\right)$ **b)** None
c) All points on the line   **d)** $\left(\frac{-21}{17}, \frac{-20}{17}, \frac{1}{17}\right)$
e) All points on the line   **f)** None   **g)** $(3, -1, 2)$

8. $(2, 6, 0)$

9. Answers may vary.
  a) $x = 6 + t$, $y = 2t$, $z = 0$; $x = 6 + 3t$, $y = 0$, $z = -2t$;
    $x = 6$, $y = 3t$; $z = t$
  b) $x = 6 + t$, $y = 2t$, $z = 0$; $x = t$, $y = -12 + 2t$, $z = 0$;
    $x = t$, $y = 2t$; $z = 4$

10. a) $6.3°$ **b)** $90°$

11. a) $\left(\dfrac{4}{6}, \dfrac{-5}{6}, \dfrac{17}{6}\right)$ **b)** $\left(\dfrac{16}{11}, \dfrac{-18}{11}, \dfrac{39}{11}\right)$

14. $(-1, 3, -2)$

15. $2x - y - 5z + 7 = 0$, $2x - y - 5z + 5 = 0$

16. Answers may vary. $[x, y, z] = [0, 0, 8] + t[1, 1, -1]$;
  $[x, y, z] = [0, 0, -4] + t[1, 0, -3]$

17. Answers may vary.
  a) $\dfrac{x - 3}{2} = \dfrac{y + 5}{3} = \dfrac{z + 1}{1}$
  c) $x - 2z - 3 = 0$, $x - 2z - 5 = 0$

19. $\dfrac{2\sqrt{30}}{5}$ units

20. a) 6 units   **b)** $\dfrac{1}{\sqrt{11}}$ units   **c)** $\dfrac{|Ax_1 + By_1 + Cz_1 + D|}{\sqrt{A^2 + B^2 + C^2}}$ units

3.5 Exercises, page 168

1. A line can intersect a plane, lie on a plane, or be parallel to a plane.

5. Answers may vary.
  a) $x = t$, $y = 3 - t$, $z = 4 - t$; $\dfrac{x}{1} = \dfrac{y - 3}{-1} = \dfrac{z - 4}{-1}$
  b) $x = 2$, $y = t$, $z = 1 - t$; no symmetric equations
  c) $x = t$, $y = 4 + 2t$, $z = 2 - 3t$; $\dfrac{x}{1} = \dfrac{y - 4}{2} = \dfrac{z - 2}{-3}$

6. Answers may vary. $\dfrac{x - 7}{1} = \dfrac{y + 2}{-6} = \dfrac{z - 4}{22}$

7. $3x + 9y - 4z + 8 = 0$

8. Answers may vary.
  $[x, y, z] = [2, 0, -1] + t[34, 26, -19]$

9. Answers may vary. $3x + 3y + 2z - 1 = 0$,
  $4x + 3y + 5z - 6 = 0$, $5x + 3y + 8z - 11 = 0$

10. $14x + 17y - 17z + 9 = 0$

11. $3x + 2y + 5z - 12 = 0$

12. $2x - y + 5z + 3 = 0$

13. b) The second value of k is the reciprocal of the first.

14. a) $11x + 14y - 3z = 0$ **b)** $12x + 13y - z + 5 = 0$
  c) $5x + 5y + 3 = 0$ **d)** $4x + y + 3z + 9 = 0$
  e) $5x + 5z + 14 = 0$ **f)** $10x + 5y + 5z + 17 = 0$

15. a) The normal vectors are scalar multiples of one another.
  b) A family of planes parallel to $x + 2y - 3z + 4 = 0$ and
    $2x + 4y - 6z + 5 = 0$

16. $16x - 9y - 5z - 18 = 0$; $3x - 2y + 1 = 0$

17. $7x - 5y + z = 0$; $5x - 4y + 2z - 3 = 0$

18. Answers may vary. $x = 2 + t$, $y = -2 - t$, $z = -2$;
  $x = -2$, $y = 2 - t$, $z = -2 + t$; $x = 2 + t$, $y = -2$, $z = -2 - t$

19. $A_2x + B_2y + C_2z + D_2 = 0$

3.6 Exercises, page 178

5. Answers may vary.
  a) $2x + 3y + 4z + 9 = 0$ **b)** $2x + 3y + 4z + 10 = 0$
  c) $x + y + z = 0$ **d)** $x + 2y + z + 7 = 0$

6. Three parallel planes

7. $\left(\dfrac{2}{5}, \dfrac{24}{5}, 2\right)$

8. a) $(1, 2, 3)$ **b)** $(4, -2, 3)$ **c)** $\left(\dfrac{-1}{4}, 4, \dfrac{5}{4}\right)$
  d) $(1, 3, -2)$ **e)** $(-1, 2, 3)$ **f)** $\left(\dfrac{-13}{10}, \dfrac{-11}{10}, \dfrac{-14}{5}\right)$

10. $x = \dfrac{16}{5} - 7t$, $y = \dfrac{22}{5} + t$, $z = 5t$

13. Answers may vary.
  a) $\pi_3 = \pi_1 + \pi_2$; $x = -12 + t$, $y = 7 - 2t$, $z = t$
  b) $\pi_3 = 2\pi_1 + \pi_2$; $x = \dfrac{6}{7}$, $y = t + \dfrac{40}{7}$, $z = t$

14. Answers may vary.
  a) $x = \dfrac{11}{5} + t$, $y = \dfrac{-2}{5} - t$, $z = t$
  b) $x = \dfrac{-5}{3} - 2t$, $y = \dfrac{-4}{3} - 3t$, $z = t$

15. a) The planes form a triangle. **b)** $(12, -17, -11)$
  c) 2 planes are parallel.   **d)** $\left(\dfrac{5}{4}, \dfrac{13}{14}, \dfrac{23}{28}\right)$
  e) $x = 5 - 3t$, $y = 1$, $z = t$

18. $y = -x^2 + 6x - 5$

19. $a = 17$, $b = -4$

21. $x = \dfrac{7a + 5b - 3c}{3}$, $y = \dfrac{-5a - 4b + 3c}{3}$, $z = -2a - b + c$

3.7 Exercises, page 188

1. a) $x = 1$, $y = 2$ **b)** $x = 2$, $y = 2$
  c) $x = 10$, $y = -25$ **d)** $x = -1$, $y = 2$

2. a) $x = \dfrac{12}{13}$, $y = \dfrac{-31}{26}$ **b)** $x = \dfrac{17}{43}$, $y = \dfrac{-92}{43}$
  c) $x = -6$, $y = 5$ **d)** $x = \dfrac{17}{8}$, $y = \dfrac{3}{4}$

4. a) Matrix 3   **b)** Matrix 2   **c)** Matrix 1

5. a) $x = 3$, $y = 4$, $z = 1$ **b)** $x = -1$, $y = 2$, $z = -5$
  c) $x = 5$, $y = -2$, $z = 3$ **d)** $x = \dfrac{1}{4}$, $y = \dfrac{-1}{4}$, $z = 0$

6. a) $x = 2$, $y = 3$, $z = 4$
  b) $x = -6 + 7t$, $y = -4 + 4t$, $z = t$
  c) Impossible   **d)** Impossible

7. a) $x = -23 - 7t$, $y = 5 + 2t$, $z = t$
  b) $x = 1 + 7t$, $y = 1 - 10t$, $z = t$
  c) $x = \dfrac{-1}{5} - t$, $y = \dfrac{8}{5} + t$, $z = t$
  d) $x = 7 + 7t$, $y = -12 - 12t$, $z = t$

9. a) Matrix 1   **b)** Matrix 2   **c)** Matrix 3

3.8 Exercises, page 194

3. a) $x = -1$, $y = \dfrac{-5}{3}$, $z = \dfrac{5}{3}$ **b)** $x = \dfrac{-32}{31}$, $y = \dfrac{51}{31}$, $z = \dfrac{119}{31}$

4. a) $x = 11 + 8t$, $y = -4 - 3t$, $z = t$
  b) $x = \dfrac{-3}{10} - \dfrac{7}{10}t$, $y = \dfrac{11}{10} - \dfrac{11}{10}t$, $z = t$

7. a) $x = 2 - 4t$, $y = 1 + 3t$, $z = t$
  b) $x = \dfrac{-3}{2} - \dfrac{9}{10}t$, $y = \dfrac{-7}{2} - \dfrac{7}{10}t$, $z = t$

8. $\$18.35$; $\$32.15$; $\$47.75$

9. 125 kg of brand X, 250 kg of brand Y, 125 kg of brand Z

10. 7.7%; 45.73%; -25%

11. a) i) $79.9°$ **ii)** $125.9°$
    b) The temperature never reaches $200°C$.

12. $18\,000$ Italian, $54\,000$ Oriental, $15\,000$ French

3.9 Exercises, page 198

3. a) $x = 32.5$, $y = 34.7$, $z = -23.1$
    b) $x = 1.5787$, $y = 2.5889$, $z = 1.2132$

4. a) i) System A   **iii)** $x = \frac{-5}{3} + \frac{1}{3}t$, $y = t$

5. b) i) $x = -1.2414$, $y = 2.1379$ **ii)** $x = 5$, $y = 2$

6. a) i) System A
    iii) $x = \frac{1}{7} - \frac{17}{7}t$, $y = \frac{10}{7} - \frac{9}{7}t$, $z = t$

7. a) $x = 5 - t$, $y = -5 + 2t$, $z = t$
    b) $x = 4.75 - 0.25t$, $y = 1.75 - 0.25t$, $z = t$

8. $10.34; \$8.73, \$12.50$

9. a) i) 1 **ii)** 5 **iii)** 14
    b) $\frac{1}{3}; \frac{1}{2}; \frac{1}{6}$

10. $1.6922, -125.15, 4182.5$

11. a) $1.1724, 9976.1$

12. $0.0148; 0.22$

Chapter 3 Review Exercises, page 204

1. A line parallel to the x-axis; a plane parallel to the xz-plane

2. A line parallel to the y-axis; a plane parallel to the yz-plane

3. $(-2, 3, 1)$

4. $(4, -1, 3)$

5. Answers may vary.
    a) $[x, y, z] = [1, 4, 2] + t[2, -1, 0]$
    b) $(3, 3, 2), (5, 2, 2), (7, 1, 2)$
    c) $x = 1 + 2t$, $y = 4 - t$, $z = 2$
    d) No symmetric equations

6. Parts a and b

7. Answers may vary.
    a) $[x, y, z] = [1, 2, 3] + t[-4, 5, 3]$
    b) $x = -1 - 2t$, $y = 3 + 4t$, $z = 2 + 4t$
    c) $\frac{x-3}{2} = \frac{y+2}{-1} = \frac{z+1}{1}$

8. a) $4x - y + 9z = 0$ **b)** $x - 17y + 3z - 1 = 0$
    c) $3x + y - z - 6 = 0$

9. π_1 and π_3

10. $8x - y - 2z + 29 = 0$

11. $x + 6y + z - 16 = 0$

12. $a = \frac{4}{3}b + \frac{5}{3}$

13. a) $3x - y + 4z - 21 = 0$
    b) Answers may vary.
    $x = 1 + 6s + t$, $y = 2 - 2s + 23t$, $z = 5 - 5s + 5t$

14. a) $(-2, 1, 5); 27°$ **b)** $x = 2 + 3t$, $y = -1 - 2t$, $z = -5 - t; 0°$

16. $\left(\frac{35}{9}, \frac{4}{9}, \frac{10}{9}\right)$

17. b) $2x + y + 2z - 4 = 0$, $2x + y + 2z + 8 = 0$

18. Answers may vary.
    a) $[x, y, z] = [0, 0, 0] + t[4, -7, -2]; \frac{x}{4} = \frac{y}{-7} = \frac{z}{-2}$

b) $[x, y, z] = \left[0, 11, \frac{17}{2}\right] + t[2, -6, -5]; \frac{x}{2} = \frac{y-11}{-6} = \frac{z-\frac{17}{2}}{-5}$

19. Answers may vary. $x = t$, $y = 5 - 3t$, $z = 4 - 2t$

20. $9x + 4y + 4z = 0$

21. Answers may vary.
    b) $5x - y + 2z - 7 = 0$
    c) $3x - 2y + 7z - 10 = 0$

22. a) $y - z - 4 = 0$ **b)** $x + 8y - 7z - 25 = 0$

23. b) $(1, 2, -3)$

25. a) $x = 1$, $y = -2$ **b)** $x = -1$, $y = 2$
    c) $x = 3$, $y = \frac{-1}{2}$, $z = 2$ **d)** $x = -6$, $y = 3$, $z = \frac{-1}{2}$

26. a) $x = -1$, $y = 0$, $z = 2$
    b) $x = \frac{1}{5} - \frac{1}{5}t$, $y = \frac{-7}{5} + \frac{2}{5}t$, $z = t$

Chapter 3 Self-Test, page 208

1. $52.1°$

4. $13x + 11y + 25z + 65 = 0$

5. $3x + 10y - 8z + 9 = 0$

6. a) $(-2, 3, 8)$
    b) Answers may vary. $x = 1 + 2t$, $y = -1 + 4t$, $z = 2 + t$

7. Answers may vary. $x = t$, $y = -1 - 2t$, $z = 2 + t$

9. a) $x = -8, y = \frac{21}{2}$ **d)** $x = 0$, $y = 1$, $z = 2$

10. 579

Performance Problems for Vectors
Problems, page 210

1. a) ii) $25, 28, 44$

2. b) $bc \cos A + ca \cos B + ab \cos C = c^2$, where c is the hypotenuse.

3. a) Answers may vary. For example, $(1, 4.6, 6.6)$, $(2, 5.3, 7.3)$, $(4, 6.7, 8.7)$

4. b) $y_2 = y_3 - \frac{x_3}{\sqrt{2}}$, $z_2 = z_3 - \frac{x_3}{\sqrt{2}}$

5. The direction vector of the line is a scalar multiple of $\left[1, \frac{1}{\sqrt{2}}, \frac{1}{\sqrt{2}}\right]$.

6. 22 square units

7. b) $|\vec{a}|\,|\vec{b}|\sin\left(\cos^{-1}\left(\frac{\vec{a}\cdot\vec{b}}{|\vec{a}|\cdot|\vec{b}|}\right)\right)$

8. a) $|\vec{v}\times\vec{w}|$
    b) $||\vec{u}|\cos\theta|$, where θ is the angle between $\vec{u}$ and $\vec{v}\times\vec{w}$
    d) $\vec{u}\cdot\vec{v}\times\vec{w}$ is positive.

10. a) 48 **b)** 12

12. a) 6

13. $3\sqrt{2}$

15. a) $5x - 3y + 5 = 0$, $7y - 10z + 5 = 0$, $7x - 6z + 10 = 0$
    b) The 3 planes intersect in the line.

17. a) Yes   **b)** Yes
    c) C lies on a circle.

19. a) P moves along the line $y = -x$.

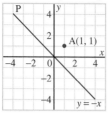

b) P moves along the line $y = -x + 0.5$.

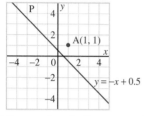

c) P moves along the line $y = -x + 1$.

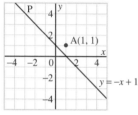

20. a) $\vec{a}$ **b)** $\vec{0}$ **c)** $\vec{a}$

21. Answers may vary. For example, [1, 2, 2] and [−8, −7, 11]

22. No

24. a) $\dfrac{12}{\sqrt{14}}$ **b)** $\dfrac{\sqrt{219}}{3}$ **c)** $\dfrac{9}{\sqrt{10}}$

26. (5, 2, 0) and (1, −1, −1)

27. b) $2x + 5y + z - 35 = 0$

28. a) $x + 2y + 2z - 6 = 0$ or $x - 2 = 0$
   b) $7x + 6y + 6z - 26 = 0$ or $x - 2 = 0$

29. a) $\dfrac{2 - 3\sqrt{2}}{14}$, $\dfrac{38 + 27\sqrt{2}}{14}$

30. $x = (36 - 9\sqrt{3} - 6\pi)$ cm^2, $y = (-36 + 18\sqrt{3} + 3\pi)$ cm^2,
$z = (36 - 36\sqrt{3} + 12\pi)$ cm^2

Chapter 4 Examples of Proof

4.1 Exercises, page 224

1. Answers may vary. For example, 2

2. Answers may vary. For example, $7 = 2^2 + 1^2 + 1^2 + 1^2$

3. Answers may vary.
   a) 0   **b)** 1   **c)** An obtuse triangle
   d) 0   **e)** 2

6. Answers may vary. For example, 41

7. a) 360°, 540°, 720°, $(n - 2)180°$
   b) 360°, 540°, 720°, $(n - 2)\ 180°$

8. a) No

---

11. i) 360°   **ii)** 360°   **iii)** 360°

13. Answers may vary. For example, the sum of two even integers is always an even integer.

14. Answers may vary. For example, the division of a square of an odd number by 4 always has a remainder of 1.

15. $\dfrac{4}{3}$; $\dfrac{5}{4}$; answers may vary. For example, when the sides of a triangle are given by 3 consecutive integers,
$\dfrac{\sin A}{\sin C} = \dfrac{\text{biggest side}}{\text{medium side}} > 1$.

16. The statement is true.

17. b) No

4.2 Exercises, page 230

1. b) No. This only proves the Pythagorean Theorem for an isosceles right triangle.

3. Gemma's response is correct as long as a is the hypotenuse of a right triangle.

4. a) $\angle ABC = \angle CBD$; $\angle BAC = \angle BCD$; $\angle BCA = \angle BDC$
   b) $c^2 - cx = a^2$
   c) $\angle ABC = \angle ACD$; $\angle ACB = \angle ADC$; $\angle BAC = \angle CAD$
   d) $cx = b^2$

5. a) Each angle in the central figure is supplementary to a right angle and each side has length $b - a$.

7. 130.83 cm

8. a) $\angle EDB$ and $\angle BCA$ are right angles, so ED and AC are parallel. Thus, ACDE is a trapezoid.
   b) See the proof that $\angle ABD$ is a right angle on page 228.

11. AM = AN $\doteq$ 7.21 cm

12. a) $y = \sqrt{\dfrac{4}{5}}x$ **b)** $y = \left(\dfrac{\sqrt{2}}{\sqrt{2} + 1}\right)x$

4.3 Exercises, page 238

1. a) ii)   **b)** ii)   **c)** i)   **d)** i)
   These choices are better because there are more zeros in the coordinates, simplifying calculations.

2. a) A(−a, 0), B(a, 0), C(a, b)   **b)** C($a + c$, b)
   c) B($\sqrt{m^2 + n^2}$, 0) C($m + \sqrt{m^2 + n^2}$, n)   **d)** C(0, $\sqrt{3}a$)

6. b) B(a, 0); D$\left(\dfrac{1}{2}a + b, c\right)$
   c) Area of △DOB: $\dfrac{1}{2}ac$; area of △AOC: $2ac$;
   area of △DOB = $\dfrac{1}{4}$(area of △AOC)

9. b) A(a, b), B(−a, b)   **c)** M(0, b)

14. A square or a rhombus

17. b) Length: width = 2: $\sqrt{3}$

4.4 Exercises, page 244

1. c) want to prove that $\vec{b} = \vec{c}$ **d)** $\overrightarrow{DB} = \vec{a} + \vec{b}$
   e) $\overrightarrow{DB} = \vec{a} + \vec{c}$

5. A parallelogram

Chapter 4 Review Exercises, page 248

1. a) Answers may vary. For example, $12 = 5 + 7$;
$20 = 17 + 3$; $100 = 71 + 29$
b) You would have to find an even number that could not be written as the sum of two prime numbers.

2. Answers may vary. For example, $\cos^2 \theta + \sin^2 \theta = 1$ for all θ

3. a) $360°$ **b)** $360°$

4. Answers may vary. For example, the product of two consecutive natural numbers is always even.

5. Answers may vary. For example, the points all lie in a straight line.

7. Length of the inside triangle: $\sqrt{3}x$; length of the outside triangle: $2\sqrt{3}x$

Chapter 4 Self-Test, page 250

1. a) False. For example, rectangles with dimensions 1×6 units and 2×3 units have the same area.
b) True in 2 dimensions, false in 3 dimensions
c) False. A rhombus also has 4 equal sides.

4. 43.3%

Performance Problems for Proof

Problems, page 252

3. 2.4
4. $h = \dfrac{ab}{c}$
6. a) 3.82 cm, 6.18 cm   **b)** 3.82 cm, 6.18 cm
7. 2
8. 6
23. b) The middle triangle
26. $\overrightarrow{c} = -\overrightarrow{a} + 2\dfrac{\overrightarrow{a} \cdot \overrightarrow{b}}{\overrightarrow{b} \cdot \overrightarrow{b}}\,\overrightarrow{b}$

Chapter 5 Deductive Reasoning

5.1 Exercises, page 263

4. a) Both angles are 60°.
b) $x°$ and $180° - 2x°$, or $\dfrac{180° - x°}{2}$

9. a) Triangle, vertex, octagon, parallel, perpendicular, radius, degree

19. a) Yes

22. a) The card with the 8 on it, the card with the circle on it, and the card with the square on it
c) He is a liar.

5.2 Exercises, page 269

2. Parts b, c, and e

5.3 Exercises, page 275

2. a) True   **b)** False   **c)** True
d) True   **e)** True   **f)** False
g) True   **h)** True   **i)** True

5.4 Exercises, page 279

1. a) 30   **b)** 440   **c)** 40   **d)** $\dfrac{1}{4}$

2. 6 candies per person per day

6. Middle square: Length $= \dfrac{1}{\sqrt{2}}s$; area $= \dfrac{1}{2}s^2$
Smallest square: Length $= \dfrac{1}{2}s$; area $= \dfrac{1}{4}s^2$

16. 7.75 cm^2

5.5 Exercises, page 286

1. Problem 1: $\dfrac{s\sqrt{2}}{2 + \sqrt{2}}$ cm, problem 2: 17.16%, problem 3: 3.33 cm

3. a) 7.07 cm

4. a) 24 cm^2

6. $\sqrt{112}$ cm

12. b) $\triangle$PBQ is isosceles.
c) $\triangle$PBQ is equilateral.

Chapter 5 Self-Test, page 290

4. a) False. For example, similar triangles have congruent angles but can be of different sizes.
b) False. For example, a right triangle

6. Bina told the truth; Anna took the radio.

Performance Problems for Deductive Reasoning

Problems, page 292

16. $\sqrt{5}$

34. Approximately 2.0565

Chapter 6 Methods of Counting

6.1 Exercises, page 306

1. a) 24   **b)** 24

2. 6 numbers: 123, 132, 213, 231, 312, 321

3. 120

4. 72

5. a) 576   **b)** 120   **c)** 144

6. 45

7. a) 32   **b)** 28

8. a) 75   **b)** 36

9. a) 10 000   **b)** 50 000 s or 13.9 h

10. a) 5040   **b)** 4960

11. a) 2   **b)** 32

12. 1024

13. a) 36^6 or 2.2×10^9

14. a) 2^{50}

15. 10^{14}

16. a) 24 **b)** 6 **c)** 12

17. a) 18 **b)** 18

18. a) 208 860 **b)** 6840

19. a) $2^4 - 1 = 15$

20. a) 10 **b)** 5 **c)** 2

6.2 Exercises, page 314

1. a) AB, AC, AD, BC, BD, BA, CA, CB, CD, DA, DB, DC, 12
b) 24

2. a) 6 **b)** 24 **c)** 120

3. a) 6; 12; 20 **b)** 6; 24; 60

4. 120

5. a) 5040 **b)** 840

6. 5040

7. a) i) 1 **ii)** 2, 2 **iii)** 3, 6, 6
iv) 4, 12, 24, 24 **v)** 5, 20, 60, 120, 120

8. a) 6 **b)** $4 \times 3! = 4!$ **c)** $5 \times 4! = 5!$
d) $6 \times 5! = 6!$ **e)** $(n + 1) \cdot n! = (n + 1)!$

9. a) 6 **b)** 30 **c)** 120
d) i) n **ii)** $n(n - 1)$ **iii)** $n(n - 1)(n - 2)$

10. a) $(n + 2)(n + 1)$ **b)** $\dfrac{1}{n(n-1)(n-2)}$ **c)** $n(n + 1)$
d) $(n + 3)(n + 4)$ **e)** $(n - r + 1)$
f) $(n - r + 1)(n - r)(n - r - 1)$

11. a) 6 **b)** 24 **c)** 120
d) 362 880 **e)** $8.065\,81 \times 10^{67}$ **f)** 11
g) 56 **h)** 60 **i)** 30 240
j) 42 **k)** 120 **l)** 720
m) 60 480 **n)** 2184 **o)** 45
p) 2 598 960 **q)** 20

12. 116 280

13. a) 60 **b)** 120

14. 120

15. a) 6 497 400 **b)** 17 160

16. 725 760

17. Parts c, d, and e

19. a) $n = 4, n \geq 1, n \in N$ **b)** $n = 9, n \geq 2, n \in N$
c) $n = 5, n \geq 1, n \in N$ **d)** $n = 3$ or $8, n \geq 3, n \in N$
e) $n = 7, n \geq 4, n \in N$ **f)** $n = 5, n \geq 2, n \in N$

20. a) $r = 2, r \geq 0, r \in N$ **b)** $r = 3, r \geq 0, r \in N$
c) $r = 4, r \geq 0, r \in N$ **d)** $r = 5$ or $r = 6, r \geq 0, r \in N$

21. $n! > 2^n$, for $n \geq 4$

6.3 Exercises, page 320

1. a) 30 **b)** 3360 **c)** 6 652 800 **d)** 37 800

2. a) 6

3. a) 30 240 **b)** 1680 **c)** 415 800 **d)** 3360

4. 1260

5. 560

7. 10

8. 3 527 160

9. a) 1 **b)** 5 **c)** 10 **d)** 10 **e)** 5 **f)** 1

10. 32

11. 360

12. a) 420 **b)** 10 **c)** 20

13. a) 70 **b)** 56
c) i) 184 756 **ii)** $\dfrac{(2x)!}{x!x!}$
iii) 125 970 **iv)** $\dfrac{(x + y)!}{x!y!}$

14. a) 200 **b)** 240

15. a) i) 6 **ii)** 30 **iii)** 90
b) i) 5.55×10^{12} **ii)** $\dfrac{(3x)!}{x!x!x!}$
iii) 3.78×10^{12} **iv)** $\dfrac{(x + y + z)!}{x!y!z!}$

6.4 Exercises, page 326

1. a) 120 **b)** 24

2. 24

3. 120

4. 48

5. a) 144 **b)** 288

7. 144

8. a) 120 **b)** 48 **c)** 72

9. 504

10. 9 395 200

11. 25

12. 120

13. 13

14. 150

15. a) 3360 **b)** 360 **c)** 60 **d)** 2520

16. a) 1260 **b)** 360 **c)** 900 **d)** 300

17. 35

18. 120

19. a) 1656 **b)** 1632 **c)** 840

6.5 Exercises, page 331

1. a) AB, AC, AD, BA, BC, BD, CA, CB, CD, DA, DB, DC
b) AB, AC, AD, BC, BD, CD

2. a) 10
b) ABC, ABD, ABE, CDE, BDE, ADE, ACD, ACE, BCD, BCE

3. 3 268 760

4. 84

5. 30

6. a) 120 **b)** 720

7. a) 210 **b)** 210

8. a) i) 1 **ii)** 1, 1 **iii)** 1, 2, 1
iv) 1, 3, 3, 1 **v)** 1, 4, 6, 4, 1

vi) 1, 5, 10, 10, 5, 1
c) i) 1, 6, 15, 20, 15, 6, 1
ii) 1, 7, 21, 35, 35, 21, 7, 1

10. a) 1   **b)** 10   **c)** 45   **d)** 55
e) 66   **f)** 120   **g)** 165   **h)** 220
i) 210   **j)** 330

11. a) $C(n, 0) = \dfrac{n!}{0!n!}$, $n \geq 0$, $n \in N$

b) $C(n, 1) = \dfrac{n!}{1!(n-1)!}$, $n \geq 1$, $n \in N$

c) $C(n, 2) = \dfrac{n!}{2!(n-2)!}$, $n \geq 2$, $n \in N$

d) $C(n, 3) = \dfrac{n!}{3!(n-3)!}$, $n \geq 3$, $n \in N$

e) $C(n, 4) = \dfrac{n!}{4!(n-4)!}$, $n \geq 4$, $n \in N$

12. 700

13. a) 4368   **b)** 376 992   **c)** 1287   **d)** 65 780

14. 201

15. a) 211 926   **b)** 241 098   **c)** 2 569 788

16. a) Super 7 lottery   **b)** 62 891 499, 13 983 816
c) 48 907 683

17. a) 210   **b)** 140

18. 864

19. a) 5   **b)** 2 or 6   **c)** 7   **d)** 8   **e)** 4 or 2   **f)** 3 or 7

20. a) 56   **b)** 28   **c)** 20

21. a) 6160   **b)** 10 752

22. 47

23. 56

25. a) 9   **b)** 24   **c)** 45

26. 41

27. a) 59 850   **b)** 43 092 000
c) 1 368 000   **d)** 547 200

28. 80 089 128

Chapter 6 Review Exercises, page 337

1. 24

2. a) 60   **b)** 36   **c)** 45

3. a) 7 200 000   **b)** 10 376 000

4. a) 10 000   **b)** 5040

5. a) 125   **b)** 30

6. 198 360

7. a) 720   **b)** 24

8. 336

9. 840

10. 657 720

11. 8640

12. 31

13. a) 1680   **b)** 360   **c)** 840   **d)** 90

14. a) $n = 7$, $n \geq 3$, $n \in N$ **b)** $n = 6$, $n \geq 4$, $n \in N$
c) $r = 2$, $0 \leq r \leq 5$, $r \in N$ **d)** $r = 3$, $0 \leq r \leq 8$, $r \in N$

15. a) $(n + 3)(n + 2)$, $n \geq -1$, $n \in N$

b) $\dfrac{1}{(n+1)(n)}$, $n \geq 1$, $n \in N$
c) $(n - r + 3)(n - r + 2)(n - r + 1)$, $n \geq r$, $n \in n$, $r \in W$

16. 7560

17. 180 180

18. 15 120

19. 10

20. a) 120   **b)** 40   **c)** 60, 60

21. 2 238 976 116

22. a) 12   **b)** 36

23. 1728

24. 576

26. 120

27. a) 18 564   **b)** 3150   **c)** 8106

28. a) 2 598 960   **b)** 24   **c)** 3744

29. a) 120   **b)** 36

30. 3360

Chapter 6 Self-Test, page 340

1. 6

2. a) 142 506   **b)** 4896   **c)** 151 200

3. a) 27 216   **b)** 90 000   **c)** 62 784

4. a) $P(n, r) = C(n, r) \cdot r!$

5. a) 120   **b)** 12

6. 7200

Chapter 7 The Binomial Theorem and Mathematical Induction

7.1 Exercises, page 346

1. a) 1   **b)** 3   **c)** 10   **d)** 20   **e)** 84   **f)** 120

2. a) $C(7, 2)$ **b)** $C(9, 5)$ **c)** $C(11, 4)$ **d)** $C(20, 14)$
e) $C(5, 3)$ **f)** $C(7, 6)$ **g)** $C(12, 9)$ **h)** $C(21, 7)$

3. Row n has $(n + 1)$ entries, so even numbered rows have an odd number of entries and odd numbered rows have an even number of entries.

6. a) 50
b) The second number in row n is $C(n, 1)$, or n.

13. a) Exit 1: 1 path; Exit 2: 2 paths; Exit 3: 1 path
b) Exit 1: 1 path; Exit 2: 3 paths; Exit 3: 3 paths;
Exit 4: 1 path
c) Exit 1: 1 path; Exit 2: 4 paths; Exit 3: 6 paths;
Exit 4: 4 paths; Exit 5: 1 path
d) Exit 1: 1 path; Exit 2: 5 paths; Exit 3: 10 paths;
Exit 4: 10 paths; Exit 5: 5 paths; Exit 6: 1 path

15. a) 70   **b)** 210

16. a) i) 1; 1   **ii)** 1; 2; 1
iii) 1; 3; 3; 1   **iv)** 1; 4; 6; 4; 1

17. a) $C(3, 3) + C(4, 3) + C(5, 3) + C(6, 3) = C(7, 4)$

18. a) $C(2, 0) + C(3, 1) + C(4, 2) + C(5, 3) + C(6, 4) = C(7, 4)$;
$C(2, 2) + C(3, 2) + C(4, 2) + C(5, 2) + C(6, 2) = C(7, 3)$

19. a) 15   **b)** 9

20. a) 170   **b)** $\dfrac{n^2 - 3n}{2}$

21. a) Each sum is a power of 2.

  b) The sum represents the number of ways any number of items can be chosen from a set of 5 items.

7.2 Exercises, page 354

1. a) $a^3 + 6a^2 + 12a + 8$
  b) $y^4 - 20y^3 + 150y^2 - 500y + 625$
  c) $1024t^5 + 1280t^4 + 640t^3 + 160t^2 + 20t + 1$
  d) $x^3 - 3x^2y + 3xy^2 - y^3$
  e) $16a^4 + 32a^3b + 24a^2b^2 + 8ab^3 + b^4$
  f) $x^5 - 35x^4 + 490x^3 - 3430x^2 + 12\,005x - 16\,807$

2. a) An a is selected from 5 of the 8 binomial factors and b is selected from the 3 remaining factors.
  b) 56

3. a) 7   **b)** 35   **c)** The 5th term

4. In each case, one letter is chosen from 4 of the 6 binomial factors and the other letter is chosen from the 2 remaining factors.

5. a) 10 terms; 11 terms   **b)** $(a + b)^{10}$; $(a + b)^9$
  c) $(a + b)^n$ has one middle term when n is even and two middle terms when n is odd.

8. a) $x^6 + 12x^5 + 60x^4 + 160x^3 + 240x^2 + 192x + 64$
  b) $x^4 - 12x^3 + 54x^2 - 108x + 81$
  c) $1 + 6x^2 + 15x^4 + 20x^6 + 15x^8 + 6x^{10} + x^{12}$
  d) $32 - 80x + 80x^2 - 40x^3 + 10x^4 - x^5$
  e) $a^4 - 8a^3b + 24a^2b^2 - 32ab^3 + 16b^4$
  f) $8a^3 + 36a^2b + 54ab^2 + 27b^3$
  g) $x^5 + 5x^3 + 10x + \dfrac{10}{x} + \dfrac{5}{x^3} + \dfrac{1}{x^5}$
  h) $243a^5 + 810a^4b^2 + 1080a^3b^4 + 720a^2b^6 + 240ab^8 + 32b^{10}$

9. a) $1 + 10x^{\left(\frac{1}{2}\right)} + 45x + 120x^{\left(\frac{3}{2}\right)} + \ldots$
  b) $x^{12} + 24x^{11} + 264x^{10} + 1760x^9 + \ldots$
  c) $256 - 1024x + 1792x^2 - 1792x^3 + \ldots$
  d) $1 - 18x + 144x^2 - 672x^3 + \ldots$

10. $a^{12} + 24a^{11}b + 264a^{10}b^2$; $59\,136a^6b^6$

11. a) $-15\,360x^3$ **b)** $7000x^5y^3$ **c)** $-112\,640a^9$
  d) $2288a^9$ **e)** $70x^8$

12. $\dfrac{7}{4}$

13. a) -1512; $20\,412$ **b)** 1760; 59 136   **c)** 0; -120

14. a) 15   **b)** 15   **c)** No

15. a) $2x^4 + 12x^2y^2 + 2y^4$
  b) $8x^3y + 8xy^3$

16. $a^3 + 3a^2b + 3ab^2 + 3a^2c + 3ac^2 + 6abc + b^3 + 3b^2c + 3bc^2 + c^3$

18. a) $1 - 6x + 12x^2 - 8x^3$; $1 + \dfrac{5}{x} + \dfrac{10}{x^2} + \dfrac{10}{x^3} + \dfrac{5}{x^4} + \dfrac{1}{x^5}$
  b) i) 11   **ii)** -26

19. 137

20. 3420

21. $1 + 7x + 21x^2$ or $1 + 14x + 91x^2$

22. $a = b = 2$

7.3 Exercises, page 360

1. a) $4 + 5 + 6 + 7 + 8$ **b)** $1 + \dfrac{1}{2} + \dfrac{1}{3} + \dfrac{1}{4} + \dfrac{1}{5}$
  c) $1 + 3 + 9 + 27 + 81$ **d)** $7 + 5 + 3 + 1 - 1$
  e) $-1 + 1 - 1 + 1 - 1$ **f)** $6 + 12 + 24 + 49 + 96$

2. a) $\displaystyle\sum_{i=1}^{100} i$ **b)** $\displaystyle\sum_{k=1}^{7} 4$ **c)** $\displaystyle\sum_{k=2}^{5} j^3$
  d) $\displaystyle\sum_{k=2}^{4} \dfrac{1}{k}$ **e)** $\displaystyle\sum_{k=3}^{12} k^k$ **f)** $\displaystyle\sum_{j=1}^{12} a^j$

3. a) iv)   **b)** ii)   **c)** iii)   **d)** vi)

4. a) $\displaystyle\sum_{i=1}^{7} 2i$ **b)** $\displaystyle\sum_{j=1}^{6} (3j - 1)$ **c)** $\displaystyle\sum_{k=1}^{5} (19 - 4n)$
  d) $\displaystyle\sum_{k=1}^{5} 4(5)^{(k-1)}$ **e)** $\displaystyle\sum_{j=1}^{4} (-1)^{(j-1)}$ **f)** $\displaystyle\sum_{i=1}^{5} 3(-2)^{k-1}$

5. a) $5 + 6 + 7 + 8 + 9 + 10$ **b)** $-2 + 4 - 8 + 16 - 32$
  c) $5 + 10 + 20 + 40 + 80 + 160$

6. a) $a + a^2 + a^3 + a^4$ **b)** $a + 2a^2 + 3a^3 + 4a^4$
  c) $a + 4a + 27a + 256a$ **d)** $-a + 4a^2 - 27a^3 + 256a^4$

7. a) $\displaystyle\sum_{i=1}^{16} (6i - 3)$ **b)** $\displaystyle\sum_{j=1}^{11} (23 - 5j)$ **c)** $\displaystyle\sum_{k=1}^{13} (4k - 6)$
  d) $\displaystyle\sum_{m=1}^{9} \left(\dfrac{1}{2}\right)^{m-1}$ **e)** $\displaystyle\sum_{m=1}^{9} 3\left(2^{m-1}\right)$ **f)** $\displaystyle\sum_{k=1}^{7} 2(-3)^{k-1}$

8. a) $4 + 6 + 8 + 10 + 12 + 14$
  b) $\dfrac{(x-1)}{1} + \dfrac{(x-1)^2}{2} + \dfrac{(x-1)^3}{3} + \dfrac{(x-1)^4}{4} + \dfrac{(x-1)^5}{5}$
    $+ \dfrac{(x-1)^6}{6} + \dfrac{(x-1)^7}{7}$
  c) $1 + 5 + 10 + 10 + 5 + 1$
  d) $3 + 10 + 35 + 126 + 462$
  e) $-8 - 32 - 128 - 512 - 2048$
  f) $\dfrac{1}{3} + \dfrac{1}{15} + \dfrac{1}{35} + \dfrac{1}{63} + \dfrac{1}{99}$

9. a) $\displaystyle\sum_{k=1}^{99} k(k + 1)$ **b)** $\displaystyle\sum_{m=1}^{25} (2m - 1)^2$ **c)** $\displaystyle\sum_{k=1}^{10} \dfrac{1}{k(k + 2)}$
  d) $\displaystyle\sum_{i=0}^{4} C(4, i)a^{4-i}b^i$ **e)** $\displaystyle\sum_{k=1}^{15} (2k - 1)(-1)^{k-1}$ **f)** $\displaystyle\sum_{j=1}^{8} j \cdot 2^j$
  g) $\displaystyle\sum_{m=1}^{7} \left[2^{(m-1)}\right]^m$ **h)** $\displaystyle\sum_{k=1}^{n} [a + (k - 1)d]$ **i)** $\displaystyle\sum_{j=1}^{n} ar^{j-1}$

11. a) $C(4, 0), C(4, 1), C(4, 2), C(4, 3), C(4, 4)$; $\displaystyle\sum_{i=0}^{4} C(4, i)$
  b) $C(1, 1), C(2, 1), C(3, 1), C(4, 1), C(5, 1), C(6, 1),$
    $C(7, 1), C(8, 1)$; $\displaystyle\sum_{j=1}^{8} C(j, 1)$
  c) $C(2, 0), C(3, 1), C(4, 2), C(5, 3), C(6, 4)$; $\displaystyle\sum_{k=2}^{6} C(k, k - 2)$
  d) $C(3, 3), C(4, 3), C(5, 3)\ldots c(n + 2, 3)$; $\displaystyle\sum_{k=3}^{n+2} C(k, 3)$

12. a) The sum of the numbers in row n is $\displaystyle\sum_{i=0}^{n} C(n, i)$.
  b) $\displaystyle\sum_{i=0}^{8} \left(\sum_{j=0}^{i} C(i, j)\right)$

13. $\displaystyle\sum_{n=1}^{19}\left(\sum_{j=1}^{n}\left(j+\frac{n^2-n}{2}\right)\right)^2$

7.4 Exercises, page 368

1. a) $\dfrac{k+1}{k+2}$ **b)** $\dfrac{k+1}{2k+3}$ **c)** $\dfrac{k+2}{k}$ **d)** $\dfrac{2k+1}{3k+2}$

e) $\dfrac{1}{3}(k+1)(k+2)(k+3)$

f) $\dfrac{1}{2}(k+1)(2k+1)(2k+3)$

7. a) $C(1,1)+C(2,1)+C(3,1)+C(4,1)=C(5,2)$

b) $C(1,1)+C(2,1)+C(3,1)+\ldots+C(n,1)=C(n+1,2)$

9. a) $C(2,2)+C(3,2)+\ldots+C(n+1,2)=C(n+2,3)$

10. b) $2n^2(n+1)^2$

c) $(n+1)^2(2n^2+4n+1)$

13. a) $S_n=\dfrac{n}{3n+1}$ **b)** $S_n=\dfrac{n}{4n+1}$

14. a) $P_n=n+1$ **b)** $P_n=\dfrac{1}{n+1}$

16. $S_n=(n+1)!-1$

19. $S_n=\dfrac{(n+1)!-1}{(n+1)!}$

Chapter 7 Review Exercises, pages 376

1. a) $C(7,4)$ **b)** $C(10,6)$ **c)** $C(n,n-r)$ **d)** $C(n,r)$

2. a) 32   **b)** 70   **c)** 35

3. a) 1; 3; 6; 10; 15

b) These numbers are found on the 2nd diagonal of Pascal's triangle.

c) For n points, there are $\dfrac{n(n-1)}{2}$ line segments.

4. a) $a^5+5a^4b+10a^3b^2+10a^2b^3+5ab^4+b^5$

b) 56

5. a) $x^5+10x^4+40x^3+80x^2+80x+32$

b) $16x^4-96x^3+216x^2-216x+81$

c) $x^6-12x^4+48x^2-64$

6. a) $128-448x+672x^2$ **b)** $10\,206x^4$

c) 210   **d)** $10x;\ 10x^{\left(\frac{3}{2}\right)}$

7. 144

8. 35

9. a) $3+6+11+18+27$ **b)** $9+16+25+36+49$

c) $-8-32-128-512$

d) $\dfrac{1}{24}+\dfrac{1}{35}+\ldots+\dfrac{1}{n(n-2)}+\dfrac{1}{(n+1)(n-1)}$

10. a) $\displaystyle\sum_{t=1}^{8}(3t+4)$ **b)** $\displaystyle\sum_{k=1}^{7}2^{2-k}$ **c)** $\displaystyle\sum_{j=1}^{10}j\cdot j!$

d) $\displaystyle\sum_{i=1}^{15}i(i+1)$ **e)** $\displaystyle\sum_{m=1}^{10}\dfrac{1}{(3m+1)(3m+4)}$

13. a) $S_n=\dfrac{n}{n+1}$ **b)** $\dfrac{51}{5050}$

Chapter 7 Self-Test, page 378

1. a) 1, 9, 36, 84, 126, 126, 84, 36, 9, 1

b) $a^8+8a^7b+28a^6b^2+56a^5b^3+70a^4b^4+56a^3b^5+28a^2b^6+8ab^7+b^8$

c) $C(11,5)$

3. 40

4. $\displaystyle\sum_{k=1}^{10}\dfrac{k+1}{\sqrt{k}}$

5. $\dfrac{1}{2}+\dfrac{3}{4}+\dfrac{5}{8}+\dfrac{7}{16}+\dfrac{9}{32}$

6. $8x^9-60x^6+150x^3-125$

7. 45

8. $2240x^3;\ 8960x^4$

9. $P_n=(n+1)^2$

Performance Problems for Discrete Mathematics
Problems, page 380

2. 165

3. 126

4. 286

5. 0.696

6. 0.785

7. a) 0.002 64   **b)** 0.304

8. $\dfrac{16}{231}$

10. $(u_n)^2-(u_{n-1})^2=u_{n-2}\times u_{n+1}$

11. $u_{n+2}-1$

12. $(u_n)^2=u_{n-1}u_{n+1}+(-1)^{n+1}$

14. $S_n=u_n$

15. a) $\dfrac{1}{56}$ **b)** $\dfrac{15}{28}$

16. a) $\dfrac{1}{924}$ **b)** $\dfrac{5}{231}$

17. 455

18. 286

19. 1 387 386

20. a) 34 650   **b)** 5775

21. a) $\dfrac{6}{1001}$ **b)** $\dfrac{120}{1001}$

22. a) 0.25   **b)** 0.439   **c)** 0.214   **d)** 1.64×10^{-4}

e) 0.999   **f)** 0.5   **g)** 0.105

23. 0.127

24. a) 0.0374   **b)** 6.93×10^{-4}

25. 0.218

26. $u_n=11u_{n-5}+u_{n-10}$

27. a) 1, 1, 3, 5, 11, 21, 43, …

b) $t_n^2=(t_{n+1})(t_{n-1})+(-2)^{n-1}$

c) $3t_n=2^n-(-1)^n$

30. a) If n is odd, $S_n=(u_n+1)^2$; if n is even, $S_n=(u_n+1)^2-1$.

b) $S_n=1-\dfrac{1}{u_{n-1}\times u_n}$

31. The sum of the nth row is u_{2n+1}.

Cumulative Performance Problems
Problems, page 389

4. b) $PQ^2=PA\times PB$

c) $PQ=PR,\ PR^2=PA\times PB$

6. a) 11   **b)** 2, 4, 6

7. 10

10. c) No

18. a) 90° or 41.4°

21. $\angle BAC = \cos^{-1}(d)$

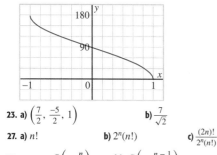

23. a) $\left(\frac{7}{2}, \frac{-5}{2}, 1\right)$ **b)** $\frac{7}{\sqrt{2}}$

27. a) $n!$ **b)** $2^n(n!)$ **c)** $\frac{(2n)!}{2^n(n!)}$

28. n even: $C\left(n, \frac{n}{2}\right)$; n odd: $C\left(n, \frac{n-1}{2}\right)$

31. The constant equals two times the area of the triangle divided by the length of one side of the triangle.

32. BE = 1.26, CA = 1.59

33. 5.66, 6.07

34. 1001

35. b) 49

37. a) 26

    b) $\left(26, 4.96 \times 10^{14}\right)$; the y-coordinate represents the number of different hands when dealt 26 cards from 52.

    d) $y = C(52, x); 0 \le x \le 52$

38. b) $y = \left(\frac{5}{6}\right)^n, y = 1 - \left(\frac{5}{6}\right)^n$ **c)** 26

39. b) $y = \frac{C(13, n) \times C(39, 13 - n)}{C(15, 13)}$

    c) i) 0.286   **ii)** 0.001 17   **iii)** 1.57×10^{-12}

40. a) 1 048 576   **b)** 286   **c)** 43 243 200

43. $f(x) = \frac{1}{x}, x > 0$

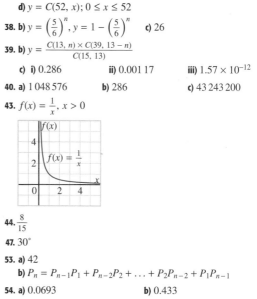

44. $\frac{8}{15}$

47. 30°

53. a) 42

    b) $P_n = P_{n-1}P_1 + P_{n-2}P_2 + \ldots + P_2P_{n-2} + P_1P_{n-1}$

54. a) 0.0693   **b)** 0.433

Index

PHOTO CREDITS AND ACKNOWLEDGMENTS

The publisher wishes to thank the following sources for photographs, illustrations, articles, and other materials used in this book. Care has been taken to determine and locate ownership of copyright material used in the text. We will gladly receive information enabling us to rectify any errors or omissions in credits.

PHOTOS

p. 2 (background), Artbase Inc.; **p. 3** (top), © Joel Berard/Masterfile; **p. 33** (centre left), Bettmann/CORBIS/MAGMA; **p. 73** (top), Artbase, Inc.; **p. 83** (centre right), Science Photo Library/Photo Researchers, Inc.; **p. 121** (centre right), Hulton/Archive by Getty Images; **p. 123** (top), Karen Shore/Kis Design; **p. 147** (centre right), Los Almos National Laboratory/ Mark Marten/Photo Researchers, Inc.; **p. 184** (top right), www.math.ucsd.edu/~okikiolu/; **p. 216** (centre right), Hulton/Archive by Getty Images; **p. 218** (background), Artbase Inc.; **p. 219** (top), Tablet from the Yale Babylonian Collection. Photographer: Bill Casselman http://www.math.ubc. ca/people/faculty/cass/Euclid/ybc/ybc.html; **p. 228** (centre right), Science Photo Library/Photo Researchers, Inc.; **p. 236** (top right), Hulton/Archive by Getty Images; **p. 259** (top), © Mark Tomalty/Masterfile; **p. 269** (top right), Bettmann/CORBIS/MAGMA; **p. 277** (top right), Courtesy of the Archives of the Institute for Advanced Study; **p. 300** (background), © Bryan Reinhart/ Masterfile; **p. 301** (top), Artbase Inc.; **p. 302** (top right), Jack McMaster; **p. 303** Ian Crysler (key card supplied courtesy of the Excelsior Hotel, Hong Kong)/Corel Stock Photo Library; **p. 308** (top right), © Ian Crysler/Corel Stock Photo Library; **p. 311** (centre right), Courtesy of Bhama Srinivasan; **p. 332** (top right), Jack McMaster; **p. 343** (centre right), Bettman/CORBIS/ MAGMA; **p. 383** (top right), Science Photo Library/Photo researchers, Inc.; **p. 385** (centre right), Reproduced by permission of the syndics of Cambridge University Library.

ILLUSTRATIONS

Dave McKay: **p. 4** (bottom right); Jack McMaster: **p. 302**, **p. 332** (top right); Pronk&Associates Inc.: **cover**, **inside front page**, **p. 4**, **p. 5** (top left), **p. 5** (centre right), **p. 51** (top right), **p. 62** (top left), **p. 74**, **p. 76** (centre left), **p. 76** (bottom left), **p. 99** (centre right), **p. 101** (centre left), **p. 110** (centre left), **p. 101** (centre right), **p. 109**, **p. 222** (top centre), **p. 222** (centre), **p. 222** (bottom centre), **p. 266** (bottom left), **p. 266** (bottom right), **p. 281** (top left), **p. 281** (centre left), **p. 330**, **p. 335** (top right), **p. 341**, **p. 364** (centre left), **p. 364** (bottom left).

DATE DUE
DATE DE RETOUR

R MᶜLEAN